Family Mediation
in Scotland

fm
FAMILY
MEDIATION
SCOTLAND

Twelve independent services covering the mainland and the islands provide family mediation in Scotland. All are affiliated to Family Mediation Scotland (FMS). (NCH is a partner in two services and Marriage Counselling in one other.)

FMS co-ordinates the work of these local services, and provides training, accreditation and registration for their mediators. It also offers an information service for professionals and the public, and seminars and conferences for professionals supporting children and young people who are affected by separation and divorce and are involved in the court process.

FMS has close links with the Scottish Office, Scottish Courts administration and the education services.

In the local services in Scotland there are over one hundred mediators who offer mediation on issues involving children. In addition, thirty of them have trained to mediate on issues of property and finance. Other services for parents, children and young people provided include support groups, children's workers and contact centres.

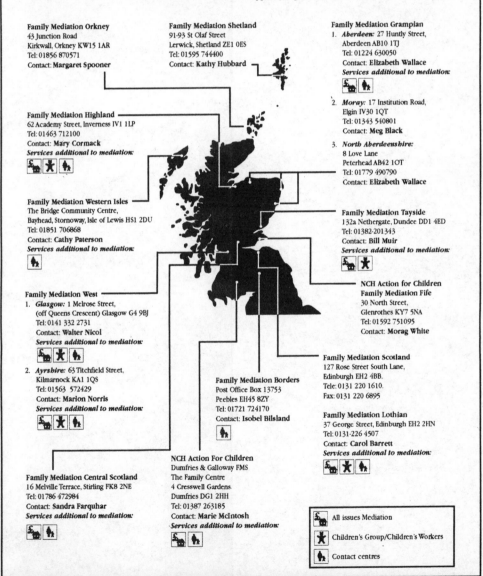

Family Mediation Orkney
43 Junction Road
Kirkwall, Orkney KW15 1AR
Tel: 01856 870571
Contact: Margaret Spooner

Family Mediation Shetland
91-93 St Olaf Street
Lerwick, Shetland ZE1 0ES
Tel: 01595 744400
Contact: Kathy Hubbard

Family Mediation Grampian
1. *Aberdeen:* 27 Huntly Street,
   Aberdeen AB10 1TJ
   Tel: 01224 630050
   Contact: **Elizabeth Wallace**
   Services additional to mediation:

2. *Moray:* 17 Institution Road,
   Elgin IV30 1QT
   Tel: 01343 540801
   Contact: **Meg Black**

3. *North Aberdeenshire:*
   8 Love Lane
   Peterhead AB42 1OT
   Tel: 01779 490790
   Contact: **Elizabeth Wallace**

Family Mediation Highland
62 Academy Street, Inverness IV1 1LP
Tel: 01463 712100
Contact: **Mary Cormack**
Services additional to mediation:

Family Mediation Western Isles
The Bridge Community Centre,
Bayhead, Stornoway, Isle of Lewis HS1 2DU
Tel: 01851 706868
Contact: **Cathy Paterson**
Services additional to mediation:

Family Mediation Tayside
132a Nethergate, Dundee DD1 4ED
Tel: 01382-201343
Contact: **Bill Muir**
Services additional to mediation:

**NCH Action for Children
Family Mediation Fife**
30 North Street,
Glenrothes KY7 5NA
Tel: 01592 751095
Contact: **Morag White**

Family Mediation West
1. *Glasgow:* 1 Melrose Street,
   (off Queens Crescent) Glasgow G4 9BJ
   Tel: 0141 332 2731
   Contact: **Walter Nicol**
   Services additional to mediation:

2. *Ayrshire:* 63 Titchfield Street,
   Kilmarnock KA1 1QS
   Tel: 01563 572429
   Contact: **Marion Norris**
   Services additional to mediation:

Family Mediation Borders
Post Office Box 13753
Peebles EH45 8ZY
Tel: 01721 724170
Contact: **Isobel Bilsland**

Family Mediation Scotland
127 Rose Street South Lane,
Edinburgh EH2 4BB.
Tele: 0131 220 1610.
Fax: 0131 220 6895

Family Mediation Lothian
37 George Street, Edinburgh EH2 2HN
Tel: 0131-226 4507
Contact: **Carol Barrett**
Services additional to mediation:

Family Mediation Central Scotland
16 Melville Terrace, Stirling FK8 2NE
Tel: 01786 472984
Contact: **Sandra Farquhar**
Services additional to mediation:

NCH Action For Children
Dumfries & Galloway FMS
The Family Centre
4 Cresswell Gardens
Dumfries DG1 2HH
Tel: 01387 263185
Contact: **Marie McIntosh**
Services additional to mediation:

All issues Mediation

Children's Group/Children's Workers

Contact centres

UK COLLEGE OF FAMILY MEDIATORS

Directory & Handbook
1998/9

UK COLLEGE OF

FAMILY MEDIATORS

Directory & Handbook

1998/9

Sweet & Maxwell

Published by
Sweet & Maxwell Limited of
100 Avenue Road
London NW3 3PF
Set by Tradespools Ltd, Frome
Printed in Great Britain by Bell & Bain Ltd, Glasgow

A CIP catalogue record for this book
is available from the British Library

ISBN 075200 634 7

Contents

Handbook

Directory

HANDBOOK

The information in the following section
has been supplied by the leading experts
in the field of family mediation. It
provides an overview of the history of
mediation, looks at key background
issues and examines the process of
mediation. Useful reference material is
also provided. The range of articles in
the handbook section combines to offer a
unique resource for those requiring more
information on the subject of family
mediation.

Introduction

Dame Margaret Booth

This is the second directory/handbook published by the UK College of Family Mediators. As before, it is intended to be a source of professional information, not only for those who mediate, but also for those who need or desire to know about family mediation and the services which are now available. With the introduction of the pilot schemes for publicly funded mediation and with the increasing number of referrals outside the pilot areas, the necessity for quick and reliable access to trained mediators by means of the directory becomes even more important. Thus the publication continues to be a significant step towards fulfilment by the College of the objects for which it was founded:

- to advance the education of the public in the skills and practice of family mediators;
- to set, promote, improve and maintain the highest standards of professional conduct and training for those practising in the field of family mediation; and to make available the details of registered mediators qualified to provide family mediation.

This edition of the directory/handbook contains for the first time the Standards and Code of Practice of the College itself, replacing the Joint Code of its founder members, the Family Mediators Association, Family Mediation Scotland and National Family Mediation. This is a crucial document. It governs the standards for membership of the College for individual family mediators as well as for organisations seeking Approved Body status. It also clearly informs those who come to mediation as to what they are entitled to expect by way of expertise and good practice from the registered members of the College whose help they seek. It marks a further stage in the development of the College as a national organisation committed to securing family mediation on a sound professional foundation.

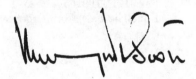

UK College of Family Mediators Who's Who

Chair	Dame Margaret Booth DBE
Vice Chairs	Kay Begg, Mediator, Bristol Family Mediation Service; Tel 0117 929 2002
	Simon Pigott, solicitor and mediator, Collyer Bristow; Tel 0171 242 7363

Governors

National Family Mediation
Tel 0171 383 5993
  Kay Begg
  Arthur Taylor
  John Shaw
  Di Eliott

Family Mediators Association
Tel 0171 720 3336
  Simon Pigott
  Penny Dunne
  Ruth Smallacombe
  Frank Fincham

Family Mediation Scotland
Tel 0131 220 1610
  The Hon Lord Caplan
  Sandra Farquar
  Hugh Donald
  Bill Muir

Chief Executive
Elizabeth Walsh
UK College of Family Mediators
24-32 Stephenson Way
London NW1 2HX
Tel 0171 391 9162
Fax 0171 391 9165
E-mail liz.walsh@btinternet.com

UK College of Family Mediators Management Structure 1998/99

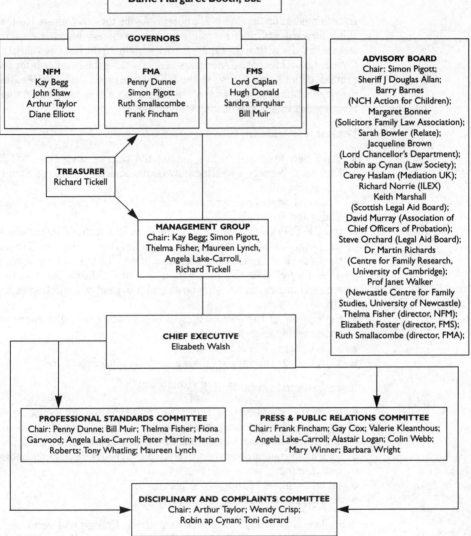

CHAIR
Dame Margaret Booth, DBE

GOVERNORS

NFM
Kay Begg
John Shaw
Arthur Taylor
Diane Elliott

FMA
Penny Dunne
Simon Pigott
Ruth Smallacombe
Frank Fincham

FMS
Lord Caplan
Hugh Donald
Sandra Farquhar
Bill Muir

ADVISORY BOARD
Chair: Simon Pigott;
Sheriff J Douglas Allan;
Barry Barnes
(NCH Action for Children);
Margaret Bonner
(Solicitors Family Law Association);
Sarah Bowler (Relate);
Jacqueline Brown
(Lord Chancellor's Department);
Robin ap Cynan (Law Society);
Carey Haslam (Mediation UK);
Richard Norrie (ILEX)
Keith Marshall
(Scottish Legal Aid Board);
David Murray (Association of
Chief Officers of Probation);
Steve Orchard (Legal Aid Board);
Dr Martin Richards
(Centre for Family Research,
University of Cambridge);
Prof Janet Walker
(Newcastle Centre for Family
Studies, University of Newcastle)
Thelma Fisher (director, NFM);
Elizabeth Foster (director, FMS);
Ruth Smallacombe (director, FMA);

TREASURER
Richard Tickell

MANAGEMENT GROUP
Chair: Kay Begg; Simon Pigott,
Thelma Fisher, Maureen Lynch,
Angela Lake-Carroll,
Richard Tickell

CHIEF EXECUTIVE
Elizabeth Walsh

PROFESSIONAL STANDARDS COMMITTEE
Chair: Penny Dunne; Bill Muir; Thelma Fisher; Fiona
Garwood; Angela Lake-Carroll; Peter Martin; Marian
Roberts; Tony Whatling; Maureen Lynch

PRESS & PUBLIC RELATIONS COMMITTEE
Chair: Frank Fincham; Gay Cox; Valerie Kleanthous;
Angela Lake-Carroll; Alastair Logan; Colin Webb;
Mary Winner; Barbara Wright

DISCIPLINARY AND COMPLAINTS COMMITTEE
Chair: Arthur Taylor; Wendy Crisp;
Robin ap Cynan; Toni Gerard

Handbook A

The Future of the UK College of Family Mediators

Elizabeth Walsh, Chief Executive

In true mediation fashion it is appropriate for the UK College itself to think forward and plan its role for when mediation becomes a mainstream activity within the family justice system. In the last two years the College has achieved the enormous task of setting the standards for the practice of family mediation in the UK, and in doing so the College has provided a template on which all mediation providers have based their training and their accreditation standards.

The last year has seen:

- three new approved bodies joining the College since the 1997/98 Directory, namely LawWise, LawGroup and the Solicitors Family Law Association;
- a judicial seminar programme taken into the regions in England, Wales and Scotland;
- the UK College consulting with the Lord Chancellor's Department, the Legal Aid Board, the Scottish Legal Aid Board, The Law Society, the Council of Legal Education, Mediation UK, the Court of Appeal ADR Project and the Association of Chief Officers of Probation amongst others, on the standards and provision of mediation in the UK;
- the piloting of the free movement of mediators from the approved bodies within each other's services;
- a UK College Code of Practice;
- a UK College Disciplinary Code and Complaints Procedure.

In the forthcoming year the UK College will:

- unify the standards and practice of mediation by assisting in assessing the core competencies of all mediators providing legally aided mediation and by unifying the forms and procedures used;
- award continuous professional development hours for ongoing mediation training;
- set up a register of approved supervisors;
- audit approved mediation bodies.

A fundamental change in the nature of the College will occur on 1 January 1999. From that date the Governors of the College will not be appointed from the Founder Bodies (National Family Mediation, Family Mediators Association and Family Mediation Scotland) but from the membership of the College. Being a full member of the College will thus take on even greater significance. But being able to vote is not the best reason for being a member. For family mediation to be a regulated and recognised alternative to judicial dispute resolution, mediators must be shown to be competent and accountable exponents of the mediation profession. The role of the UK College is to ensure that that is so.

A Short History of Family Mediation

Dame Margaret Booth

Until 1963 it was an absolute bar to the grant of a decree of divorce or judicial separation in England and Wales that the parties had reached an agreement in respect of their affairs. It was not until 1 January 1971, with the implementation of the Divorce Reform Act 1969, that this prohibition was finally abolished. But even by then the concept of conciliation, as it was then known, had started to take root. The Committee on One-Parent Families, in its report published in July 1974 (the Finer Report), had the foresight to envisage conciliation not in any narrow sense but in the comprehensive sense of assisting parties to reach agreement or reduce the area of conflict in respect of every matter arising from the breakdown of their marriage. Thus, conciliation, or mediation as it was later to become known, became recognised and accepted as the means by which divorcing or separating couples could be assisted to communicate with one another and to reach their own informed decisions about some or all of the issues between them.

The first independent Family Conciliation Service was set up as a pilot project in Bristol in 1978 to assist separating or divorcing parents to make agreed arrangements for their children. At about the same time, in South East London and in Surrey, senior court welfare officers set up a system of volunteer conciliators as an alternative to the ordering of welfare reports by the courts. Thereafter, the concept and practice of conciliation grew so influential that it was termed 'a conciliation movement'. In 1981 a three-year research project was started at Bristol University, and in 1982 an inter-departmental committee was set up with a brief to review the situation and recommend whether further facilities for conciliation should be promoted, although the results of these initiatives proved not to be wholly positive. Despite this, the successful, and continuing, conciliation scheme applicable to children's issues was established in the Principal Registry of the Family Division in January 1983. Support for conciliation was also forthcoming in the 1985 Report of the Matrimonial Procedures Committee which had been required by the Lord Chancellor 'to recommend reforms which might be made ... to encourage settlements'.

As more new services came into being in England and Wales, the need for a single body to support them and to co-ordinate practice and training became apparent. Thus, in 1981 the first national organisation was inaugurated under the name of the National Family Conciliation Council (NFCC). Later it became known as the National Association of Family Mediation and Conciliation Services and finally, in 1993, its name was refined to National Family Mediation (NFM). By 1986 the Council was hosting an international conference in London and in that same year it produced a Code of Practice and Statement of Aims and Objectives worked out in conjunction with the Solicitors Family Law Association and agreed with The Law Society. Although the services affiliated to the Council were then still concerned only with children's issues, in 1990 a pilot project to include comprehensive or All Issues Mediation was initiated in five different services and its successful outcome enabled the work of these services to be expanded.

The second national body within this jurisdiction, the Family Mediators Association (FMA), developed from a London pilot project introduced in 1985 to offer All Issues Mediation, then still outside the code of practice of the services affiliated to the NFCC. This project, known as Solicitors in Mediation, also aimed to make legal expertise available in the process by pairing a solicitor mediator with a family mediator. The good outcome of this venture led to the inauguration of the FMA in 1989.

In Scotland the first out-of-court voluntary family mediation service was established in Lothian in 1984 and this, too, was quickly successful. Further regional services followed, with an increasing number of referrals coming from the courts and from solicitors. The Scottish Association of Family Conciliation Services was established in 1986 at the initiative of the regional services, and thereafter it promoted the development of conciliation throughout Scotland, taking responsibility for ensuring common standards as well as providing training, consultancy and support. In 1992 Family Mediation Scotland (FMS) was set up, to which the services are now affiliated.

The year 1988 saw the publication of the English Law Commission's discussion paper The Ground for Divorce which paved the way for the subsequent Family Law Bill. Its proposals envisaged mediation as an integral part of a process over time, leading to divorce or legal separation. The public and Parliamentary debate which took place in the following years culminated in the Bill receiving the Royal Assent on 4 July 1996 and, for the first time, mediation was placed on the statute book. In May 1997, in preparation for the implementation of the Family Law Act 1996, pilot schemes in 13 areas across England and Wales introduced publicly funded mediation services provided by means of franchise contracts with the Legal Aid Board (see Sarah White's section 'Legal Aid Board Family Mediation Pilot Project' below).

The intense interest which was generated in the concept and practice of mediation highlighted the need to end the fragmentation and inconsistency of services in England and Wales. Recognising this, and to alleviate the situation, in 1994 NFM and FMA co-operated to produce their first joint Code of Practice. Shortly after, on 24 January 1995, the constituent members of both the NFM and FMA held a joint symposium at which the resolution was taken to form a steering committee with a view to establishing a single professional body. It was also resolved to invite FMS to send representatives to sit on this committee, an invitation which was at once accepted. As a result of the intensive work which followed, the UK College of Mediators came into being on 1 January 1996. Its constitution provides that, during a three-year transitional period, the College will be run by representatives nominated by the three national bodies which alone constitute its membership. This will end on 1 January 1999 when those persons whose names are listed as members on the College Register will automatically become its voting members and will assume responsibility for its future.

Memoranda of Understanding and Mediation Summaries: A Discussion Document

Peter Martin

This discussion document has been prepared with a view to the standardisation of Memoranda of Understanding and Mediation Summaries. By the time this directory/handbook is published, the final proposals agreed upon will become part of the recommendations for good practice of the UK College of Family Mediators. There are, of course, many acceptable variations of practice both from organisation to organisation, and from individual to individual. The intention of the good practice recommendations will be to ensure a consistent and high standard of the finished article.

(1) What are Memoranda of Understanding or Mediation Summaries?

Memoranda of Understanding (the National Family Mediation and Family Mediation Scotland terminology) and Mediation Summaries (the Family Mediators Association term) are summaries of the results of a mediation process, the proposals reached by the couple (where proposals have been reached), and summaries of the background information upon which the proposals are based. The documents may include financial proposals in All Issues Mediation and a Parenting Plan where the couple have children.

(2) Why are they Needed?

Memoranda and Summaries are needed for the couple to confirm not only what took place in the mediation, but also to confirm the conclusions reached so that these may be referred back to and so that the couple's decisions are clear. They are also needed in All Issues Mediation for presentation to each person's independent legal advisor to be turned into a fully binding agreement. This may also be the case in respect of a Parenting Plan where the proposals are to form the basis of a court order regarding the children. Memoranda and Summaries are in many ways the open face of a mediation, particularly in All Issues Mediation. The professionalism of the mediator and effectiveness of the process will often be judged by third parties by what they read. Well-presented Memoranda or Summaries are a good advertisement for mediation. Badly-prepared and rambling Memoranda or Summaries may confirm existing prejudices about mediation and indicate that the process itself was badly presented and rambling.

(3) Who are the Memoranda or Summaries for?

They are firstly for the parties themselves. The reasons for this are set out above. Secondly, they are for the mediators to provide an additional record of the results of the mediation. Thirdly, they are for third parties. Those writing Memoranda or Summaries should bear in mind that these will be read by third parties who do not necessarily have background information about the couple. In particular, this applies to the parties' own legal advisors. The Memorandum or Summary therefore needs to be sufficiently comprehensive and clear to be fully understood by, for example, a solicitor who is seeing the individual for the first time and is being asked to turn the proposals into an agreed order. It should therefore not only set out what is proposed, but also why it is being proposed.

(4) Types of Memoranda of Understanding and Summaries

(a) Interim Summary

The couple may often find an Interim Summary extremely helpful. The Interim Summary will identify the issues and the tasks on which they are working and on which additional information may be required. An Interim Summary should always be legally privileged, even if it is a summary of financial assets. Where a required wording is used to confirm that privilege exists, that required wording should be within this document. An Interim Summary of the financial position in All Issues Mediation may be extremely helpful in allowing individuals to consult their own independent solicitors on issues of disclosure or completeness of disclosure, and possible settlement options.

(b) Interim Agreement

In certain circumstances an Interim Agreement may be appropriate. Such circumstances are extremely limited, since an Interim Agreement may well be legally binding and may be referred to in court proceedings. Interim Agreements may be more often used within a parenting program, for example to record the arrangements for contact. A written summary of agreed arrangements for contact which is referrable to the court can sometimes avoid misunderstandings and provide certainty which is extremely helpful to separating parents. In matters concerning children the court will of course make the ultimate decision whatever the agreement records. In All Issues Mediation, Interim Agreements should be used only on the rarest occasions to deal with financial issues, since such an agreement may prejudice either party's position in relation to future overall settlement. Therefore, care should be taken to ensure that it is Without Prejudice to the final settlement, and that any agreement that has been reached does not so prejudice either party that it effectively decides the issues between the couple. The most common (and sometimes most difficult) requirement for an Interim Agreement may relate to the sale of the former matrimonial home and the utilisation of the net proceeds of the sale. Such an agreement should only be entered into if the parties are also independently legally advised and the agreement itself approved by the parties' solicitors before signing. The financial disclosure and data upon which any such agreement is based should be recorded in an open schedule as in 4(e) below.

(c) Parenting Plan

In any mediation in which the couple have children, a Parenting Plan should be considered. In mediation in which only Children Issues are being considered, the final Mediation Summary or Memorandum of Understanding will largely consist of such a Parenting Plan. A Parenting Plan may also be prepared as an Interim Summary. In All Issues Mediation, the Parenting Plan should form part of the final Memorandum or Summary. The current FMA practice does not use the term 'Parenting Plan'. It is recommended that this term be adopted to emphasise that the couple are parents, rather than using the more legalistic 'contact arrangements' or similar terms.

(d) Final Legally Privileged Mediation Summary or Memorandum of Understanding

The content and form of this final document are considered in more detail below. Essentially it should summarise the mutually acceptable proposals for settlement, where such have been reached. It should provide sufficient background information to be understandable in itself, without additional explanation from the parties. Where some or all issues remain unresolved, there should be a neutrally worded statement of each party's position to enable and assist further steps that might be required to reach settlement. It should pinpoint any issues that have not been dealt with at all. It may also contain financial information and the background to the financial proposals including, where they exist, each party's contentions as to 'ownership' of particular assets and similar matters.

(e) Open Summary of Financial Information

In All Issues Mediation there should be an Open Summary of the financial information that has been disclosed. This document should not be legally privileged so that it is clear to the party's legal adviser, and if necessary to the court, upon what financial basis proposals are being put. It will provide a detailed list of the financial resources and other relevant facts about each party's financial circumstances. Supporting documents produced within the mediation should either be attached to this or referred to as having been disclosed to both parties. It should also record a statement by both parties either that full disclosure has been given, or that disclosure is incomplete. This summary should be signed both by the mediators and by the parties themselves.

It should be noted that the above is not in accordance with the universal practice of NFM or FMS, but a number of services have adopted the above view. The current Memoranda of Understanding and 'standard' documents that I have seen, however, contain the financial information within the Without Prejudice document. This substantially negates the whole purpose of having full disclosure within a mediation and can lead to additional expense as solicitors have to re-check and/or re-work the information provided within the Memorandum to safeguard the interests of their clients. This is because financial information given on a Without Prejudice basis needs to be repeated on an open basis before any solicitor should advise that it is safe to reach settlement terms.

(5) Form and Content of Memoranda/Summaries

The precise form of a Memorandum of Understanding or Summary varies among organisations, and even between mediators within the same organisation. It is not suggested that the form of a Memorandum should be prescribed. It is important that the Summaries whilst being professional and businesslike should also convey the warmth and care shown by the mediators. Whilst always being professional, they should be neither legalistic nor too informal. Balance is important. Within NFM and FMS, the Memorandum of Understanding (which term from hereon is used only for the Without Prejudice document) is phrased to come from the individuals themselves, although it is not signed by them. Within FMA a more neutral third party phraseology is used. There is no significant reason to recommend one approach over the other.

From the point of view of content, the following is felt to be essential within every document:

(a) Open Summary of Financial Information

This is only required in All Issues Mediation. As recommended above, it must be a separate document from the Memorandum and should not contain any details of proposals, only information. It should contain:

(i)   A statement confirming that the Summary is an open document recording the financial information disclosed by each. The statement should also confirm that the need for full financial disclosure has been explained and the extent to which any independent verification has been undertaken. The FMA has a required wording of such a statement for insurance purposes. It is recommended that this or a similar statement be adopted. It is set out in the recommendations at the end of this document.

(ii) Details of the financial documents disclosed should be set out. Copies of the detailed Financial Memoranda completed by the clients should be attached, together with the additional documentation, or alternatively confirmation given that each party already has such documents in their possession. It is preferable for the former course to be adopted, but substantial copying of documents results from this, with consequent cost implications. If documentation is not attached, an index of the documents disclosed should be included.

(iii) Details of the financial circumstances should be set out. For ease of reference these should be scheduled, with appropriate notes or explanations given separately. The notes and explanations must not deal with the Without Prejudice negotiations but only refer to issues of agreed fact.

(iv) The Open Summary and schedule forming part of this should contain full details of the assets, liabilities, income, expenditure levels and any other relevant financial information. The date to which information has been provided must be set out. Ideally it should show the current ownership of these assets, whether in joint or individual names and if so whose. The Summary can make it clear that in setting out the current ownership of assets, no statement as to individual rights is implied. A schedule which does not identify current ownership is, however, almost useless from the lawyer's perspective in turning what are hopefully proposals for settlement into a court order without substantial additional investigation and expense.

(b) Memorandum of Understanding

The Memorandum of Understanding or Mediation Summary is the Without Prejudice, privileged Summary. The contents of this may vary from case to case since this Summary will deal with the issues that the parties wish to deal with. In general terms, however, in an All Issues Mediation, the Memorandum of Understanding should contain the following essential elements. Reference is made below to a number of areas where information (and I mean information not advice) needs to be provided. If the mediators themselves are not able to provide such information they must ensure it is provided before completing the mediation.

(i) A prescribed statement confirming that the document is legally privileged and does not record or create a binding agreement. This statement should also confirm that the parties have been advised to obtain independent legal advice. All member organisations have a required wording for this paragraph, although such wording varies. There does not appear to be any major advantage or disadvantage of the varying wordings, but it may assist if (subject to insurance requirements) a single wording could be agreed. The statement should also confirm that the parties have signed a separate Open Summary of Financial Information and confirm the distinction between that, which can be disclosed, and the Memorandum of Understanding which is privileged. It is suggested that the statement also clarifies that the Memorandum of Understanding can be produced and shown to involved third parties, such as the individual's solicitor.

(ii) Background Information: Sufficient background information should be given to ensure that the Memorandum and the Open Summary are understandable to a third party. It should detail the essential matters of the names, ages and dates of birth of the parties and their children, and whether the couple are still living together and brief historical information if it is relevant. Some brief comment as to the process of the mediation, such as the number of sessions, may also be helpful within this.

(iii) The issues that the parties wished to deal with should be set out so that the parameters of the mediation can easily be seen.

(iv) Parenting Plan: This must be clear and concise and must always deal with issues of residence and contact. It is recommended that the term Parenting Plan be adopted as a standard phrase within the Memorandum of Understanding. The Parenting Plan should also deal with other issues that have arisen in connection with the children's welfare, paying particular attention to issues such as education and religious upbringing. Where the couple have been in basic agreement in relation to the children's issues this should be mentioned to show why a brief note is appropriate rather than a lengthy exposition.

(v) Child Support: Issues of maintenance for the children should always be dealt with. If the Child Support Agency is not involved and not intended to be involved then it should be noted whether or not a Child Support Calculation has been done in any event. Where there is no Child Support Agency Assessment, the Memorandum must confirm that the couple have been informed of the Child Support Agency and the manner in which it works. It should further confirm that the couple have been told that the Child Support Agency may override any agreement in respect of maintenance reached between them should either party apply.

(vi) Separation/Divorce: The Memorandum should not only record the intentions of the couple in this respect, but also confirm in respect of married couples (in England and Wales) that the effect of the Family Law Act and the manner in which it is to work has been explained, particularly where the couple intend to divorce after a period of separation. In Scotland the relevant date/date of separation/valuation date to value the assets which are matrimonial property must be established.

(vii) Matrimonial/Family Home: The decision of the couple in relation to this should not only be set out, but also the manner of its original purchase and funding.

(viii) Capital and Other Assets: Where relevant, the source of these as well as the proposed division should be set out. The competing claims and details of the issues between the couple in respect of any assets should be made clear, whilst not repeating the arguments that occurred within the mediation.

(ix) Financial Support: The extent and period of financial support proposals should be dealt with. In particular, if the payments are to be time-limited, confirmation as to whether or not any extension of the time limit is to be possible should be confirmed. The effect of dismissal of rights should also be dealt with.

(x) Pensions: In view of the current provision in respect of this, it is essential that the Memorandum deals with the pensions specifically. A reminder of the explanation given as to current pension law would be helpful. If there is to be no pension splitting or earmarking and the matter has been dealt with within the overall division of assets (which as a matter of interest, is still the norm), the manner in which this has been done should be made clear.

(xi) Inheritance: Confirmation that the provisions of the Inheritance Act were explained should be given. The extent to which issues of possible future inheritance were taken into account should also be confirmed. This may not apply to Scotland.

(xii) Wills: Confirmation that the effect of divorce on wills and the necessity to make new wills was discussed should also be given.

(xiii) Tax: Confirmation that the general tax effect of the proposals had been considered, or confirmation that the couple have been advised to take advice on this aspect, should be given.

(xiv) Division of Contents/Personal Possessions: The extent to which this was dealt with within the mediation should be clarified, in particular if it is agreed, for example, that the parties are going to divide it by themselves, the process by which they are to do this and to solve arguments (for example by equal division by value in the event of dispute) should be confirmed.

(xv) Other Issues: Included within this should be details of the parties' intentions to co-habit or remarry, or the fact that either or both have no such intention. Details of any other issues that arose should be dealt with. These will vary from mediation to mediation. In particular whether or not any of the particular Section 25 factors were taken into consideration should be dealt with. The implications of a dismissal of claims should be confirmed as having been discussed where appropriate. In particular, if the mediator had any qualms about disclosure this must be mentioned to flag-up the issue to the parties' independent advisors. The timing of the proposals should also be dealt with. Issues that may arise from any intention to re-marry must also be clarified. A commitment to return to mediation to help sort out future problems can be helpful.

(xvi) Summary of Proposals: The proposals in respect of each individual item should be made clear when discussing it within the body of the Memorandum. A Summary of Proposals should also clearly set out the proposals in such a way that a third party, particularly a solicitor, will simply be able to refer to this Summary in order to draft an agreement or consent order between the parties.

The Open Summary and Memorandum also act as a checklist of those items a mediator should cover. As such they should be produced, albeit in shortened checklist form, even if the couple do not wish this to be produced to them or to be paid for by them.

(6) Summary of Proposals and Recommendations

There are a number of issues of best practice arising from the above. In particular, those matters contained in section five provide a useful checklist both in relation to the documentation to be produced, but also in relation to those matters which the mediators should ensure are dealt with within the mediation. The following specific proposals and recommendations are made for adoption as part of a practice standard:

(a) The term 'Parenting Plan' should be adopted to emphasise the role of the couple as parents.

(b) The Open Summary of Financial Information must be a separate document setting out the factual basis upon which the mediation has proceeded and any proposals are based.

(c) There should be a standardisation of terms. The open summary of financial information should be called the Open Summary of Financial Information. The Without Prejudice document should be called the Memorandum of Understanding. The term Mediation Summary on its own can be confusing.

(d) Standard paragraphs should be utilised as follows:

(i)   Open Summary of Financial Information: 'This Open Summary records on a formal and open basis the financial information disclosed by each of us and which has formed the basis of our discussions in mediation and any proposals that have resulted from such discussions. The need for full financial disclosure has been explained, and supporting documents produced where practical and where requested. It is acknowledged that no independent verification has been undertaken by the mediator as to accuracy or completeness. Where any independent verification has been obtained, this is referred to specifically in the Summary. Both parties confirm that their financial disclosure is complete (or set out what information remains outstanding). We have agreed to value our assets as at the (insert date) and that the values should form the basis of any proposals for financial settlement. A separate Summary relating to the discussions in the mediation, the outcome and any proposals made which is "Without Prejudice" and legally privileged has also been provided.'

(ii)   Memorandum of Understanding: 'This Memorandum is legally privileged. It does not record or create a binding agreement between (insert names), and any proposals set out in this Memorandum have not been set out with the intention of creating legal relations by the creation of this document. It is intended to facilitate each of them obtaining independent professional advice which the mediator(s) have recommended them to do before they take any steps to enter into an agreement, whether through solicitors or informally between themselves. Unless and until they decide to enter into a binding agreement, no such binding agreement exists between them. Mr and Mrs (insert name) have signed an Open Summary of the information disclosed by each of them. They understand that this may be produced to the court (unlike this Summary) and have had the necessity for full and complete disclosure explained to them. This Memorandum of Understanding may, of course, be produced to legal advisors upon the basis that it is and remains a privileged document.'

(e) The Open Summary should be signed by the couple and by the mediator(s). The Memorandum of Understanding should only be signed by the mediator(s). Where a detailed Parenting Plan has been produced and the parents feel it would be useful to have it signed in a formal way, the Parenting Plan should be reproduced as a separate document headed as such.

(f) All of the documents produced by way of financial disclosure, including in particular any financial questionnaires completed by the parties, should either be annexed to the Open Summary or an index of the documentation produced should be set out.

(g) A schedule of the assets and liabilities, income and general expenditure should be produced as part of the Open Summary (total expenditure rather than the individual items being sufficient), indicating the existing ownership of all assets and liabilities.

(h) A Summary of any proposals should be clearly and succinctly set out at the end of the Memorandum of Understanding.

(i) The matters set out in section five of this document should be adopted (with such additions or deletions as after discussion seem appropriate) as a best practice checklist of the issues which mediators should consider in all mediations.

I would like to thank Fiona Garwood of FMS and Paul Foster, who is both an FMA and NFM mediator, for their valuable input into the production of this discussion document. I would also like to thank Angela Lake-Carroll and acknowledge that many of the ideas and comments within this document probably originate from her through our working together on FMA training over the years. I also acknowledge that my knowledge of Scottish family law is sparse to say the least. There may be a number of differences in relation to legal issues which will need to be taken into account before this discussion document becomes formal College policy. The principles remain the same, however. They should just be read in a different accent. Finally, I must thank my partners in Osmond Gaunt & Rose for allowing me the time to continue to work in mediation despite the financial disincentives.

Peter Martin is an FMA Mediator and Member of the UK College Professional Standards Committee.

Mediation—Looking to the Future: An Overview of Key Issues

Professor Janet Walker

The year 1996 was a landmark in the history of family mediation in the UK. Gulliver[1] has described mediation as the 'gradual creation of order and co-ordination between the parties', and a similar narrative could be applied to the developments and transitions in the organisation and positioning of family mediation during the last 20 years, culminating in 1996 in the establishment of the UK College of Family Mediators, and the formal recognition of mediation within the family justice system. While the leading mediation agencies were coming together in a spirit of co-operation to provide a firmer, more coherent professional foundation for both policy and practice, another significant path was being laid on which to build a more enduring framework for the delivery of family mediation services in England and Wales. The Family Law Act 1996 is expected to promote a more conciliatory, consensual approach to the dissolution of marriage, and thereby encourage greater use of mediation by couples who will be required to resolve disputes about the arrangements for children, finances and property before a divorce is granted. Mediation 'is intended to be a pervasive factor in the new divorce process'[2], and although the Act will apply only in England and Wales, it signifies such a dramatic shift in the acceptance and funding of mediation as an alternative dispute resolution process in family proceedings that it is bound to have far-reaching implications for developments elsewhere, and in particular for the work of the UK College.

Having survived for many years in a climate of scepticism, mediation seems set fair to attain a more assured position in the family justice system. Its advocates could be forgiven for believing that, finally, mediation 'is an idea whose time has come'[3]. Some might argue that mediation is facing a new beginning, with opportunities to shape the future with greater confidence. Nevertheless, there are a number of debates to be had and decisions to be made both prior to the implementation of the Family Law Act and also after a new system is up and running. For the purposes of this brief glimpse into the future, it is possible to group the issues which must be addressed into three main categories: organisational structures and arrangements; professional competencies; and principles and objectives of policy and practice.

The Shape of Things to Come

During its early history, mediation in the UK developed in a piecemeal, fragmented manner, with little in the way of formal co-ordination between a variety of services located across the statutory, voluntary and private sectors. A deeply-embedded child-saving philosophy has characterised much mediation practice, and some of the services within the voluntary sector are supported by leading children's charities. But what began more as a movement for divorce reform has steadily had to embrace demands for increased professionalism and national standards. While the new legislation does not set out to regulate mediation, it nevertheless requires certain standards of service delivery and quality assurance to be met if public funding is to be made available.

Mediation has been organised primarily within four main bodies: National Family Mediation and Family Mediation Scotland in the voluntary sector; the probation service in the statutory sector; and the Family Mediators Association in the private sector. We are now witnessing significant changes as the UK College becomes a membership body, and increasing numbers of services and providers gear up for legal aid franchising, and national standards are being adopted.

Services in the voluntary sector are the most likely to face change. They stand to gain considerably from the availability of legal aid for those couples who cannot afford to pay. The perpetual insecurity of these services has raised many concerns among more established professions about the credibility and expertise of mediators who provide their services mostly well below market rates, although most services ask clients for donations or nominal contributions. These services now have to demonstrate that they are self-sufficient and not dependent on public funding to stay in business. Research suggests that clients are not looking for cheap-and-cheerful services, but for something which is unquestionably professional. The standard they frequently use to make their judgment is the same as the standard they apply to lawyers[4]. Mediators in the private sector, at least half of whom are also practising lawyers, have had to bring a business-like orientation to the service they offer right from the beginning, particularly in respect of charging more realistic fees, but the numbers using their services have remained very low.

The Legal Aid Board began its programme for franchising mediation providers during 1997. This process makes substantial demands on services, many of which have historically been run on large amounts of goodwill and commitment and minimal funding.

The next few years will reveal whether current service structures are robust enough or the most appropriate to meet the challenges and opportunities now available. As value-for-money questions are asked, relatively small voluntary sector mediation services may disappear in favour of larger units, or mediators may become self-employed, or enter multi-disciplinary professional partnerships[5]. Even lawyers trained as mediators see the future of mediation as dependent to a large extent on the way in which issues concerned with funding, organisation, training and quality assurance are managed[6]. And there is the critical question of the role the probation service will play in a new era of mediation practice. There are fears[7] that models of inter-disciplinary co-operation between mediation providers which appear to have flourished in recent years may not survive the new proposals for public funding which could encourage greater competition than previously. It will be interesting to see how both national and local partnerships and consortia respond to a rapidly changing landscape in respect of mediation funding, and the need for nationally available and quality assured service provision by the millennium.

Determining Professional Competence

Over the years, judges, lawyers, probation officers, counsellors, family therapists and others have aspired to mediation practice, and there has been no shortage of debate, sometimes heated, about the competencies required. The move to All Issues Mediation in the late 1980s brought the skills and expertise needed by mediators into sharp focus. The position of the Law Society has been to support the growth of mediation in principle, but to argue that 'the involvement of a lawyer in the mediation process is essential when property and financial matters are being considered'[8]. As more lawyers have trained and practised as mediators, their technical expertise has been absorbed into the mediation process, yet there remains ambivalence about the extent to which mediation is or ever can be a real alternative to negotiation through lawyers, and therefore about whether mediation should be encouraged to develop as a separate profession distinct from the practice of law, social work and counselling. It is clear that many lawyers continue to view mediation as a useful adjunct to the traditional lawyer-led process, but not as a substitute for it, and a significant number have expressed the view that mediation as a separate profession would not be necessary if all lawyers adopted a conciliatory approach to matrimonial disputes.[9]

The UK College has developed national standards for selection, training and accreditation for mediators, yet other professional bodies, such as the Solicitors Family Law Association, are developing their own training standards. Diversity is commonplace in other jurisdictions, notably in North America, where training is offered by a wide variety of individuals and agencies, with professional associations (such as the Academy of Family Mediators) offering similar sorts of validation process to those offered by the UK College. Choice would seem to be healthy in so far as it does not seek to segregate potential mediators into groupings which may ultimately work to the detriment of better co-ordination and effective organisational structures. Indeed, until issues of structure are determined, it is possible that the potential benefits of a truly multi-disciplinary approach to what is undoubtedly a boundary-crossing activity may not be fully realised. It will be unfortunate if professional rivalries and 'turf' issues impede progress.

What is emerging is a greater focus on the importance of a coherent theoretical framework, the significance of which has perhaps been overshadowed in the past by the almost exclusive interest in delineating skills and techniques, to the extent that mediators have not been provided with explanatory models that inform practice regardless of their professional backgrounds. This is clearly an important task given that there is likely to be a surge in demand for training.[10] If this can be achieved, then there is every chance that diversity may be seen as a strength. Both lawyers and non-lawyers engage in a rhetoric of cross-disciplinarity, but until now the rhetoric has not been sharply defined, nor very detailed. Mediation represents a complex process of accommodation in the face of changing views about what it can and should be. It is most unfortunate that in its formative years mediation has been so positively contrasted with negotiation by lawyers. Such polarity is not only misleading, but deeply divisive at a time when co-operation and co-working seem to be essential.

Defining Principles and Objectives

Despite the existence of a variety of organisational and practice models, most mediators share a common set of principles and are guided by common objectives. There is a strong belief in the UK that mediation must be a confidential and voluntary process in which the mediator is impartial between the parties and neutral as to outcomes. There is a high level of agreement that the mediation process should enhance communication, maximise the exploration of alternative outcomes, address the needs, wishes and feelings of all parties, help participants to reach agreements perceived by them as fair, and provide a model for future conflict resolution.[11] The Government White Paper[12] which preceded the Family Law Bill set an agenda for mediation which would extend its remit still further to include the identification of marriages capable of being saved, helping couples accept responsibility for the ending of the marriage, dealing with feelings of hurt and anger, addressing issues which may impede a couple's ability to negotiate settlements, and focusing on the needs of children and the importance of shared parental responsibility. This is a tall order, and mediators are now considering just what is realistic and possible, bearing in mind that mediation is not a universal panacea.

As family mediation moves from the margins to the mainstream of family justice, some thorny issues must be re-examined. There is growing realisation, for example, that mediators must screen for and provide adequate safeguards in relation to domestic violence[13]. Although there is no universal agreement about whether a history of domestic violence should preclude any attempt at mediation, most mediators do not think that mediation is appropriate for couples where abuse has been a persistent feature or is severe and ongoing. Much of the feminist criticism of mediation is of settlement-oriented, mandatory programmes in which coercion is a feature. Increasingly, the key question is probably not whether to mediate in spousal abuse cases, but what special steps must be taken to protect an abused partner who nevertheless wishes to mediate.[14] Mediation may be acceptable if the process is individually tailored, separate interviews are offered, and legal protection is a priority, but this issue needs a more considered debate during the pilot projects, and before the Family Law Act is implemented.

How to ensure that the parties are encouraged to consider the welfare, wishes and needs of their children is another matter on which further thought is necessary. Mediators are already conscious of the need to consider the position of children, and this is addressed in training. Occasionally children are directly involved in mediation, and some services now offer counselling support for children. The extent to which the use of parenting plans may be introduced into mediation practice is a matter for experimentation. Such plans as are used in other jurisdictions, notably Australia and North America, are highly practical and detailed documents which go far beyond more basic questions of residence and contact. Such detailed negotiation may appear to be overly interventionist and directive to those espousing a minimalist, dispute resolution approach, and it remains to be seen whether it is a viable option in the longer term. During 1998, the use of parenting plans will be tested in some areas as part of the Family Law Act pilots, in order to discover whether parents find them useful.

A Period of Expansion

As mediators and the Legal Aid Board prepare for the implementation of the Family Law Act, there is no way of knowing what the demand for mediation will be in the future. There is optimism that numbers attending mediation will increase, but so far there is little evidence of this happening. Concern was expressed during the passage of the Family Law Bill through the House of Commons that a two-tier system of mediation could emerge: voluntary sector services provided for legally-aided clients with no choice over which service they can access, and the possibility of private mediation for those who could afford to pay and exercise choice. Even if this were the position, the concern ought to be less about any difference in quality between the two, and more about how inequalities in choice might add to conflict between the spouses, or deter would-be clients from choosing to mediate.

Whatever organisational and practice structures emerge, and however codes of practice are refined, the government has placed substantial reliance on mediation to reduce the bitterness in divorce and place responsibility for managing the dissolution in the hands of those seeking it. If mediation is to begin to justify this level of faith and financial investment, it is essential that couples are able to make better informed choices. This implies that there must be an end to the confusion surrounding the purpose and nature of mediation. Many of those debating the new provisions in Parliament were struggling to grasp the concept of mediation and distinguish it from counselling. An attitude survey conducted for the government in 1995 found that when mediation was explained to them, over 80 per cent of the sample thought mediation would be either 'fairly' or 'very useful'. Explaining mediation carefully and precisely is a particular feature of the information meeting, attendance at which will become compulsory when the Family Law Act is implemented. The government has decided that various models for the provision of information should be tested, and the first five pilots were launched in June 1997. During 1998, a further six pilots are planned. Some of these pilots are taking place in areas where franchising of mediation services is taking place. Two new videos showing mediation in practice have been produced for the information meetings. Preliminary findings from the evaluation suggest that those attending information meetings consider themselves to be better informed about mediation than previously, and some of them are indicating their intention to try mediation. What we do not know is whether being better informed about mediation will encourage more people to mediate their disputes in the future. It has been commonly held that without better public under-standing of what mediation is, how it fits with other services, including legal advice and representation, and how to assess whether it is an option worth trying, the 'enormous potential' accorded to mediation may never be realised. The information meeting pilots should begin to test this assertion.

▨ References

1   Gulliver, P H (1979) *Disputes & Negotiations: A cross-cultural perspective*. Academic Press, London.

2   Cretney, S M & Masson, J M (1997) *Principles of Family Law*. 6th edn, Sweet & Maxwell, London.

3   Vroom, P; Fassett, D & Wakefield, R A (1981) 'Mediation: The Wave of the Future', *American Family*, 4, pp 8–13.

4   Walker, J; McCarthy, P & Timms, N (1994) *Mediation: the Making and Remaking of Co-operative Relationships an evaluation of the*

effectiveness of comprehensive mediation. Relate Centre for Family Studies, Newcastle University, Newcastle upon Tyne.

5 McCarthy, P & Walker, J 'The longer-term impact of family mediation', *Findings*, No 103. Joseph Rowntree Foundation Social Policy Research.

6 Posey, J (1995) 'Looking to the Future: observation on Government's proposals: a Co-ordinator's Response', *Family Mediation*, Vol 5, No 2, p 14.

7 McCarthy, P & Walker, J (1995) 'Mediation and Divorce Reform: The Lawyers' View', *Family Law*, Vol 25, pp 361–64.

8 Pemberton, A (1996) 'Mediation and Divorce Reform Proposals', *Family Law*, Vol 26, pp 220–221.

9 The Law Society (1991) *Response to National Family Conciliation Council Policy Paper on a National Family Conciliation Service.* The Law Society, London.

10 McCarthy, P & Walker, J (1995) 'Mediation and Divorce Reform: The Lawyers' View', *Family Law*, Vol 25, pp 361–64.

11 Walker, J (1997) 'Family Mediation' in McFarlane J (ed) *Rethinking Disputes: The Mediation Alternative.* Cavendish Publishing Ltd, London.

12 Folberg, J (1985) 'Mediation & Child Custody Disputes', *Columbia Journal of Law & Social Problems*, 19 (4) pp 1–36.

13 Lord Chancellor's Department (1995) *Looking to the Future: Mediation and the Ground for Divorce.* Government White Paper Cm 2799. HMSO, London.

14 Hester, M & Radford, L (1996) 'Domestic Violence & Child Contact Arrangements', *Findings*, No 100. Joseph Rowntree Foundation Social Policy Research.

15 Erickson, S K & McKnight, M S (1990) 'Mediating Spousal Abuse Divorce', *Mediation Quarterly*, 7 (4) pp 377–88.

Update on UK Research

Professor Janet Walker

There can be few advocates of an adversarial legal system when it comes to the resolution of matrimonial disputes. Family mediation appears to be the sensible alternative, so much so that practitioners have not always appreciated the emphasis placed by policy makers on the need for empirical evidence as to its benefits. Until the mid-1980s there was little systematic research on the effectiveness of mediation, and in 1989 Kressel & Pruitt[1] concluded that the sustained study of mediation was still in its infancy, although they noted that it was way ahead of equivalent research on the more traditional, adversarial system.

The UK can lay claim to a respectable body of mediation research, much of which has influenced policy and practice. Early studies of mediation concentrated on measuring settlement rates, but researchers and practitioners alike quickly realised the limitations of simply counting the number of agreements when the focus in mediation is not only on outcomes but also on process. In a recent review of research, Irving and Benjamin[2] group studies into three categories: process studies; outcome research; and those studies which consider predictors of successful mediation. While few UK studies have specifically attempted to do the latter, there are some important studies of process and outcomes, which indicate some of the predictors.

Understanding Process

Process studies ought to show what interventions have what sort of effects, with which kind of clients, and in what types of contexts. Most fall short of this ideal, but they do shed light on what takes place within mediation. Some of the most detailed studies have involved conversation analysis of audio-taped sessions. In the UK, Dingwall and Greatbatch[3] have done most work in this area, as a result of which they have questioned mediator neutrality, arguing that in their orchestration of settlements, mediators subtly ensure certain sorts of outcomes. While these may be socially highly desirable, and legally acceptable, they nevertheless impose a particular, and often implicit, value system which may not always be appropriate, and may militate against couples seeking their own mutually acceptable solutions. In their study of the management of arguments by disputants in mediation sessions Dingwall and Greatbatch[4] found that some arguments continue until a mediator intervenes, but many are ended by the disputants themselves, without either having to offer concessions or to submit. They conclude that general statements about the management of conflict in mediation are premature. Looking at process studies in the United States, Irving & Benjamin concluded that 'successful' mediators tend to intervene actively, encouraging productive exchanges and discouraging destructive conflict.

Our own research[5] has examined process, concentrating particularly on the consumer view, enhanced by the perspectives of mediators and lawyers, and non-participant observation. These studies show that practice setting makes a difference, frequently shaping what mediators do or do not do. More importantly, the research reveals just how

Handbook A

demanding mediation is for clients and for mediators, particularly in respect of All Issues Mediation in which financial disclosure and division of assets can require considerable patience and stickability. We have found that clients:

- may experience fatigue in mediation;
- value the safety and fairness of the process;
- would like more opportunity for single appointments, particularly at the start;
- look for guidance from mediators (perceived as 'experts');
- dislike being pressured into making agreements;
- need to talk about the past in order to plan the future;
- feel constrained if the process is too rigid;
- value professionalism.

▪ Assessing Outcomes

Outcome studies usually focus on agreements, client satisfaction and costs. Across the studies in North America and the UK, agreement rates vary between 50–80 per cent. Although our evaluation of All Issues Mediation took place in its early days, the findings suggested that it is more effective than mediation which is restricted to child issues. Some 80 per cent of couples reached agreements (39 per cent on all issues, and a further 41 per cent on some issues). In addition:

- the majority of users were satisfied with the service;
- satisfaction was not dependent on reaching agreements;
- mediation assisted in the recreation of friendly relationships;
- users were helped to cope with stress, reduce resentment and tension, and improve communication.

The limitation of most outcome evaluation is its relative short-term focus, yet many would argue that if mediation is to be of any real value, it must produce results which survive in the longer term. Our follow-up study of mediation clients some three to four years afterwards[6] shows that users of All Issues Mediation, as compared with those restricted to children's issues, were:

- more likely to feel that mediation had helped them maintain good relationships with their ex-spouses, and feel less bitter;
- more content with child-care arrangements and had fewer disagreements about contact;
- able to reach agreements which had survived the critical test of time.

One of the most important findings is that actually reaching agreements in mediation is an important factor in respect of the longer-term benefits, having a substantial impact on the quality of post-divorce life and also on the cost of getting divorced. Determining the costs associated with mediation has proved to be somewhat elusive, however, and this is an area which is likely to be the subject of further (difficult) research. Our early research suggested that mediation might impose an additional cost as an adjunct to legal representation; more recent research indicates that, in the clients' view at least, mediation can substantially reduce the cost of divorce.

Predicting Successful Mediation

There is no consensus among the available studies as to the best predictions of achieving mediated agreements, although mediators favouring a problem-solving approach seem to be more effective than those who are more settlement-oriented, and users prefer the former, too. There is some evidence that agreement is more likely if clients perceive that the mediator can help them gain insights into their feelings, when disputes are relatively recent and less severe, and when clients possess good communication skills and are willing to cooperate. It is clear that mediation is not suitable for everyone, and assessing who might benefit is an important matter for future studies.

Learning from Research

Research in the UK has consistently pointed to the benefits of a multi-disciplinary approach. Mediation is valued as one of a number of important services which meet a variety of needs, and in 1996 it found its place on the statute books as one of the key elements within the Family Law Act. For the first time, mediation will be publicly funded through the Legal Aid Board. Prior to implementation of the Act, new research has been commissioned to determine, among other things, the relative benefits and cost effectiveness of contracting for the provision of publicly funded and quality assured family mediation through different supplier arrangements: and the relative costs and benefits both for users and the tax payer. In addition to the establishment of a number of databases and economic analysis, qualitative research will study the intake process, and what goes on in mediation by means of conversation analysis. By the millenium, the body of knowledge about mediation practice in the UK is likely to be increased substantially as a result, and the amount of information about mediation available to the public will be similarly increased. It remains to be seen how far a new framework for mediation within a wholly different approach to divorce process confirms or questions previous findings.

References

1 Kressel, K & Pruitt, D G (1989) *Mediation Research: The Process & Effectiveness of Third Party Interventions.* Jossey-Bass, San Francisco.

2 Irving, H H & Benjamin, M (1995) *Family Mediation: Contemporary Issues.* Thousand Oaks, Sage, California.

3 Dingwall, R & Greatbatch, D (1991) 'Behind Closed Doors: A Preliminary Report on Mediator/Client Interaction in England', *Family & Conciliation Courts Review*, 29(3), pp 291–303.
(1993) 'Who is in Charge? Rhetoric & Evidence in the Study of Mediation', *Journal of Social Welfare & Family Law*, 6, pp 367–85.

4 Dingwall, R & Greatbatch, D (1997) 'Argumentative Talk in Divorce Mediation Sessions', *American Sociological Review*, Vol 62. Feb, pp 151–170.

5 Ogus, A I; Walker, J A; Jones-Lee, M; Cole, W; Corlyon, J; McCarthy, P; Simpson, R & Wray, S (1989) *Report of the Conciliation Project Unit on the Costs and Effectiveness of Conciliation in England and Wales.* Lord Chancellor's Department, London.
Walker, J, McCarthy, P & Timms, N (1994) *Mediation: the Making*

and Remaking of Co-operative Relationships—an evaluation of the effectiveness of comprehensive mediation. Relate Centre for Family Studies, Newcastle University, Newcastle upon Tyne.

6 McCarthy, P & Walker, J (1996) 'Evaluating the Longer Term Impact of Family Mediation', Report to the Joseph Rowntree Foundation, Oct, pp 47.

Family Law for Mediators

Paul Foster

This is an introductory guide to be dipped into as necessary. We have endeavoured to state the law accurately as at January 1998.

The Law of Divorce

The law relating to marriage breakdown was radically changed by the Family Law Act 1996. This statute is not yet fully effective, but reference should be made to David Hodson's section 'Family Mediation and the Family Law Act 1996' below for full details of the changes.

Marriage has aspects of both contract and status. Once a couple has gone through a ceremony of marriage it may be possible for the marriage to be declared a nullity, although nullity proceedings are very unusual. If the marriage is valid, it may be suspended by a decree of judicial separation, or ended by a decree of divorce. The person starting the proceedings is called the petitioner, while the one on the receiving end is the respondent. The court document which starts the proceedings is called the petition. To start the ball rolling the petitioner sends to the court:

(a) a petition;
(b) a statement in prescribed form setting out the arrangements for the children of the family (plus sufficient copies of each);
(c) a cheque for the fee (currently £150); or
(d) if applicable, a form granting exemption from court fees; and
(e) if a solicitor is acting, a certificate stating whether the solicitor has discussed the prospects for reconciliation and giving the names of persons qualified to help with that process. There are no sanctions on the solicitor for failing to do so.

Nullity

As stated, this is a rare order. The petitioner must show that the marriage was void from its beginning or is voidable. A void marriage never existed and is established by proof of one of the following grounds:

(a) invalidity within the terms of the Marriage Acts (eg prohibited degrees of relationship);
(b) bigamy;
(c) both parties are the same sex;
(d) marriage is polygamous with one party domiciled in England and Wales.

A voidable marriage exists until a decree absolute ends it. To succeed, the petitioner must show one of the following grounds:

(a) inability to consummate;
(b) wilful refusal to consummate;
(c) lack of valid consent;
(d) unfitness of one party due to mental illness;
(e) respondent suffering from a communicable venereal disease;
(f) pregnancy of the wife by another.

Applications under the last four grounds cannot be made after three years, save with leave of the court. In practice, there are few advantages in bringing proceedings to void a marriage and most petitioners rely upon unreasonable behaviour (see later). However, it is worth noting that proceedings for nullity can be brought within the first year of the marriage.

Divorce

The sole ground for divorce is that the marriage has irretrievably broken down. No petition may be presented during the first year of the marriage. Irretrievable breakdown must be proved and this can only be done in a limited number of ways prescribed by the Matrimonial Causes Act 1973.

The prescribed ways of proving breakdown (known as 'facts') are:

(a) that the respondent has committed adultery and the petitioner finds living with the respondent intolerable (although not necessarily intolerable because of the adultery);

(b) that the respondent has behaved in a way which makes it unreasonable to expect the petitioner to go on living with the respondent (invariably known as 'unreasonable behaviour');

(c) desertion for two years prior to the presentation of the petition;

(d) separation for two years as above with the consent of the respondent;

(e) living apart for five years.

Most decrees are based upon unreasonable behaviour petitions brought by wives.

Costs

The petition often includes a claim (known as a prayer) for costs against the respondent. In practice these claims are often compromised or abandoned. Who should pay for the divorce is, of course, a suitable issue for mediation. If the court has to decide, it will normally award costs against a respondent if the petition is based on facts (a) or (b).

Calculating Time

Facts (c), (d) and (e) require that a prescribed continuous period of time has elapsed before the presentation of a petition. The Act provides that in calculating time no account is to be taken of a period or periods of up to six months during which the couple resumed cohabitation although these periods are not counted in computing the period of separation. The idea being to encourage attempts at reconciliation. The clock is stopped but the continuity is not broken.

Financial Hardship Bars

Parliament was concerned to protect financially weak spouses from the consequences of divorce until such time as the court had a chance to consider their position. To this end:

(1) A respondent to a two or five year petition can apply to the court to delay the granting of a decree absolute until the court is satisfied as to the reasonableness of the provision being made by the petitioner.

(2) A respondent to a five year divorce can apply to the court to refuse a divorce on the grounds of 'grave financial or other hardship'. These provisions are not often used in practice and with the advent of pensions earmarking will become rare indeed. Having said that, similar provisions appear in the Family Law Act 1996.

Judicial Separation

The effect of a decree of judicial separation is that the spouses are no longer bound to cohabit and the court can sort out their finances. The marriage is not dissolved however. The only people who normally find judicial separation appropriate are:

(a) people who have not been married a year but who need the court to make orders relating to capital or property;
(b) spouses whose marriages break down but whose religious faith denies them the possibility of civil divorce; and
(c) petitioners whose spouses are approaching retirement (usually wives) and who do not wish to lose pension benefits by reason of divorce.

To get a decree of judicial separation the petitioner must prove any one of the five facts above but need not assert that the marriage has broken down irretrievably.

Procedure

Most divorces and separations are granted under what is known as 'The Special Procedure'. This is a process conducted by post. When the respondent has acknowledged receipt of the petition and indicated that it will not be defended, the petitioner swears an affidavit confirming the truth of the petition and Statement of Arrangements for the Children and this is sent to the court. A district judge reads the paperwork and if satisfied that it is in order and that the petitioner has proved his grounds, the judge will move on to consider if she needs to exercise her powers under the Children Act 1989. The judge will, if satisfied, certify that the petitioner is entitled to a decree *nisi* and the court will fix a date for its pronouncement. If the judge is concerned about the arrangements for the children, she may call for further evidence or, in extreme circumstances, delay the divorce.

Six weeks and one day after the date of the decree *nisi*, the petitioner may apply for the divorce by applying for the decree absolute. Again this is done by post on a prescribed form and a fee (of £20) is payable. If the petitioner does not apply then the respondent may do so three months after the earliest date upon which the application for the decree absolute could have been made.

Defended Divorce

Sometimes respondents cannot accept the allegations against them or that the marriage is over. They have a right to defend the divorce by filing a document called an Answer and paying the appropriate fee (currently £100). The court will then give directions for trial and, at worst, a judge will have to decide if the petitioner is entitled to his divorce. Defended divorces are sad affairs. Even if successful, the respondent's victory is invariably pyrrhic and he will find that the lawyer's bills have substantially depleted the family coffers.

Mediators can provide a great service by taking time with the couple to explore the ending of the marriage and whether there is scope for agreeing the basis, both legal and factual, upon which it is to be ended. Until such time as The Family Law Act 1996 comes into force, we live with a divorce law which requires the initiator to rely upon fault-based

Handbook A

material if the divorce is to occur while the couple are still together or within two years of separation. It is surely good practice to alert the couple to the potentially polarising impact of this aspect of the law and to seek to negotiate ways of minimising the hurt.

Cohabitation

When unmarried people who have lived as husband and wife separate they do not have the same rights that married people have. English law has no concept of common law marriage (strictly speaking it does, but it is not what most people think it is!). Cohabitants do have rights to be protected from domestic violence (see later). They have no right to maintenance and there is no concept of 'palimony.' In relation to property, cohabitants may be able to rely upon the title deeds, or an agreement or in some cases upon some special legal rules known as the rules of equity. We shall look at each in turn.

The title deeds

The starting point is the title deeds. What do they say? Frequently they will be decisive. If the family home is in joint names then if the house is held by the owners as 'beneficial joint owners', they each own all the property and the survivor would automatically inherit it if the other one died. The net sale proceeds would be split equally if the house were sold. Alternatively it will be held as 'tenants in common', in which case the couple will have defined the individual shares they each own in the property. For example, '70 per cent to John and 30 per cent to Jill.' John and Jill are free to will their shares as they wish.

Couples should get detailed competent legal advice on which method is right for them before they buy, but this does not always happen, or if it does the importance of the decision is not appreciated in the heady atmosphere of the start of the relationship. Mediators therefore need the couple to get legal advice on the effect of the title deeds early in the mediation. Of course, the clients may decide to depart from the effect of the deed, but they must do so with their eyes open and for mutually understood reasons. The law will normally only allow a variation of the terms of the original conveyance at the request of one owner only if it can be proved that there has been significant fraud, duress or mistake.

Contract

The couple may have entered into a cohabitation agreement. These are rare and if well-drafted may answer most of the problems clients habitually bring to mediation. These agreements have seldom been tested in the courts. It is thus not possible to state categorically whether or not the courts would uphold any particular agreement. In general terms we imagine that if the agreement

- had been made between a couple of roughly equal bargaining power, and
- that each partner had an opportunity to receive legal advice before entering into the agreement, and
- that the effect of the agreement is not to produce a manifestly unjust result in present circumstances,

then the courts would be likely to give the agreement great weight. Again, early legal advice is essential.

If only one of the owners wants the property to be sold, a new Statute is now in force which sets out some of the factors which the Judge must take into account in making her decision.

■ Equity

These rules become relevant if an unmarried cohabitant or former cohabitant is seeking to establish an interest in property without having his or her name on the title deeds. They are formidably complex. Beware! Basically the courts look to see if the conduct of the parties towards each other makes it unfair to deny the weaker party an interest. However, the rules are technical. The details of the conduct are all important. This is lawyer's law not broad-brush justice. The questions it is worth asking are:

(1) Is there an express agreement, arrangement or understanding between the parties which has been acted upon to the claimant's detriment?

(2) Have there been direct contributions to the purchase of the property by the claimant?

(3) Have there been improvements to the property by the claimant in circumstances where it was either agreed expressly or can be implied that they would acquire an interest in the property as a result?

(4) Has a promise been made to the claimant in relation to the house upon which she has relied and acted to her detriment? This last area (known as 'proprietary estoppel') is in a state of flux. Highly skilled legal advice is needed.

Mediators who reflect on the above will realise that the law invites cohabitants to pay attention to their past actions and words in order to establish property interests. This approach does not sit happily with the future focus of mediation. Therefore, it may be that until this area of law is reformed there will be tension between cohabitants' legal remedies and their preferred solutions in mediation. We would, however, stress that while this is perfectly valid, it is vital that the cohabitants understand their legal position before concluding memoranda of understanding. Having said that, this is a lawyer's paradise, so do not be surprised if the cohabitants return from their solicitors with very different views of their legal situation!

■ Children

The key document is the Children Act 1989 (in this section referred to as 'the Act'). This codifies much of the private and public (ie involving local authorities) law relating to children. Some key concepts are outlined below.

Welfare of the Child

In any decision relating to the upbringing of a child or the administration of a child's property, the welfare of the child is said to be paramount. That is to say it is the only—not merely the most important—factor to be taken into account. That does not tell us much. How do the courts decide what is in the child's welfare? The Act provides a checklist which the court is obliged to have regard to in certain defined circumstances, and which is of value whenever 'welfare' questions arise. The factors are:

Handbook A

(a) the ascertainable wishes and feelings of the child concerned (considered in the light of his age and understanding);

(b) his physical, emotional and educational needs;

(c) the likely effect on him of any change of circumstances;

(d) his age, sex, background and any characteristics of his which the court considers relevant;

(e) any harm which he has suffered or is at risk of suffering;

(f) how capable each of his parents, and any other person in relation to whom the court considers the question to be relevant, is of meeting his needs;

(g) the range of powers available to the court under the Act in the proceedings in question.

We suggest these are commonsense factors which couples frequently have in mind when negotiating in mediation. What does the child need? Will change be harmful? Will he suffer? Which of us is better able to care for her etc? The reader will note that at the top of the list come wishes and feelings. It was not apparently intended to make this factor the most important, but clearly each factor must be assessed for importance. Wishes and feelings will be given increasing weight as the child matures. Children mature at different rates, but frequently the wishes of a child approaching puberty or beyond will be decisive.

Delay is Harmful

The Act says that delay is presumed to be harmful for the child. The court is required in every case to fix a timetable leading to a final hearing. The court tends to be proactive in the management of the case. It will authorise the filing of evidence and permit the reasoned and justifiable involvement of outside relevant experts.

Parental Responsibility

Parental responsibility is defined in the Children Act 1989 as 'all the rights, duties, powers, responsibilities and authority which by law a parent of a child has in relation to the child and his property'.

Who has parental responsibility?

Parents who were married to each other at the time of their child's birth or who have subsequently married both have parental responsibility for their natural children. If the parents have not been married to each other then only the mother of the child has parental responsibility for that child automatically.

Who can acquire parental responsibility?

Only an unmarried father can apply for parental responsibility of a child. A non-parent who has a residence order will have parental responsibility for a child during the lifetime of the residence order. A guardian appointed in a will or by a court order will also have parental responsibility as will parents who have adopted a child.

How can the father get parental responsibility?

An unmarried father can acquire parental responsibility either by the making of a court order on the application of the father, or the mother and father can enter in to a parental responsibility agreement. If the father applies for a parental responsibility order then the court will grant the parental responsibility order if the father has shown sufficient commitment to the child and there is sufficient attachment between them, and the court is satisfied about the reasons for the father's application. The court must always have the welfare of the child as its paramount consideration when deciding whether to grant a parental responsibility order.

Alternatively, if the mother agrees to the father having parental responsibility without the necessity for a court application, then the parents can enter into an agreement. The parental responsibility agreement must be made in a form set out in the regulations and it must be witnessed by a Justice of the Peace, a justice's clerk or a court official authorised by a judge. The person witnessing the signature will need to identify both parents to prevent any forgery of the parental responsi-bility agreement and will need to see the child's birth certificate. Once a parental responsibility agreement is made, it has to be registered at the Principal Registry of the Family Division. A parental responsibility order or a parental responsibility agreement can only be brought to an end by an order of the court.

What does parental responsibility mean?

If a father is granted parental responsibility, it does not mean that he will have a right to interfere in the day-to-day decisions that are made for the child, nor can he interfere in the mother's life. Parental responsibility is there to encourage the parents to inform and possibly consult each other in respect of important steps in the child's life. Whether or not the father has parental responsibility does not affect the father's obligations in relation to the child, eg for maintenance, and it does not affect his right to apply for other orders relating to a child, eg a contact order.

What effects does parental responsibility have?

(1) If you want to remove a child from the country to live abroad then the consent of all persons with parental responsibility is required and if this is not forthcoming then a court order will be required. A child can, however, be taken out of the country for up to one month for the purpose of a holiday without the consent of any other person with parental responsibility or by any person with a residence order in respect of the child.

(2) A person with parental responsibility can object to a child's surname being changed. It seems to be the law that a child's name should not be changed without the consent of all persons with parental responsibility for him.

(3) A person with parental responsibility acquires various rights regard-ing a child's education, ie that person can be informed by the local education authority as to the child's progress when he attends school and has the right to be notified of other school events, etc.

(4) A person with parental responsibility has the right to receive medical reports relating to the child and to consent to medical treatment for the child.

(5) A person with parental responsibility can sign various documents, eg passport applications.

(6) Subject to not acting inconsistently with a court order, a person with parental responsibility can act unilaterally and without consultation with the other parent.

(7) A person with parental responsibility can object to a child being 'accommodated' by a local authority and can remove the child from local authority care unless a care or emergency protection order is in force.

(8) A person who has parental responsibility for a child may not surrender or transfer any part of that responsibility to any other person, but can arrange for some or all of their responsibility to be met by one or more persons acting on their behalf.

Section 8 Orders

These are the orders which the court can make to resolve private disputes between parents. The ideas underlying them are not unexpected, but it is wise to pay close attention to the wording of the definition of each order. The possible orders are as follows:

Contact orders

A contact order is an order requiring the person with whom the child lives or is to live to allow the child to visit or stay with the person named in the order, or for that person and the child otherwise to have contact with each other.

Notes on contact orders

Contact with his/her natural parents is seen as a fundamental right of the child which should be observed unless there are exceptional reasons why the child should be denied that right. Contact may be direct (staying or visiting), indirect (eg cards, letters), or supervised. An order for parental contact will cease to have effect if the parents live together for a continuous period of six months after the order. Although the court may order contact with others (for example grandparents) such applicants have no right to see the child, and the child's welfare will determine the outcome.

Residence orders

A residence order is an order settling the arrangements to be made as to the person with whom a child is to live.

Notes on residence orders

The court may make a residence order in respect of two or more persons and define the time the child spends in each household—s.11(4). This enables the court to order shared residence although that is still an unusual solution to be imposed by the court. A residence order lapses if two parents with parental responsibility live together for more than six months. While a residence order is in force:

(a) no person may cause the child to be known by a new surname;
(b) the person with the residence order may take the child out of the country (ie England and Wales) for up to 28 days in any one year;
(c) no other person may remove the child from the country without the permission of the court, unless they have the written consent of each person with parental responsibility.

So, for example, John and Sue both have parental responsibility for their son Thomas. There is a residence order in favour of Sue. She may take Thomas to Ibiza for a fortnight's holiday without consent. John needs her consent (or the court's) before he can take Thomas to see his brother in

France. Sue will need consent to go to Australia for six weeks in the autumn.

(d) There is no presumption that a child is better off with one parent than the other, but there is a rebuttable presumption of fact that a baby would be better off with its mother.

Prohibited steps order

A prohibited steps order is an order that no step which could be taken by a parent in meeting his/her parental responsibility for a child, and which is of a kind specified in the order, shall be taken by any person without the consent of the court.

Notes on prohibited steps orders
These are orders to regulate aspects of parental responsibility. If it is wished to stop behaviour which does not form part of the legitimate exercise of parental responsibility, they are not appropriate. They can be directed against non-parents and even in exceptional circumstances non-parties. These orders cannot be used to regulate contact between the parents themselves.

Specific issue orders

A specific issue order is an order giving directions for the purpose of determining a specific question which has arisen, or which may arise, in connection with any aspect of parental responsibility for a child.

Notes on specific issue orders
These are used to decide issues such as where a child is to go to school, whether a child should have an operation, and whether a parent should be given leave to remove a child permanently abroad.

▩ Domestic Violence

The Law is contained in Part IV of the Family Law Act 1996. That Act begins by setting out certain general principles in s 1. Section1(d) states that any risk to one of the parties to a marriage and to any children of violence from the other party should, so far as reasonably practicable, be removed or diminished. 'Family' is widely construed. Protection is given to both married and unmarried couples, although controversially, where the parties are not married s 41 of the Act requires the court, 'to have regard to the fact the parties have not given each other the commitment involved in marriage'. It remains to be seen whether this politically motivated addition to the Act has any discernible consequences in practice.

What is 'Violence'?

The Act provides no comprehensive definition. It is clear from the statute and case law that the court will take into account not only the actual or threatened use of force but also other forms of emotional, physical and sexual harassment. The court will always pay more attention to an applicant who has acted promptly to bring her case before the court and who is able to provide independent evidence, for example a medical report, of the harm she has suffered.

Two Main Classes of Order

The Act provides for the making of non-molestation orders and occupation orders. To an extent their meaning is self-explanatory, but technical rules abound. Whenever it is faced with an application for one of these orders, the court has to ask itself three main questions:

(1) What is the connection between the applicant and the respondent (ie between the person bringing the proceedings and the defendant)?
(2) Having regard to the criteria in the Act, does the evidence show in this case that the applicant is entitled to an order? Or to put it another way, how is the discretion to be exercised?
(3) Should a power of arrest be attached?

We shall now consider each of these questions for each of the two types of order.

Non-Molestation Orders

What is the connection between applicant and respondent?
The parties must either be 'associated' or parties to the same family proceedings. 'Associated' is defined in s 62(3) of the Family Law Act 1996. The definition is extremely broad and helps resolve a number of shortcomings in the old law. A person is associated with another if:

(a) they are or were married or lived together;
(b) they have lived or live in the same household (employees, tenants, lodgers and boarders are excluded);
(c) they are relatives ('relatives' is defined in the Act);
(d) they are or were engaged;
(e) they are parents of or have parental responsibility for a child.

How does the court exercise its discretion?
This is straightforward. The court must have regard 'to all the circumstances including the need to secure the health, safety and well being—
(a) of the applicant ...... and
(b) of any relevant child.' Section 42(5).

Apart from the history of molestation or violence set out in the applicant's statements, the court will pay attention to any medical or psychiatric reports filed on her behalf.

Should there be a power of arrest?
A power of arrest is a clause added to the injunction made by the court directed to the police. It empowers a police officer to arrest the respondent and bring him before the civil court which made the order if the respondent breaks the order or is about to do so, or the officer has reasonable grounds to believe this is the case. If granted, it is extremely useful to applicants who otherwise have the burden of enforcing any breaches of the order by taking further court action themselves. Under the old law, powers of arrest could only be added in limited circumstances and were in practice only given in cases of serious violence. Now the court must add a power of arrest whenever the respondent has used or threatened violence against the applicant or a relevant child unless in all the circumstances of the case the court is satisfied the applicant or child will be adequately protected without such a power being added.

It remains to be seen how the court interprets this provision. We imagine there will be many more powers of arrest issued than previously. On the other hand, the judicial hostility towards powers of arrest may persist.

Other points

Non-molestation orders will normally be made for a limited time and may be made without notice being given to the respondent in circumstances of real emergency.

Occupation Orders

These orders allow a person to enter or remain in occupation of a dwelling and/or exclude a respondent from all or part of a dwelling or an area surrounding it. For a full definition see s 33(3).

What is the connection between applicant and respondent?

To be entitled to apply for an occupation order, the applicant must:

(a) be entitled to occupy the dwelling in question because s/he has a legal right, eg the applicant must be an owner or tenant or contractual licensee; or

(b) be a spouse; or

(c) be a former spouse; or

(d) be a cohabitant or former cohabitant.

Applicants in categories (a) and (b) have a slightly stronger position than applicants in the other two categories. The respondent must be an associated person. This has the same meaning as for non-molestation orders (see above).

How does the court exercise its discretion?

The Act provides a checklist of factors which the court must take into account when deciding whether or not to make an occupation order. The factors include needs, resources, conduct, specific matters relating to the marriage or cohabitation, and the needs of any children of the relationship or for whom both parties have or have had parental responsibility. These factors are spelt out in great detail in the Act.

If the court is being asked to exclude a respondent from his home, it must also consider whether the applicant or any relevant child is likely to suffer significant harm as a result of the respondent's conduct if the order is not made. It must also balance the harm which the respondent will suffer if excluded against the harm which the applicant or child are likely to suffer if he is not. It must perform this exercise in every case. If the parties are married, the court must make the order if the balance of harm is in favour of the applicant. If they are not, the court may make the order. This subtle difference of approach in applying the balance of harm test when dealing with unmarried parties is reinforced by the provision in s 41 referred to in David Hodson's section 'Family Mediation and the Family Law Act 1996' below.

Duration of orders

This is a bit complicated. If the applicant is a spouse or former spouse with a legal entitlement, the order can last until either party dies. If the applicant is a former spouse with no legal entitlement, the order can last for up to six months and may be extended for one or more additional periods of six months. If the applicant is a cohabitant or former cohabitant, the order may last for up to six months and may be extended for one further period of six months, but not more. In practice, the parties will either reconcile or proceed to resolve their property dispute by agreement or in further court action, for example, by applying to the courts for an ancillary relief order in divorce proceedings.

Supplementary provisions

The court may make additional orders dealing with the payment of rent and mortgage, the repair and maintenance of property and the use of furniture.

Should a power of arrest be attached?

Exactly the same rules apply as with non-molestation orders. The court has to consider the use or threat of violence and may attach a power of arrest unless satisfied the applicant will be safe without one.

Excluding the Abuser

These notes are not concerned with public law (ie care proceedings) but in passing it may be noted that the Act contains an important amendment to the Children Act which enables a court to exclude a suspected abuser when making an interim care order. This addresses the often made criticism that it is wrong for an abused child, rather than the alleged abuser, to be removed from his home when the authorities intervene to protect the child.

Mediation and Domestic Violence

All skilled mediators would wish to be sensitive to the issue of domestic violence. While there appears to be a professional consensus that mediation may be possible even where domestic violence has occurred or been threatened, Parliament, the Legal Aid Board and family mediation's professional bodies have all recently considered this issue in depth. Mediators are reminded of the existence of the College's approved Code of Practice.

Section 27 of the Family Law Act inserts a new s 13B into the Legal Aid Act 1988 requiring mediators who receive public funds to comply with a code of practice which must require the mediator to have arrangements designed to ensure:

(a) that parties participate in mediation only if willing and not influenced by fear of violence or other harm; (and)

(b) that cases where either party may be influenced by fear of violence or other harm are identified as soon as possible.

The Act also contains (Sched 1 para 4) a provision enabling the court to exempt the parties from the usual requirement that a financial arrangement has to be reached before the granting of a divorce order if a non-molestation or occupation order is in force. Domestic violence is also a factor which may come to displace any presumption in favour of mediation contained in the new Act, and would be a relevant issue in deciding whether a spouse could get access to legal aid for legal representation without attending a meeting with a mediator.

▪ Financial Provision

This section is of particular relevance to mediators engaged in All Issues Mediation (AIM). Naturally, in the limited space available we can do no more than provide a brief *aide-memoire* to highlight points of particular concern or risk and stimulate further thought and research.

Clients in All Issues Mediation will no doubt be encouraged by the mediators to seek independent legal advice. Not infrequently the clients will return to the mediation having gathered from their respective solicitors very different views of the likely result if they were to go to court. We therefore emphasise in this section the highly discretionary nature of this area of family law to assist mediators in understanding the challenges which have to be confronted by advising solicitors. We begin, however, by briefly describing the procedures which lead to the court making a decision.

Procedures

If a spouse who is a party to divorce or judicial separation proceedings wishes to seek a financial order from the court, the procedure to be followed will be different depending on whether or not the proceedings are taking place in one of the so-called 'pilot' courts. As their name implies these are county courts in which a new and sophisticated procedure for resolving matrimonial financial disputes is being piloted.

Non-pilot Courts

The applicant files a form indicating the nature of the orders sought in general terms, together with a sworn statement. This statement is usually a mixture of financial information, marital history, supposition and (hopefully) persuasive argument in favour of a particular outcome. The courts encourage applicants to be concise and precise but these statements often suffer from the twin curses of prolixity and imprecision.

The respondent is required to file a similar statement in reply giving details of his or her means within 28 days. Usually the parties' solicitors will then serve requests for further information and discovery (ie disclosure) of relevant financial documentation. This stage of the process can be both time-consuming and expensive. Recalcitrance or evasion (real or imagined) may induce applications to the court for specific orders for disclosure. There will eventually come a time when the parties consider the matter is ready for trial. Routinely in some district registries and always in cases of complexity, there will be a pre-trial review at which the parties will have a chance to negotiate through their lawyers, and district judges will press the parties to define the issues which divide them and seek to identify the evidence which the court will need to make a decision. Final directions will be given, including directions for the filing of a trial bundle and, if needed, a chronology. The matter will then come before a district judge (unless very weighty) who will read the papers and hear evidence and argument before making a decision.

Pilot Areas

The following courts are involved in the pilot scheme as at January 1998:

Barnsley County Court
Bath County Court
Blackwood County Court
Bolton County Court
Boston County Court
Bow County Court

Bristol County Court
Bury County Court
Crewe County Court
Guildford County Court
Harrogate County Court
Hertford County Court
Kingston County Court
Maidstone County Court
Northampton County Court
Salford County Court
Southampton County Court
Southport County Court
Stafford County Court
Staines County Court
Stoke-on-Trent County Court
Taunton County Court
Teeside County Court
Trowbridge County Court
Tunbridge Wells County Court
Willesden County Court
Wrexham County Court

The Procedure

About three months after the financial proceedings are started, there is an initial hearing (known as the First Appointment) at which the judge will check what issues are in dispute and what further information is required from either party in order to enable the dispute to be resolved. Both parties will already have completed and exchanged a prescribed form setting out detailed information about their financial circumstances at least five weeks before the First Appointment. If the issues are not resolved at that time then a further court hearing will be arranged once any additional information has been obtained. At that hearing (known as the Financial Dispute Resolution or FDR Appointment) the judge will be entitled to see any offers or proposals made by either party (including without prejudice proposals). The judge will take an active role in trying to help the parties resolve the case there and then without the additional expense and delay of a final court hearing. Occasionally the judge may treat the First Appointment as an FDR if both parties agree. If the case is settled then an order will be made by consent. If not, the final hearing will be arranged which will be dealt with by a different judge who will not be entitled to know of any without prejudice offers. The court timetables are strictly applied and one party can be ordered to pay the other's costs if the rules are not complied with. The court procedure from the time of the financial application until a final hearing is likely to take between five and eight months, although many cases settle along the way.

The Process of Mediation and the Court Process Compared

All mediators who have undergone training in All Issues Mediation will be familiar with John Haynes' IUVD process, first devised by Steve Erikson in the USA:

- *identify* the assets;
- *understand* the assets;

- *value* the assets;
- *divide* the assets.

The court process broadly follows the same path. As can be seen, the initial steps are concerned with identifying what forms part of the cake to be divided and verifying the details through the procedure known as discovery. The court has a discretion to order parties to give full and relevant disclosure and will exercise it in favour of disclosure unless the expense of producing the information outweighs the likely benefits. There is legal authority placing a duty upon legal advisers involved with matrimonial financial disputes to be alive to the possibility of a negotiated settlement and to make an offer or offers of settlement as soon as there is sufficient information to meaningfully do so. The valuation of assets is invariably ordered by the court unless the value is a matter of public record (eg quoted shareholdings) or is agreed. Both processes are now greatly concerned to take pensions into account. This is an area where it seems the law is only slowly catching up with the wishes of the public as frequently expressed by them in mediation. Where the processes differ is, of course, that compulsory powers are available to the courts to compel the payment of maintenance and the transfer and settlement of property and it is to these we now turn.

The Powers Available to the Court on Divorce and Judicial Separation

As the law now stands, these powers are for the most part available only on or after decree *nisi* and do not become exercisable until decree absolute. This must be contrasted with the position after the introduction of The Family Law Act 1996. On or after the making of a decree nisi or granting a decree of Judicial Separation, the court may make any one or more of the following orders.

(1) A periodical payments order for a spouse or child, subject to the provisions of the Child Support Act 1989
This is a maintenance order. It is often limited in time and the time limit can be either variable or definite and final. Prior to the expiry of a final time limit for their duration, maintenance orders can be varied as circumstances change. They are not index-linked. The Child Support Act limits the circumstances in which the court can make maintenance orders for children.

(2) An order for secured periodical payments
Unusual but useful, this enables the court to direct that specified property be charged or deposited as security for the payment of maintenance.

(3) A lump sum order for spouse or child
The payment of a sum of capital. Only one such order may be made, although the payment can be by instalments, bearing interest if paid late, and the timing and amount of the instalments may be varied. Otherwise not variable.

(4) A property adjustment order
The court's power to direct that property belonging to one spouse be transferred to the other, either outright or on terms. Property may be transferred or settled. *Ante-* and *post-*nuptial settlements may be varied or reduced. Once made these orders are *not* variable. Upon making one of

the above orders the court may also order the sale of any property in which either spouse has an interest, and may attach conditions to the sale.

Essential point: Orders for maintenance can be changed. Capital orders usually cannot!

Interim Measures

The court has the power to direct that temporary maintenance be paid. This is known as maintenance pending suit. The court may also freeze assets likely to be disposed of by a spouse in order to defeat a just claim. These injunctions can be vital if weaker parties are not to be defrauded, but they must be obtained quickly and often without the other spouse having advance knowledge of the application for them. Mediators need to be alert to the possibility of matrimonial assets being disposed of or irrevocably altered during mediation, and be ready to urge the clients to seek legal advice and if circumstances justify it suspending or terminating the mediation.

How does the Court Exercise its Powers?

Like so many areas of family law, the judge is given a range of powers (as we have just seen) and is also given a discretion as to how to operate them. The discretion, although wide, is not untrammelled. It must always be exercised in a reasoned way and must take into account certain factors defined in the Matrimonial Causes Act 1973. These so-called s 25 factors lie at the core of resolving matrimonial financial disputes through litigation. We have found in practice that they can be used with sensitivity in mediation to assist couples struggling to devise their own criteria of fairness. We summarise them as follows:

(a) The income, earning capacity and resources each party has or is likely to have in the foreseeable future, including earning capacity, which it would be reasonable to expect a party to take steps to acquire.
(b) The financial needs obligations and responsibilities which each party has now or will have in the foreseeable future.

Comment
These two factors are concerned with needs and resources. They are present and future-focused. Evidentially they involve not only the production of documents establishing what is earned, owned or owed but also allow the introduction by both sides of more speculative material regarding earning capacity and future gains and losses. As a result of a recent change, the court must take pensions into account. The foreseeable future test does not apply to pensions.

(c) The standard of living enjoyed by each party prior to the breakdown of the marriage.
(d) The age of each party and the duration of the marriage.

Comment
The court aims to preserve standards of living, but as the world knows this is not possible in practice. Earning capacity is related to age and proximity to retirement. Applicant spouses who have only been married for a short time cannot in general expect to do as well as those who have been married for some years. Cohabitation prior to marriage is not

equated to marriage by the courts. One suspects many clients in mediation would take a different view.

(e) Any physical or mental disability of either party.

(f) The contributions each party has made in the past or will make in the foreseeable future. These include direct (eg £50,000) and indirect (eg looking after the home or caring for the family) contributions.

Comment

Point (e) probably speaks for itself. Clearly, medical evidence is going to be all-important. The courts do not attach as much weight to past contributions as many spouses (usually husbands!) would like. To this extent the courts share the future focus of mediation, although we would suggest that this should not be used as an excuse for a less-than-meticulous examination of who has brought or contributed what to the marriage if that is what the clients want.

(g) Conduct if it would be inequitable to ignore it.

(h) On divorce or nullity (ie *not* judicial separation) benefits which a party to the marriage will lose the chance of acquiring.

Comment

Conduct is rarely a factor. Reported cases include reckless gambling, attempted murder of spouse and various forms of conduct which directly impacted on finance in a very negative way. Adultery and what may perhaps be described as 'routine' unreasonable behaviour are nearly always ignored by the courts.

Point (h) is of particular relevance to pensions and is considered separately.

■ Points of Particular Difficulty or Interest

Pensions

Pensions are complicated. They are also increasingly important. For many couples their pension funds are by far the most valuable asset they possess. They are bound to be significant issues in many AIM cases. They must be considered in all. Failure adequately to consider pension provision has already resulted in solicitors being successfully sued. Mediators are almost bound to be in the firing line before long. Because pensions are difficult it is easy to feel lost in a maze. When lost, the mediator is perhaps more susceptible to losing control of the process. We would suggest that the threads which will always lead you to safety are:

- to remember a pension is just another asset (albeit a complex one);
- to hang on to the process;
- to be ready to invite the clients to seek information and advice from third parties. Pensions will certainly generate lots of homework!

The basic skills still work:

(a) *identify* the exact details of the relevant pensions;

(b) *understand* what benefits the pension offers and what benefits will be actually or potentially lost because of the divorce;

(c) an attempt must be made to *value* the fund as it stands and the benefits it will pay in the future;

(d) *divide* (although this must be understood differently in relation to pensions as explained below).

A pension is both an asset acquired during the marriage and a means of providing an income in later life for both clients. This dual nature may well be reflected in the negotiations as clients develop themes and positions based upon entitlement (the pension viewed as an asset) and need (the pension viewed as future income). Both perspectives are valid, but it often helps to tease them out and to make the values and concerns which are informing their negotiations explicit, *and* write them on the flip chart!

Identifying the pensions

There are various types of pensions as described in the following list:

(1) State pensions including widows' benefits.
(2) Private pensions sub-divided as follows:
    (a) Statutory pension schemes. These are pensions provided under statute for state employees.
    (b) Occupational pension schemes. The most commonly encountered, eg the BAe pension scheme.
    (c) Small self-administered schemes. These are pensions set up by directors of small companies with substantial shareholdings.
    (d) Retirement annuity contracts. Personal pensions started before 1 July 1988.
    (e) Personal pension schemes. As above set up after 1 July 1988.
    (f) Very occasionally you may come across unapproved schemes.

Remember to ask both clients for details of present and previous occupational schemes. People sometimes forget frozen pensions from the past.

Understanding

This will come from asking the right questions. We think consideration should be given to reviewing the current budget forms used by College members or preparing a supplementary questionnaire/*aide memoire*.

The following information should always be obtained:

(a) the rules of the scheme;
(b) the explanatory booklet (if there is one);
(c) the date of joining;
(d) details of any rights transferred in from another scheme;
(e) a copy of the latest benefits statement;
(f) a statement of projected benefits, as follows (all projections/estimates):
    (i)   the lump sum payable on death in service;
    (ii)   the spouse's pension payable on death in service;
    (iii) the lump sum on commutation (pensioners will normally elect to commute);
    (iv) the pension payable if no commutation and with commutation;
    (v)   the spouse's pension following retirement;
    (vi) the normal retirement date;
    (vii) the current transfer value (this has assumed special significance since the earmarking provisions came in);
    (viii) have any expression-of-wish/nomination forms been completed and if so, in whose favour?

This may look a daunting list. It may help you get your head around it to bear in mind that you will typically find:

(a) a lump sum payable on death in service;
(b) a lump sum payable on retirement if benefits are commuted;
(c) a widow's/dependants' pension;
(d) a pension (of course!).

The above information will help you discover the current value of the fund (the transfer value), and the estimated values of the other benefits which will or may be payable or lost.

Essential point: Remember that following divorce the divorced spouse will not qualify as widow or dependent. Those benefits will be lost.

Displaying the information

We think we all have much to learn in this area and practice will develop. Our practice is to display the transfer value on the assets sheet with, frequently, marginal notes describing other vital information (eg projected annual pension). However it is done, it is important to remember that a pension is not realisable capital like, say, a building society account. It is therefore deeply misleading to total it with the other assets. We would suggest using a different column and maybe a different colour ink to emphasise this point.

Also, we should be aware that this information may take weeks or even months to obtain. There will be pressure to get on with other tasks and it is all too easy to forget about *that* pension! Therefore, mark the chart to indicate that the data is awaited.

In passing, we note that there are several different methods of calculating the transfer value which are the subject of (to the writer) largely incomprehensible debate between actuaries. The new law requires schemes to produce something known as the CETV (current equivalent transfer value). This will probably become the standard comparator. We have found it useful to draw a diagram, as a time line, showing:

(a) the date pensionable employment started;
(b) the date of the marriage;
(c) the date when the marriage effectively ended; and
(d) the date of anticipated retirement.

This can be useful when considering issues of entitlement.

Dividing the pension

As the law stands, pensions cannot be split. A section in the Family Law Act (s 16) provides legislation which may enable splitting in the future. For technical reasons this probably does not achieve what it is intended to achieve, and in any event there is little prospect of splitting being brought in before the millennium. Therefore, division here must refer to a range of remedies and solutions short of actual splitting which couples may select in order to:

(a) acknowledge a wife's deemed entitlement to a pension fund accumulated in her husband's name while she raised a family;
(b) provide for the future income needs of either or both spouses;
(c) compensate a spouse for lost benefits.

This chart sets out a range of ideas:

Remedy or solution	Comment
Offsetting	Using other available assets to compensate the other spouse.
Earmarking	Only applies where petition issued after 1.7.96 (for explanation, see below).
Splitting	Not available yet, if ever.
Variation of Settlement	Based on case of Brooks v Brooks. Uncertain and technical rules may permit re-writing of terms of certain pension schemes to benefit ex-wives.
Adjourning of application for lump sum	Up to maybe five years maximum. Unnecessary if you can earmark.
Insurance	Maybe endowment and term policies can be used imaginatively to compensate the wife for the lost benefits.
Nomination	Can only be ordered by a court after 6.4.97.

Offsetting

This is concerned with the provision of a lump sum or property to compensate the weaker spouse. The difficulties are:

(a) few couples have sufficient resources to achieve a realistic level of compensation;

(b) the proper value of compensation can be very difficult to calculate;

(c) how the couple will weigh unknown factors: eg, prospects of remarriage or future cohabitation, future redundancy affecting the projected fund values, premature death of either spouse (eg suppose I give her £200,000 today for her pension and she dies next week?);

(d) computing the appropriate discount for accelerated payment.

Clearly some of these issues must be negotiated by the clients, but others can be clarified by outside advisers. In particular, it can be an informative but depressing exercise to discover what lump sum would be needed now to provide a pension at age 65 of £10,000 pa (for example, the clients must decide what they need).

Variation of settlements

This is a complicated area. It will normally only be relevant in the case of self-administered schemes. The wife will have to show that she has an interest in the pension fund and it constituted a pre- or post-nuptial settlement. Mediators should strongly urge clients to take professional advice if they think such a scheme exists.

Earmarking

It is early days. Earmarking may prove useful, but lawyers do not yet have a feel for how these powers will be used by the courts. Our guess is that there will be relatively few orders made where the beneficiary of the order is under 40-ish. We may be wrong! It will certainly make competent lawyers 'pension-sensitive'. Make sure you are too. The courts must now have a regard to pensions and may direct the trustees/managers of the scheme to pay the whole or a percentage of the pension or of the lump sum payable on death to the applicant when such sums fall payable. The courts may also direct a pensioner to commute the whole or part of his/her benefits or direct the pensioner to nominate the other spouse as a beneficiary of any benefits which may be nominated.

Pitfalls and problems

(1) The court cannot compel the spouse to retire.
(2) The orders are *variable*. (Think of the potential for future litigation!).
(3) The remarriage of the wife will terminate any order made for periodical payments and possibly for a lump sum also, depending on the wording of the order. The mediator must find out what the couple want to happen. More 'what ifs' for your pensions checklist.
(4) The court cannot compel the pensioner to continue making contributions, although presumably the couple could agree, that 'he' would undertake to the court to do so.
(5) There is no widow's pension if the husband dies before retirement.
(6) Many couples want a clean break. If they earmark they don't get it, although she will get the earmarked component of a lump sum payable in that event.

Conclusions

The proper negotiation of pension provision may well prove to be one of AIM'S greatest challenges. We feel that practice in this area is developing and may well need further thought. It is of note that pensions are of less importance in many USA jurisdictions where much current AIM practice originates. It is difficult to see how the task can be done professionally without careful acquisition, organisation and display of relevant data, and the regular use of skilled outside professionals. Mediation services may need to build up a referral bank of mediation-sensitive financial advisers and accountants.

Cohabitation

The court will take the resources of a cohabitant into account to the extent that the resources:

- increase the income or capital of the cohabiting spouse;
- reduce the expenses of the spouse;
- meet or diminish the needs of the spouse;
- are likely to do any of the above in the foreseeable future.

Cohabitants are not under a duty to maintain children of another relationship or an ex-spouse.

Redundancy Payments, Inheritances, Damages and the Like

These are potential resources which the court is required to take into account when performing the balancing exercise required by s 25. The court will not take inheritances into account unless they have already been received, or are certain to be received (eg the rare case where property is bound to be inherited by a surviving child under foreign law), or will be received in the reasonably near future. This last condition is construed restrictively. If an aged close relative with property who is expected to die shortly, and upon death to benefit one party to the proceedings, the court may order an adjournment of the lump sum application. Damages for personal injury are resources to be taken into account, although the court will bear in mind their purpose was to compensate the victim to whom they were awarded and will seek to analyse the composition of the damages and ring-fence that part of the damages which was awarded for the victim's pain and suffering.

Bankruptcy

Upon bankruptcy the bankrupt's assets vest in his trustee in bankruptcy, who is under a duty to realise them for the benefit of the bankrupt's creditors. The major asset is frequently the matrimonial home. Statute operates to effectively prevent the sale of the home for a period of 12 months from the making of the order provided it is occupied by the bankrupt's spouse and/or minor children. After a year the trustee normally succeeds unless the occupying wife can point to truly exceptional circumstances of which homelessness is insufficient. While a technical subject outside the scope of these notes, mediators should also be aware that certain transfers made by the bankrupt prior to his bankruptcy are reviewable by the trustee.

The Family Home

Spouses have a right to occupy the matrimonial home so long as the marriage subsists regardless of whether or not they own the home or have a financial interest in it. This right of occupation may be restricted, terminated or suspended by the court. The right can be registered so that any persons seeking to buy or otherwise deal with the property will be deemed to have notice of the right and take subject to it. It is therefore important for mediators to urge spouses to take advice where the matrimonial home is in the sole name of the other. They may need to register their rights by instructing their solicitor to register what is known in the trade as a Class F. If the court has to decide the future of the matrimonial home it will normally do one of the following things:

(1) Order a sale of the property with a division of the net sale proceeds between the spouses upon sale.
(2) Order a sale at some point in the future upon the happening of some event with a division of net sale proceeds after sale. If the trigger for a sale is the death of the occupying spouse or (her) earlier remarriage it is known as a Martin Order. If the trigger is the occurrence of the earliest of a number of defined events including the children of the family finishing education (secondary or tertiary) it is known as a Mesher Order. The exact triggering events are always a matter for negotiation or the court.

The court may leave the property in, or transfer it into, joint names to be held upon trust as above. Alternatively, it may transfer it into the sole name of one spouse and protect the interest of the other by making it a condition that the transferee grants a charge (like a mortgage) to the other spouse for a defined amount, or more usually percentage, of the value of the property.

(3) Order an outright transfer of the home to one spouse.

Mortgages

Mortgagees must be given notice of applications for property adjustment orders affecting their security. Any order of the court will take effect subject to pre-existing mortgages and may require the lender's consent. The court may order a spouse to transfer a matrimonial home to the other but cannot order the mortgagee (lender) to release the transferring spouse from the mortgage. He therefore remains liable under the mortgage.

This problem is addressed by a formula whereby the receiving spouse promises the court to use her best endeavours to seek a release of the other spouse from the mortgage. This release is entirely a matter of discretion for the lender. If the lender refuses to release, the spouse also promises to indemnify the transferring spouse against any future liability under the mortgage. This is an imperfect solution since the only circumstances in which the transferor is likely to look to enforce the indemnity are ones in which by, definition, it is unlikely the other spouse will be able to do so.

Child Support

The Child Support Act 1991 came into force on 5 April 1993. Before then child maintenance was determined by the courts. It is not possible in the limited space available here to provide a detailed explanation of the formula and the workings of the Act. For most divorcing couples the amount of child support payable will now be decided by the Child Support Agency. Clients in mediation may look to the mediator for guidance on the amount of child support they should be paying in the light of the formula contained in the Act. Our view is that mediators should approach this task with caution. We find it a little hard to understand why this is any more the proper province of the mediator than working out what the client's tax liability would be.

The calculation is not an easy one (as the performance of the agency itself has in the past testified) and an inaccurate calculation may be worse than useless. Moreover, the calculation is sensitive to certain variables, as will be seen, and it may therefore be necessary to do the calculation a number of times on the basis of different initial assumptions. Quite apart from this, there is the danger of drifting into an advisory role quite incompatible with the role of mediator. Despite these cautionary notes, we do feel that a family mediator should aspire to have at least a rudimentary understanding of the Act and its operation in practice.

The fundamental principles

(1) Section 1 of the Act states that both natural parents (this includes adoptive but not step parents) have an obligation to maintain their children. The Act only deals with natural parents' obligations towards their children. Other matrimonial legislation deals with spousal maintenance and maintenance for children treated as children of the family upon divorce.
(2) Where the Child Support Agency has jurisdiction to make an assessment in respect of a child, the court may not make or vary any order in respect of that child. The court may however convert a written agreement into a consent order.

(3) Claimants of certain prescribed welfare benefits (most noticeably income support and family credit) must use the agency unless the parent with care can show she or the child would suffer harm or undue distress.

When does the agency not have jurisdiction?

(a) where the child is not the natural or adopted child of the parents;
(b) where the child is over 19 or aged between 17 and 19 and not in full time education;
(c) in respect of sums for educational expenses;
(d) to provide for expenses for a disabled child;
(e) where the paying parent is a high earner and the higher additional element (see later) provides insufficient maintenance for the child;
(f) where either parent or the child is habitually resident abroad.

In all these cases application must be made to the court. The court also has power to make capital orders for a child (eg Matrimonial Causes Act 1973, s 23 and Children Act 1989, Sched 1).

The language of the Act

The Act defines certain technical terms. Some of these (most obviously 'absent parent') do not appear to sit comfortably with the philosophy of mediation or indeed of the Children Act. Mediators may therefore need to reflect before casually importing these terms into their practice.

- *a qualifying child* is a child in respect of whom the agency has jurisdiction;
- *a person with care* is the person with whom the child has his home or who has care of the child for at least 104 nights during any 12-month period. Note, however, that this is an oversimple definition and reference should be made to the legislation or standard text books for more accuracy;
- *an absent parent* is a parent who is not the person with care and who does not live in the same household as the child.

How it works

Once a parent makes an application to the agency, an assessment is carried out. Financial information is gathered from the parents (if not already known to the agency because, for example, the applicant is in receipt of benefits) and the child support payable is calculated by applying the formula to the facts of the case.

The formula

The amount of child support payable comprises a figure known as the basic element plus an additional element in the case of wealthier parents. Both elements are derived from a formula which requires the manipulation of defined components.

Stage 1—Work out the maintenance requirement
The maintenance requirement is intended to represent the minimum amount necessary for the maintenance of the qualifying child or children. It is calculated by deducting the child benefit for the qualifying children from specified amounts under the income support legislation.

Stage 2—Work out the assessable income

Assessable income is the net income of the absent parent less the absent parent's allowable expenditure. The allowable expenditure includes:

- his actual housing costs subject to an upper limit;
- an allowance for work-related travel costs for travel over 150 miles each week;
- an allowance for certain capital transfers prior to 5 April 1993;
- one half of the absent parent's actual pension contributions.

Stage 3—Calculate the protected income

As its name suggests, this is a calculated minimum below which the absent parent's income as a result of the assessment must not be allowed to fall. It is based upon income support figures for the absent parent's whole family (including step-children). To this figure are added a basic sum plus a safety margin and the parent's council tax and a travel allowance.

Stage 4—Work out the maintenance assessment

The first step is to add the assessable incomes of the two parents and divide the result by two. If the result is less than the maintenance requirement, the absent parent's liability is limited to one half of his assessable income.

If the result is more than the maintenance requirement, the amount of child support payable comprises a basic element (BE) plus an additional element (AE). The purpose of the calculations is to provide an extra 25 per cent of the surplus assessable income remaining after the maintenance requirement is met.

$$BE - A \times G \times P$$

where A = absent parent's assessable income

$$G = MR / A \times G \times P$$

and P = 0.5

$$AE = (1 - G) \times A \times 0.25, \text{ subject to a maximum ceiling.}$$

Shared care

Arrangements exist for reducing the maintenance assessment where care is shared between the parents and the child spends at least 104 nights with the absent parent.

Interim assessments

The agency has power to impose an interim assessment where there has been a failure to respond or an inadequate response from the absent parent. The above is only a brief outline of a complex area. We suggest that whenever child support considerations arise, the clients should be advised to approach the agency and to consider taking legal advice.

References

Wall, J (ed) *Rayden & Jackson on Divorce & Family Matters* (looseleaf), 17th edn, Butterworths.

Bevan, H & Parry, M (1995) *Child Law*. 2nd edn, Butterworths.

Duckworth, P (1995) *Matrimonial Property & Finance*. 5th edn, FT Law & Tax.

Bird, R (1997) *The Child Support Calculation Pack 1997/98*. Jordans.

Salter, P (ed) (1997) *Pensions & Insurance on Family Breakdown*. 2nd edn, Jordans.

Bracewell, The Hon Mrs Justice (ed) (1997) *Family Court Practice 1997*. Jordans.

David Hodson

The Family Law Act 1996 introduces the most important changes in family law, certainly for the past 25 years, probably since 1857 when divorce left the Ecclesiastical Courts, and in some respects in the history of the English legal system. It introduces no-fault divorce whereas previously England has always had fault as the sole or partial basis for obtaining a divorce. It lengthens materially the average time for a divorce, from 4–6 months to at least 13, or possibly 21, months. It allows both parties to commence the divorce proceedings together and for either or both parties to seek the final divorce. In many cases, it requires that the final financial arrangements be in place before the final divorce order can be made.

However, the law reforms are not the only radical changes. Alongside, and being implemented at the same time, is a complete new process and infrastructure for those going through spousal separation and divorce. This will have a crucial bearing on the future work and role of family mediators in divorce. Moreover, the new law itself will not work unless the new process and infrastructure is fully in place and operational. The government recognises this, and the new law will not come into force until a number of pilot projects, including mediation, have been fully worked through and have shown that the surrounding infrastructure can work (see Sarah White's section 'Legal Aid Board Family Mediation Pilot Project' below).

The Act is fundamentally important for mediation and mediators. It brings mediators, along with counsellors, onto the centre stage hitherto occupied only by lawyers. Family mediation is vital if the Act is to work as intended. The Act anticipates that very many cases presently being resolved through solicitors' negotiation, sometimes through court-based litigation and occasionally by the parties direct, will be resolved through mediation. The Act was perceived as quite heavily Treasury driven. They hope that cases resolved through mediation should cost the public purse less than those resolved through the primary involvement of lawyers. While many in the Lord Chancellor's Department and in Parliament were aware of the wider and longer term benefits for the parties of a mediated settlement, it was the public costs savings (ie a lower legal aid bill) that enabled the green light to be given to the legislation.

The government has repeatedly said that mediation cannot, by its nature, be compulsory. However, there is anxiety that the provisions in the Act and its operation in practice may often result in it being perceived by legally aided parties as compulsory. The relevant provisions are referred to below. This is a crucial issue that is being addressed during the pilot projects. The challenge to mediators and mediation organisations is to protect the voluntariness of entry to mediation and re-emphasise the consensual nature for those taking part.

It was also made explicit by the government that there were three additional reasons for encouraging mediation. First, marriages which are capable of being saved are more likely to be identified through mediation than through the legal process. An essential aspect and principle of the new legislation is that every opportunity should be taken to save saveable marriages. The perception was that this did not occur through the legal process. Secondly, spouses are enabled in mediation to take responsibility for the breakdown of the marriage, and can acknowledge responsibility for the ending of the marriage. They are helped to deal with matters of fault, blame, anger and hurt with the minimum of bitterness and hostility. Thirdly, couples are encouraged to look to their responsibilities of marriage and parenthood, and to co-operate in making arrangements for the future rather than focusing on the past. These themes are part of the responsibility and burden that mediation is expected to carry under the new Act.

The Family Law Act received Royal Assent on 4 July 1996. However, there will be a number of pilot projects, involving information meetings and mediation, before the Act is fully implemented. It is likely to come into force some time in 2000, depending on progress in the pilot projects. There are transitional provisions which will allow couples already separated on the date of implementation, to count their period of separation towards the period for the divorce under the new legislation. Existing divorce proceedings will not be immediately affected and will continue.

Part IV of the Act concerns domestic violence, consolidating and improving the present law and procedure, and has been much welcomed by all those helping victims of domestic violence. Part IV also provides for rights of occupation of the family home for both spouses and co-habitants. Part IV came into force in October 1997 and is, in many ways, completely separate to the remainder of the Act.

General Principles

Section 1 of the Act requires the court and any person exercising functions in respect of Parts II and III (separation and divorce procedure, and legal aid and mediation, respectively) to have regard to certain general principles. These are:

(a) that the institution of marriage is to be supported;

(b) that the parties to a marriage which may have broken down are to be encouraged to take all practical steps to save it;

(c) that a marriage which has irretrievably broken down should be brought to an end with minimum distress to the parties and to the children, with questions dealt with in a manner designed to promote as good a continuing relationship between the parties and any children as is possible and without costs being unreasonably incurred; and

(d) that any risk to any party or children of violence from the other party should so far as reasonably practical be removed or diminished.

Clearly, this affects the couple concerned and the court dealing with the cases in hand. It also affects government departments involved in the making of rules, regulations and practice directions. These general principles are likely to have a pervasive impact on the specific implementation of the Act as well as being directive for mediators, lawyers, etc.

Timetable

At present, the inter-relationship of the timetable for a divorce with discussions regarding the children and finances is not particularly important. Financial and children matters can be resolved before the divorce starts, alternatively the decree absolute can be pronounced in many cases with financial and children matters still being discussed

All this will change with the new reforms. Final financial orders will invariably be needed before there can be a final divorce. Moreover, the process will be much longer. As the time for first applying for the divorce gets closer, there will be increasing pressure by the parties on mediators and lawyers to resolve financial issues. Clients will be increasingly anxious that steps are taken at the earliest possible time so that there is no slippage or other delay for the final order. Legal aid will be available for mediation but only once the proceedings themselves have commenced. Accordingly, it will be important for mediators to be aware at any mediation session of the particular stage that has been reached in the divorce timetable. Set out below is a summary timetable of the key stages of the divorce process.

Important Dates in the Divorce Process

Day 1: Information meeting.
Three months: File statement of marital breakdown at court.
14 days: Statement deemed to be served and nine- (or 15-) month period of reflection and consideration begins.
Nine months: Earliest date for application for separation order or divorce order, but see following.
Six months: Extended period of reflection and consideration if children under 16 or one party applies for further time for reflection.
12 months: Latest time to apply for separation order or divorce order after end of nine- (or 15-) month period of reflection and consideration.
One month: Likely period between application for separation order or divorce order and date of making final order if all other arrangements are satisfactorily in place.

Information Meetings

One criticism of the present divorce law is that a divorce can be obtained without proper consideration for the consequences and implications. The government was keen, therefore, to ensure that no-one commenced proceedings for a separation or divorce without fully considering the consequences. There is an obligation to attend an information meeting before a person can commence proceedings. There will be certain exemptions, eg for those who are physically unwell, in prison or in circumstances where attendance is practically impossible. The government has set up pilot projects to examine the best way in which the information meetings can be conducted. Even after proceedings have commenced, if the other party intends to apply to the court in respect of a child or in respect of property or financial matters, or contest any such application, they too must attend an information meeting.

Although rules and regulations will more specifically determine the content and conduct of the information meetings, there will definitely be information about:

- marriage guidance and other marriage support services;

- mediation;
- legal representation;
- legal aid;
- the importance of the welfare, wishes and feelings of children;
- how to help children better cope with the breakdown of marriage;
- the sort of financial issues that can arise;
- protection against domestic violence; and
- general information about the divorce and separation process.

A party seeking to commence proceedings leading to a separation or divorce order cannot do so until at least three months after attending the information meeting, the so-called 'cooling off' period.

The information meeting provider has a duty to give information about mediation. It is almost certain that this will include the names and addresses of local mediation services. Great care will have to be taken by the information meeting providers to ensure that there are no allegations of favouritism or bias in the names that are given out. (Family lawyers and counsellors, and their respective organisations, have similar concerns.) Nevertheless, under guidance from the national mediation organisations, this may prove a good opportunity for local mediation services to inform and educate the local information meeting providers and for their details to be given to all attending the information meetings. *The UK College of Family Mediators Directory & Handbook* is very useful in this context.

Marriage Support Services

Another criticism of the present divorce law is that the system does nothing to help save saveable marriages. The three-month period between the information meeting and the commencement of proceedings is designed as a 'cooling-off' time when parties are specifically intended to consider whether the marriage is saveable. To this end, the information meeting can refer one spouse or the couple together to a meeting with a marriage counsellor, which will be state-funded under certain circumstances. Moreover, during the main period of the proceedings ('the period of reflection and consideration') the parties may attend marriage-counselling sessions which again will be state-funded under certain circumstances. Sections 22 and 23 make provision for the government, through the Legal Aid Board, to enter into contracts with marriage counselling services for the provision of marriage counselling during the divorce process. This will be another area for examination during the pilot projects.

Statement of Marital Breakdown

Instead of a petition for divorce or judicial separation as at present, a Statement of Marital Breakdown, referred to as a 'statement' will commence proceedings. It can be made singly or jointly. It must state that the maker or makers of the statement are aware of the purpose of the period of reflection and consideration and wish to make arrangements for the future. Court rules will specify the exact contents of the statement. A statement is ineffective to obtain a divorce order if made in the first year of marriage, continuing the present bar on divorce petitions presented within one year.

Certificate as to Marriage Services, Reconciliation and Mediation

Where a solicitor acts for the maker of a statement of marital breakdown, he or she must file a certificate that the party has been informed about the availability of marriage support services and mediation, and that the party has considered any child's welfare, wishes and feelings, and that names and addresses of persons qualified to help effect a reconciliation or in connection with mediation have been given.

The significance of this reform is that at present, solicitors acting for the petitioner only have a duty to certify whether the prospects of reconciliation have been discussed and if so whether the names and addresses of marriage support services have been given. The reforms not only add mediation to marriage support services, but also cast a specific duty to inform about marriage support and mediation, and give names and addresses of persons qualified to help. The relevance for mediators is that all family law solicitors will now need to have names of local mediators and mediation services to give to clients commencing divorce proceedings, in order to comply with this requirement. This provides good educational opportunities, which should be seized by local groups. Moreover, it is still the case that many solicitors, particularly those who would not be regarded as family law specialists, do not understand what mediation is, and are often sceptical about its benefits. This opportunity should be used to educate and inform.

Period for Reflection and Consideration

Marital proceedings commence on the filing of a statement of marital breakdown. There is then a period for the parties to reflect on whether the marriage can be saved and to have an opportunity to effect a reconciliation, and to consider what arrangements should be made for the future. This is known as 'the period for reflection and consideration'. It begins 14 days after the court receives the statement, in order to allow for service, unless there has been inordinate delay in service in which case the time can be extended.

The period for reflection and consideration lasts nine months. However, if there is any child under 16 or one party seeks time for further reflection, there is an additional six-month period before an application for a divorce order can be made. This six-month period does not apply if there is an occupation order or non-molestation order (the two new forms of domestic violence protection orders) in favour of the applicant for the divorce order or a child of the family, or if the court is satisfied that delaying the making of the divorce order would be significantly detrimental to the welfare of any child of the family.

At the end of the nine-month period, or 15-month period if applicable, either party can apply for a separation order or divorce order. There is only 12 months in which to do so after the end of the nine- or 15-month period for reflection and consideration, after which the proceedings lapse and a fresh statement must be made. It is possible for the parties to give notice jointly that they are attempting a reconciliation, whereupon time ceases to run. If the joint notice of attempted reconciliation lasts for more than 18 months, the proceedings lapse and there must be a new statement.

The Parties' Arrangements for the Future

The government was very concerned that in many cases at present, the final divorce is made some time before the final financial arrangements are put in place. Accordingly, under the Act, there can be no divorce or separation order unless the parties' arrangements for the future are satisfactorily in place. This is shown in one of four ways, namely:

- a court order dealing with financial arrangements;
- a negotiated agreement as to their financial arrangements;
- a declaration by both parties that they have made their financial arrangements; or
- a declaration by one, to which no objection has been notified by the other, that there are no significant assets of either party and no intention by either party to apply for financial provision and therefore there are no financial arrangements to be made.

There are exemptions from this requirement in four categories. The overriding requirement is that the applicant has tried to reach agreement about the parties' financial arrangements, other than in (c). The exemptions apply when:

(a) the other party has delayed in complying with the requirements of the court or been obstructive, or the court was prevented by third parties from obtaining necessary financial information;

(b) the ill health, disability or injuries of the applicant, other party or child has meant that it has not been possible to reach agreement about financial arrangements and this is unlikely in the foreseeable future;

(c) it has been impossible to contact the other party; or

(d) there is an occupation order or non-molestation order in favour of the applicant or a child of the family against the other party.

These four requirements and four exemptions along with orders preventing divorce (see below) are likely to be the focus of much disagreement, tactical manoeuvrings and litigation.

Mediators must be aware that their clients may be under or feel under pressure to reach a financial settlement as the period of reflection and consideration comes to an end. A spouse who may be keen to have a divorce may put pressure on the other spouse to agree terms as a pre-requisite to the divorce order. A spouse may be under pressure from a fiancé(e) to agree financial terms for the divorce and the consequential remarriage. These pressures may not be evident save by the mediator being aware of the closeness to the end of the period of reflection and consideration (whether nine- or 15-months).

It is also necessary that requirements regarding the welfare of the children be satisfied. This is an extension of the present s 41 of the Matrimonial Causes Act 1973. As now, the court must ascertain whether there are any children of the family and whether it should exercise any of its Children Act powers. The court can direct that the divorce or separation order is not to be made if it is likely that any of the Children Act powers are going to have to be exercised or the court is not yet in a position to exercise that power without further consideration of the case, and there are exceptional circumstances which make it desirable that the divorce or separation order should not be made. The court has to treat the welfare of the child as paramount.

In coming to a decision, the court has to take account of the wishes and feelings of the child, the conduct of the parties, the general principle that the welfare of the child is best served by having regular contact with those who have parental responsibility for the child and maintaining as good a continuing a relationship with the parents as possible, and any risk attributable to the child by the proposed living arrangements.

Orders Preventing Divorce

Where dissolution of the marriage could result in substantial financial or other hardship to the other party or to a child and it would be wrong in all the circumstances, including the conduct of the parties and interests of any child, for the marriage to be dissolved, the court is able to order the temporary or permanent prevention of a divorce. It will probably be used by lawyers in the same way as the present s 10(2) of the Matrimonial Causes Act 1973 (temporary delay of final divorce to overcome any prejudice by loss of insurance or pension benefits). The interrelationship of the requirements for satisfying the parties' arrangements for the future and these hardship orders preventing divorce will depend significantly on implementation by lawyers and the courts.

The Specific Initiatives for Mediation

A major thrust of the government's proposals for divorce reform is that many more cases should be referred to mediation instead of being resolved through court-based litigation. There will undoubtedly be an encouragement given at the information meeting to consider mediation, and a solicitor acting for the maker of a statement of marital breakdown has an obligation to inform about the availability of mediation. Moreover, the court has power to direct at any stage that each party attend a meeting for the purposes of enabling an explanation to be given of the facilities available for mediation and an opportunity for each party to agree to take part in mediation. The direction may be given at the request of either party or on the court's initiative. The direction specifies the person who will conduct the meeting and then requires a report stating whether the parties have complied with the direction by attending the meeting and whether they have agreed to take part in mediation. The court's power to adjourn includes adjournment to enable disputes to be resolved amicably. At the end of the adjournment, the court will require a report as to whether the parties have taken part in any mediation, any agreement reached, the extent of any resolution of a dispute, the need for further mediation and how likely it is that further mediation will be successful.

For the first time, legal aid will be available for mediation and the Legal Aid Board is entering into contracts with mediation services and mediation practices. This has a significant bearing on solicitors, as a person shall not be granted legal aid for legal representation unless he or she has first attended a meeting with a mediator to determine whether mediation appears suitable and, if so, to help the person applying for legal aid for legal representation to decide whether instead to apply for mediation. This provision, with its perceived prevention of immediate access to legal representation, has caused concern to many lawyers and will be carefully scrutinised in practice during the pilots.

Provision is made for parties to have legal aid to take part in mediation, but the statutory charge may continue to apply—this will be tested in the pilots. Mediators must comply with a code of practice to ensure that parties are participating in mediation only if willing, to identify cases where there may be influence of violence or harm, to keep the possibility of reconciliation under review and to ensure that each party is informed about the availability of independent legal advice. Mediators must also ensure that the parties consider the welfare, wishes and feelings of each child and consider the opportunity for a child to express his or her wishes or feelings.

Applying for the Separation Order or Divorce Order

References to decrees *nisi* and absolute and to judicial separation are abolished. There will only be a separation order or a divorce order. It is only at the end of the nine- or 15-month period of reflection and consideration, as applicable, that either party has to specify which of the two orders they are seeking. If one party makes the original statement of marital breakdown, the other party is nevertheless entitled to apply for the final order. The Act does not specify, but it is likely that there will be four weeks between the application for the divorce/separation order and the making of the order. A divorce order cannot be made with reference to a statement made within the first 12 months of marriage.

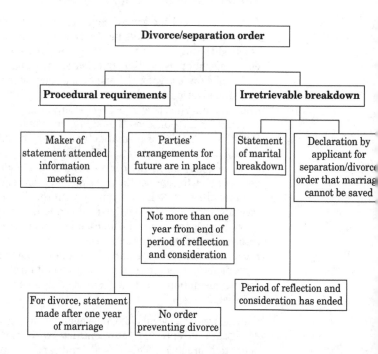

A divorce order or separation order can only be made if the marriage has broken down irretrievably. However, evidence for this is simply compliance with a number of procedural steps:

(a) requisite attendance at an information meeting;
(b) the parties' financial arrangements are satisfactorily in place;
(c) there is no order preventing the divorce;

(d) the necessary period for reflection and consideration has ended;

(e) the applicant for the separation/divorce order has made a declaration stating that having reflected on the breakdown and considered the requirements as to the parties' arrangements for the future, it is believed that the marriage cannot be saved; and

(f) not more than 12 months have elapsed from the end of the nine- or 15-month period for reflection and consideration.

In these circumstances, the separation order or divorce order will be made. If there is an application for both orders, the application for the divorce order takes precedence provided there is no order preventing divorce in force and the statement was made after the first anniversary of the marriage. It is possible in certain circumstances to convert a separation order into a divorce order without having a further period for reflection and consideration.

Financial Provision

The Act makes a number of changes to the court's power to grant financial provision, specifically increased powers to grant interim lump sum and interim property adjustment orders. Moreover, the Act allows final financial orders before the final separation/divorce order if the court is satisfied that the circumstances of the case are exceptional and that it would be just and reasonable for the order to be made. Perhaps the first most obvious change for practitioners is the wholesale rearrangement of ss 21–24 Matrimonial Causes Act 1973. This is set out in Sch 2 of the Act.

Pension Rights

The Act lays the foundation for pension splitting powers for the courts. However, it will require further legislation, certainly secondary legislation by way of rules and regulations, and very probably further primary legislation. It is unlikely to be in force until the year 2000 while full consultation takes place, but the principles are now clearly provided for by Parliament in the Act.

At present, for divorce petitions issued after 1 July 1996 the court has pension earmarking powers. However, it has always been accepted that this was only a halfway house towards full pension splitting powers. Earmarking creates real problems in practice. The government has repeatedly said that there are many technical difficulties with implementing pension splitting. There are fiscal issues; there are vast sums invested in pension companies, and there will have to be significant changes in the way the funds are operated in order for pension splitting to be fully enforced. Nevertheless, the pension companies support pension splitting, and full justice and fairness to many spouses on divorce demands that pension splitting powers are available. Unfortunately, full implementation will not arrive quickly. For now what is significant is that the principle of equal sharing of pensions built up during a marriage has been accepted and can be a good starting point in negotiations in mediation.

Pilot Projects and Commencement

As a result of the government's bad experience with the Child Support Act 1991, and because the infrastructure of the divorce process for couples is just as important as the new law, the government is setting up a number of pilot projects across the country. These will not cover the law itself, but mediation services, marriage-counselling services, inter-relationship with legal representation, and information meetings. The practical experience gained through these pilot projects is likely to influence substantially the workings of the new divorce process.

The new law and court procedures are heavily dependent on rules and regulations. Just as implementation of the Children Act 1989 required completely new regulations in the Family Proceedings Rules 1991, so it is highly likely that there will be new rules and regulations before the Act is fully in force. At present, it is anticipated that the provisions of the Act regarding divorce and separation will be brought fully into effect in 2000. However, it is also clear that the government will not bring in the new law until the divorce process and the surrounding infrastructure of mediation, counselling, information meetings, etc is working well. The commencement date may therefore have to be reviewed during the pilot projects. Part IV, which deals with domestic violence and rights of occupation of family homes, was brought in on 1 October 1997.

Practice Management

The radical changes in the Act, and especially the commercial opportunities for mediation practices accompanied by the demands of the Legal Aid Board, mean that many mediation practices will have to undertake dramatic changes. The UK College and the main mediation organisations will be offering guidance. However, to a certain extent, local practices will need to take the initiative.

The Future

The Family Law Act makes major changes. It has every potential to improve radically the conduct and resolution of family law matters on spousal separation and divorce. Mediators and mediation organisations, locally and nationally, now have a tremendous opportunity within the English legal system, to provide a much-needed service alongside lawyers and counsellors to help those going through marriage break-down.

David Hodson is a specialist family law solicitor, and partner in The Family Law Consortium, Covent Garden, London, WC2. He is a family mediator, having trained with The Family Mediators Association. He is chairman of the Solicitors Family Law Association Good Practice Committee and a member of its National Committee.

Legal Aid Board Family Mediation Pilot Project

Sarah White

Introduction

Part III of the Family Law Act 1996 (the Act) enables the Legal Aid Board (the Board) to secure through franchise contracts the provision of family mediation services for clients eligible for legal aid. The delivery of family mediation is a new area of activity for the Board and it is important when developing and expanding services throughout England and Wales, that arrangements are piloted and subject to ongoing evaluation by independent researchers. It is also important to maintain a commitment to consult with the key representative bodies and more widely throughout the pilot project.

To assist in developing proposals for piloting family mediation services, the Board has researched the current provision of services offered by National Family Mediation (NFM), Family Mediators Association (FMA) and other service providers. Discussions have also been held with academics and senior officers of NFM, FMA, the UK College of Family Mediators, NCH Action for Children, the Probation Service, the British Association of Lawyer Mediators, The Law Society, the Solicitors Family Law Association, the Institute of Legal Executives, the Legal Aid Practitioners Group and others.

The Approach

The aim of the pilot project is to enable the Board to ensure that arrangements are in place to meet the demand for mediation services created by the Act. This will be achieved by facilitating the development and expansion of the most effective arrangements for the provision of publicly funded and quality assured family mediation services for eligible clients throughout England and Wales. The Board's objectives are to determine:

(a) the relative benefits and cost effectiveness of contracting for the provision of publicly funded and quality assured family mediation services through different supplier arrangements;

(b) the most effective quality assurance and contracting arrangements for the delivery of publicly funded mediation services;

(c) the level of quality assured legal advice necessary to support publicly funded family mediation and the most cost effective arrangements for providing it;

(d) the relative cost/benefits, for both the assisted person and the taxpayer, of the provision of publicly funded mediation and the supporting legal advice compared to the current legal aid arrangements.

Following visits to mediation services and discussions with key representative bodies, the Board prepared draft proposals. During the summer of 1996 the proposals were circulated on a confidential basis to key representative bodies for comment. They were revised following comments received and the wider consultation exercise commenced with publication of the document Family Mediation Pilot Project Proposals in October 1996. As the purchase of family mediation services is a new

Handbook A

activity for the Board, it has been necessary to set out in detail proposals covering the duration of the pilot project. Following the consultation exercise and discussions with the key representative bodies, the proposals were further revised and in February 1997 the Board published its key reference document *Franchising Family Mediation Services*, which incorporates:

- Section 1: The Approach
- Section 2: Draft Code of Practice
- Section 3: Draft Family Mediation Franchise Specification

Timetable

In the approach, the Board has adopted an implementation plan for the pilot project which has four overlapping phases. The project commenced in September 1996, with the initial consultation and preparation stages and selection of areas and suppliers. Phase I of the pilot itself started in May 1997. Selection of participants in Phase II will begin during the latter part of Phase I, ie November 1997 to March 1998 and Phase II pilot contracts will be finalised by May 1998. The final testing of the draft franchise and contracting arrangements will take place in Phase III, from March 1999, prior to the introduction of ongoing arrangements in Phase IV, which will start in mid-2000.

Selection of Areas

In the Autumn of 1996 the Board invited family mediation services wanting to be involved in Phase I of the pilot project to complete and return an expression of interest form. Services were asked to provide detailed information including the number of trained mediators; which organisation they were trained by; the number of mediation enquiries received; the number of completed mediations; and the type of mediation offered, ie children-only issues or including property and finance matters. The data taken from the forms has enabled activity throughout England and Wales to be mapped out. In order to ensure a sufficient volume of cases to inform the research project, the key criterion for the Board when selecting the areas was the volume of cases dealt with by services.

The Board had originally envisaged operating Phase I in three to five areas and including between 20 and 30 suppliers. It was clear, however, both from comments received and from the forms submitted that the provision of family mediation services is very limited, with fewer than 100 suppliers currently providing any significant volume of mediation work throughout England and Wales. In the circumstances it has been necessary for the purposes of Phase I to involve 12 locations and around 33 suppliers. The Phase I areas are: London, Birmingham, Bristol, Bromley, Cambridge, Cardiff, Coventry, Durham, Greater Manchester, Newcastle, Northampton and Peterborough.

In Phase II the Board will continue to develop and expand the services involved in the Phase I areas. Further pilot areas and suppliers are currently being chosen for Phase II. The areas where the greatest volume of family work occurs are being identified, and this will inform the selection of areas and services, in addition to the criteria used in selecting Phase I areas and services. The number of areas will be increased to extend the pilot to cover as many population centres as possible. This expansion will help to extend the availability of publicly funded family mediation services to other areas throughout England and Wales. In Phase II the Board will continue to refine the quality assurance arrangements, taking data both from the researchers and also the Board's audits of services to inform this process. It is anticipated that by the end of Phase II, in March 1999, the number of suppliers involved will have increased to between 80 and 100.

Models of Mediation

A key element of the pilot project will be the testing of a range of supplier arrangements. Set out at paragraph 1.23 of *Franchising Family Mediation Services* is a description of four models which will be monitored and evaluated. The models identified are:

(a) specialist mediation services, including in-court services—NFM, NCH Action for Children and others;

(b) association/federation/consortium arrangements—FMA and others;

(c) partnership arrangements between family law firms and mediators or mediation services;

(d) solicitors with in-house mediation services, either permanent staff or partners who are mediators or mediators brought in on a fee basis and paid by the firm—SFLA and others.

The Board is keen to test a range of different models and would welcome suggestions of other viable arrangements which could then be considered for inclusion in the pilot project.

Block Contracting a Publicly Funded and Quality Assured Service

The pilot contracts will be developed during the four phases of the pilot project:

Phase I

This will be an enabling contract allowing the Board to fund service providers for the purpose of testing various arrangements. Initially, it is likely to take the form of a block contract based on an estimated volume of work. It will require compliance with a Draft Code of Practice, key aspects of the Draft Family Mediation Franchise Specification and certain monitoring requirements. The assumption in Phase I is that funding will provide resources and facilities to deal with a predicted level of demand. In the circumstances, the Board would seek to reduce the ongoing level of funding only if demand was significantly below that anticipated in the contract.

Phase II

The Board may wish to test a number of different contracting arrangements. The relative advantages of different contract payment arrangements in terms of quality assurance and cost effectiveness will be monitored and evaluated. The arrangements could involve contracting for an agreed level of resource, block contracting for an agreed volume of cases, fixed prices paid on a case-by-case basis, unit price payments by sessions and others. With a block contract there would be an agreed payment under the contract for a block of cases to be dealt with. Central to the viability and effectiveness of such a contracting arrangement would be the degree of similarity of cases, so that a unit price could be applied with which both the Board and the provider were satisfied.

Phase III

By the start of Phase III it is assumed that there will be a clearer picture of demand, how it is developing and the most effective supplier arrangements for meeting it. As these may vary in different parts of England and Wales there will be a need for a range of different supplier arrangements, provided by both not-for-profit and private sectors, to meet different demands and to provide reasonable access.

Phase IV

The contracting arrangements, including the contract terms, will be finalised in preparation for the launch of ongoing contracting arrangements in early 2000. It is intended that suppliers with provisional contracts will be invited to tender for three-year contracts. The three-year contracts will be reviewed on a rolling basis so that the supplier will know at least a year in advance if the contract is to be terminated or extended.

Family Mediation Franchise Specification

The Board is committed to the franchising initiative as a way of further developing the quality assurance of services, which began with the franchising of legal aid services. In considering the delivery of a quality assured service it is appropriate to consider the requirements set out in the Draft Family Mediation Franchise Specification ('Draft Specification'), which is incorporated into the key document *Franchising Family Mediation Services* and has also been published as a separate document.

The Draft Specification incorporates a Draft Code of Practice which includes the provisions of s 27 of the Act. These require a mediator to have arrangements designed to ensure that parties participating in mediation do so only if willing, that they are not influenced by fear of violence or other harm, and that where either party may be so influenced these factors are identified as soon as possible and dealt with as appropriate. Reconciliation is to be kept under review and each party is to be informed about the availability of legal advice. Section 27 also requires mediators to have arrangements in place that are designed to ensure that the parties are encouraged to consider the welfare, wishes and feelings of each child and to identify whether, and to what extent, each child should be given the opportunity to express his or her wishes and feelings in mediation. The requirements in both documents will be tested during Phase I, following which any revisions will be incorporated into a revised Draft. This will be published for consultation before a further Draft Code and Specification are made available for testing in Phase II.

The Draft Specification contains management criteria which will be set to ensure that professional standards are maintained. They will include requirements in respect of: premises; providing supervision; file review; and managing people employed by the service. There will be additional requirements, currently being used by the Board in promoting a quality assurance framework, which relate to auditing services through transaction criteria, an audit tool that attempts to check whether key transactions in the mediation process have taken place. As the pilot progresses, outcome measures will also need to be developed. These will be informed by the research project which will seek to identify the success rate of mediation, durability of mediated settlements and client satisfaction. Services will need to meet minimum requirements before being included in the pilot, and the Board's liaison managers will work with individual services, helping them to move towards meeting the overall quality requirements. The assumptions made in respect of the standards required to deliver a quality service will also be tested and reviewed in light of the research and findings of the Board's audits.

It is important to the development of a quality service that issues concerning the quality of the mediator, and not just the mediation process, are addressed. It is not the Board's role to regulate the mediation profession and to this end key elements of the Draft Specification are based largely on the work of the UK College of Family Mediators and the work of key bodies such as NFM, FMA, BALM, the Probation Service, the Law Society and the Solicitors Family Law Association. The Board is pleased to support the work of the UK College's Advisory Board, which brings together the key representative bodies to consider key issues concerning the establishment of a mediation profession. In particular, the Board is pleased to work with these organisations when considering key issues concerning selection of mediators, training, supervision, accreditation and regulation. The Board is committed to supervision as a means of providing a quality service. The role of supervision in the mediation process will be subject to the scrutiny of the researchers and also detailed discussions with the key representative bodies.

■ Research Project

There are a number of key issues which will be tested during the pilot project. The research team will monitor and evaluate both the objectives of the project and also the arrangements set out in Part III of The Approach in the main document. The research will be one of the major elements during Phase I and II of the pilot. A consortium has been appointed, of which Professor Gwynn Davis from Bristol University will be Academic Director. The contract will be held by the research organisation Social Community Planning Research (SCPR), which is led by Dr Patten Smith. The other researchers involved are Dr Gwyn Bevan, from the London School of Economics, who will provide an economic analysis of mediation services, and Professor Robert Dingwall and Dr David Greatbatch from Nottingham University, who will monitor the mediation process. Dr Adrian James from Hull University will undertake a study of the institutional impact of the pilot and Professor Gwynn Davis will examine the intake assessment.

The research data to be collated will include case reports completed on each mediation client, together with control data to be collected from solicitor firms not involved in the mediation pilot. A panel study will also be undertaken, involving follow-up interviews of around 1,000 separating couples who have been through the mediation process. A small number of cases will also be followed up with in-depth interviews. Although quantitative data will be collected on all clients involved in mediation, it is important that the research includes a qualitative element as this will enable the researchers to bring into the overall analysis clients' views on the mediation process. The research project will be monitored by the Board's Advisory Group which includes staff from both the Board and the Lord Chancellor's Department, the researchers and independent academics.

Section 29

The Board will be piloting and introducing section 29 in the Phase I and II areas by the end of 1998. Section 29 requires a legally aided client to attend before a mediator, prior to the Board considering an application for legal aid for legal proceedings, to allow the mediator to assess whether mediation is suitable to the parties, the case and all the circumstances.

Conclusion

The approach adopted by the Board and the timescale for implementing the pilot project are challenging. It is important, therefore, that the Board maintains its commitment to consult with key representative bodies and more widely on progress and on any proposed changes to the approach as currently set out in the key reference document. Interim reports on the research project will also be published so that all concerned with the pilot are aware of progress, any proposed changes and the reasons for them.

Family Mediation and the Law in Scotland

Fiona Garwood, Maureen Lynch and Hugh Donald

Introduction

Mediators need to have knowledge of the legal framework as it affects the users of their services. They should be aware of the main features of the divorce and relevant family law, associated court orders, court and legal processes, any rules of court which apply and they need to have an understanding of the legal aid system and child support regulations. It is not the mediator's role to give advice, legal or otherwise; but it is their responsibility to ensure that clients have correct legal information and access to legal advice. For example, mediators can provide information on a court procedure; but would not recommend a course of action or give advice or any opinion on a likely outcome. This section provides an overview of the Scottish legal system relevant to family mediation in Scotland. It outlines the main features of the Scottish divorce legislation and the legal processes within which mediators in Scotland operate. It highlights those which are different from England and Wales.

Chart of Differences in Law Between Scotland and England & Wales

Legislation which applies across the UK

Child Support Act 1991, Pensions Act 1995 (Scottish provisions came into force August 1996.)

Scottish statutes which have parallel legislation in England & Wales

Scotland: **Children (Scotland) Act 1995**, *England & Wales*: **Children Act 1989** These define parental responsibilities, rights and duties in relation to children and set out duties and powers available to public authorities to support children and their families and to intervene when the child's welfare requires it.

Scotland	*England & Wales*
Divorce (Scotland) Act 1976 Sets out irretrievable breakdown of marriage as the sole ground for divorce in Scotland.	**Matrimonial Causes Act 1973,** as amended. Due to be superseded by **Family Law Act 1996.**
Matrimonial Homes (Family Protection) (Scotland) Act 1981 Covers exclusion orders, transfer of tenancy, powers of arrest, protection of cohabitees, division and sale of property.	**Domestic Violence and Matrimonial Proceedings Act 1976** and **Matrimonial Homes Act 1983**, but **Part IV Family Law Act 1996** from October 1996.
Family Law (Scotland) Act 1985 Makes provision for financial and other consequences of decrees of divorce.	**Matrimonial Causes Act 1973** as above. Makes provision for financial and other consequences of decrees of divorce. Also **Family Proceedings Rules 1991** Statutory Instrument containing rules of court and procedure governing divorce, judicial separation and nullity, financial claims, children proceedings and other areas of family law litigation. See also **Family Law Act 1996** which amends ancilliary financial provision in Matrimonial Causes Act.

Scottish legislation with no similar provision in England & Wales

Civil Evidence (Family Mediation) (Scotland) Act 1995 An Act to make provision for the inadmissibility as evidence in civil proceedings in Scotland of information as to what occurred during family mediation.

Note: This chart was prepared with the assistance of David Hodson of the Family Law Consortium.

The chart above highlights the significant pieces of legislation which apply across the UK, ie the Child Support Act 1991, and statutes which have parallel legislation in England and Wales and are covered in Paul Foster's section 'Family Law for Mediators' below. It also highlights Scottish legislation which has no parallel in England and Wales. The following paragraphs outline the Scottish court system, relevant Scottish legislation, the rules of court which apply in Scotland, Scottish legal aid and legal terms commonly used in Scotland.

The Scottish Court System

The District Court

This court deals with minor criminal matters only. The cases proceed before one or more magistrates sitting with a qualified clerk. This court has no jurisdiction regarding children.

The Sheriff Court

The sheriff court has both a criminal and a civil jurisdiction and deals with the vast majority of cases in Scotland. Scotland is divided into six sheriffdoms and each has a sheriff principal. There are fifty sheriff court districts, each of which has at least one sheriff. A sheriff must be legally qualified and have had at least ten years in practice. Sheriff principals and sheriffs are addressed as 'My Lord' in court and 'Sheriff' when off the bench. Most family actions are heard in this court. A sheriff also hears cases for child protection orders or where parents are objecting to a local authority assuming parental rights, and deals with referrals from the children's panel where the parents or child do not accept the alleged grounds of referral. Criminal cases involving children (between the ages of 8 and 16) can be presented in the sheriff court only with the leave of the Lord Advocate (Scotland's chief law officer). Special provisions apply if the child is charged along with an adult.

The Court of Session

This is a civil court and all judges have the same rank and title, 'Senators of the College of Justice'. The Court of Session sits only in Edinburgh. This court has wide powers of jurisdiction including jurisdiction regarding actions involving status—for example, illegitimacy, nullity of marriage. It may deal with divorce, and family matters like the sheriff court; but in practice most cases now go to the sheriff courts. Both the sheriff court and the Court of Session have powers to refer parties to mediation under Rules of Court (see Rules of Court below).

The High Court of Justiciary

This court has jurisdiction to try all crimes (although many serious crimes are heard in the sheriff court) and has an exclusive jurisdiction in murder, treason, rape and incest cases. It is a court which sits both in Edinburgh and on circuit. The trials proceed before a single judge and jury and the court's power is restricted in the same way as the sheriff court in relation to the prosecution of children.

The House of Lords

This is the final appeal court for civil cases. Cases are heard by an appellate committee of the House of Lords consisting of five Law Lords.

Rule of Court Referrals to Scottish Family Mediation Services Flow Chart

Dispute Between Parents Over Children
(May Also Involve Grandparents)

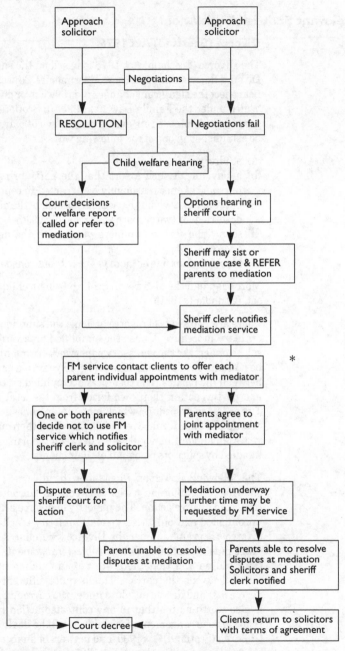

* In places where contact centres are available, their use is an option at any stage.

By convention, when the court is hearing Scottish cases, at least two of them are Scottish judges.

Note: The above is based on Child Care Law. A Summary of the Law in Scotland, *BAAF Practice Series ll.*

■ Relevant Scottish Legislation

Divorce (Scotland) Act 1976

The Divorce (Scotland) Act 1976 is based on the same principles as the Divorce Reform Act 1969 (now Matrimonial Causes Act 1973) and will not reflect the significant changes in provision for divorce in England and Wales under the Family Law Act 1996. In Scotland there remains one ground for divorce, irretrievable breakdown of marriage, and this has to be established in one of the following ways:

(a) adultery;
(b) behaviour, of such a sort that the party bringing the action (the pursuer) cannot reasonably be expected to continue living with the party against whom the action is brought (the defender);
(c) desertion for two or more years (hardly used);
(d) separation for two or more years with the defender's consent to divorce ;
(e) separation for five or more years without consent of the defender.

More than half the divorces in Scotland where children are involved, are sought under (a) or (b).

There are two kinds of divorce actions: the simplified procedure and the ordinary procedure. Under the simplified procedure, the parties themselves undertake the necessary paperwork. To qualify for this there must be no children of the marriage under 16 years old or any financial claims between the parties. The cost for the simplified procedure in 1997 is £55 and parties obtain their own forms from the local sheriff clerk's office. The ordinary procedure, which amounts to almost two-thirds of current Scottish actions, would cover divorces where there are children under 16 years old and/or financial claims between the parties. These actions are handled by solicitors on behalf of their clients.

The following flowchart illustrates the divorce process in Scotland, showing the different paths between an uncontested action and a contested divorce action. The majority of divorce actions in Scotland are uncontested and only a very small minority reach a proof. Actions for divorce are granted under the Divorce (Scotland) Act and the sheriff or judge must be satisfied that suitable arrangements have been made for the children and that there are no outstanding financial or property claims between the parties. This is quite different from the system of decree *nisi* and decree absolute under the current English legislation. It is also worth noting that in any contested action in Scotland, matters relating to arrangements for children will be dealt with under the new Children (Scotland) Act 1995, and matters of finance and property under the Family Law (Scotland) Act 1985 (see below). A further significant difference is the Rule of Court which enables a sheriff or judge to make a referral to mediation in any family action where an order in relation to parental responsibilities or parental rights is an issue. See Rules of Court in Scotland relevant to family mediation, below.

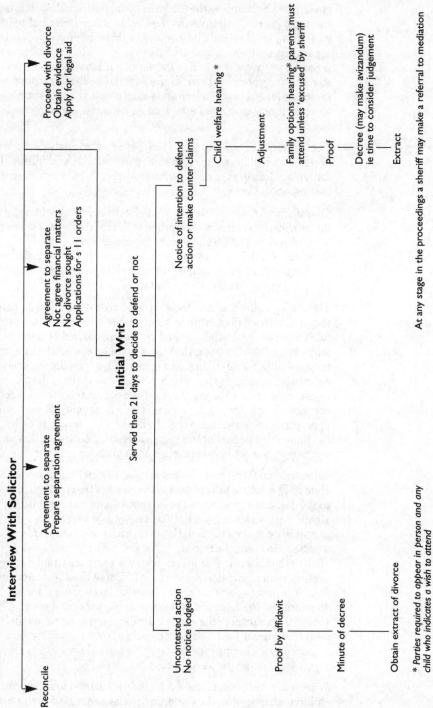

The Divorce Process in Scotland Flow Chart

Interview With Solicitor

Reconcile

Agreement to separate
Prepare separation agreement

Agreement to separate
Not agree financial matters
No divorce sought
Applications for s 11 orders

Proceed with divorce
Obtain evidence
Apply for legal aid

Initial Writ
Served then 21 days to decide to defend or not

Uncontested action
No notice lodged

Notice of intention to defend
action or make counter claims

Child welfare hearing *

Proof by affidavit

Adjustment

Family options hearing* parents must
attend unless 'excused' by sheriff

Minute of decree

Proof

Decree (may make avizandum)
ie time to consider judgement

Obtain extract of divorce

Extract

* Parties required to appear in person and any
child who indicates a wish to attend

At any stage in the proceedings a sheriff may make a referral to mediation

Children (Scotland) Act 1995

Arrangements for children when parents separate and divorce are governed in Scotland by the Children (Scotland) Act 1995. It is based on the same general principles as the Children Act 1989, and reflects the view that parents should be involved in their children's lives even after separation or divorce; that all decisions in relation to children should place the welfare of the child as the paramount consideration; that courts should intervene only when they are sure that such intervention is better for the child, and that children and young people should be provided with an opportunity to express a view when decisions are being made about them.

The Children (Scotland) Act 1995 defines the relationship between parents and children in terms of parental responsibilities. It also contains a definition of what parental responsibilities are. Parents have the responsibility to:

(a) safeguard and promote the child's health, development and welfare;
(b) provide, in a manner appropriate to the child's stage of development, (i) direction and (ii) guidance to the child;
(c) if the child is not living with the parent, to maintain personal relations and direct contact with the child on a regular basis;
(d) act as the child's legal representative.

These responsibilities and their parallel rights are given to parents if they are married to each other. Unmarried mothers automatically have full parental responsibilities and rights; unmarried fathers, however, may obtain these by going through a procedure to establish a parental responsibilities and rights agreement. This procedure involves the completion of a simple form which may be obtained from the offices of any registrar or from Citizens' Advice Bureaux or from family mediation services. When the form is completed, it should be sent with the appropriate fee to the Register of the Books of Council and Session. When the unmarried father obtains parental responsibilities in this way, they can only be removed again through an application to the court.

All individuals with parental responsibilities and rights in relation to a child have a duty to have regard to the views of the child before making a major decision in relation to the exercise of parental responsibilities and rights. Parents also have a duty to have regard to the views of the other parent in a similar situation. However, each parent is considered to be in a position to exercise parental responsibilities and rights independently of the other parent. The orders which a court may make to regulate arrangements for children under the Children (Scotland) Act 1995 are: residence orders, contact orders, specific issue orders and prohibited steps orders. The definition of residence orders makes it possible for each parent to be named in the residence order, even if the child is only living with that parent for a short time during any week or any month. It is intended that 'staying over' contact between a child and a parent will be regulated through the use of residence orders.

When a court is asked to make a decision in relation to arrangements for children after divorce, the Children (Scotland) Act 1995 places a duty on the court to give the child concerned an opportunity to express his/her view about the application. If the child expresses a view, the court is required to have regard for the view expressed. When an application for an order is lodged, the pursuer's solicitor will be directed to send a form to each of the children concerned, outlining what is being asked for from the court and informing the child of his/her right to express a view. If the child expresses a view in writing, then the sheriff may decide to maintain the confidentiality of the child's views throughout the legal process. The child's written expression of view would therefore be placed in an envelope marked 'confidential' which would not be available to any of the other individuals involved in the court apart from the sheriff. The Children (Scotland) Act 1995 made it possible for children to be independently represented by a solicitor even in circumstances where there was not a conflict of interest between the child and the parent. It is therefore possible, and in some sheriff courts very likely, that a child may be given the opportunity to express his/her view through a solicitor.

The rules which are used within the court process to put into practice the principles of the Children (Scotland) Act 1995, include a rule which establishes the duty for the convening of a child welfare hearing when arrangements for children after separation and divorce are disputed by the parents. This hearing is intended to be held as early as possible in the legal process. Both parents are required to be present at the hearing and the child may also be present at the sheriff's discretion if they wish. These child welfare hearings are designed to be less formal than the court process. The sheriff may, and frequently does, speak directly to the parent rather than through his/her agent. The hearings will be held in private in the court with only those directly involved in the application being present. They are designed to provide an early opportunity to resolve issues around the arrangements for children so that children may be protected from the effects of conflict between their parents.

A Rule of Court also makes possible the referral of parents to a family mediation service. This may take place at any point in the legal process and it does not depend on there being a legal dispute between the parents over arrangements for their children. Where there is agreement that contact should take place, but the details of how it will happen have not been agreed by the parents, then the sheriff may refer the couple to a family mediator.

Family Law (Scotland) Act 1985

The Family Law (Scotland) Act is the key piece of legislation setting out the provisions for aliment (maintenance), financial and other consequences of decrees of divorce and the property rights and legal capacity of married people. Some sections on aliment for children have been superseded by the Child Support Act 1991.

The principles

There are five main principles which underpin the Act contained in s 9 of the Act:

(a) that the net value of the matrimonial property is to be shared fairly between the parties;

(b) that fair account should be taken of any economic advantage derived by either party from contributions by the other and of any economic disadvantage suffered by either party in the interests of the other party or of the family;

(c) that any economic burden of caring for children of the marriage after divorce is shared fairly between the parties;

(d) that the party who has been dependent to a substantial degree on the financial support of the other party should have financial support to enable him or her to adjust to the loss of that support for a period of not more than three years.

(e) that a party who at the time of divorce seems likely to suffer serious financial hardship as a result of the divorce should be awarded some financial provision to relieve this hardship over a reasonable period. (This is seen as being an exception rather than the rule).

Types of order available on divorce

(a) aliment:
  - spouse—interim/backdated
  - child (if outwith jurisdiction of Child Support Act)—top-up/ educational expenses/for disabled child;
(b) capital sum;
(c) transfer of property;
(d) periodical allowance;
(e) incidental orders including:
  - 1 for sale of property
  - 2 for valuation of property
  - 3 regulating occupation of matrimonial home
  - 4 regulating use of furnishings and plenishings in matrimonial home
  - 5 as to date from which interest shall run on any amount awarded.

The factors

Section 11 of the Act details the factors to be taken into account by the court when applying the above principles. These factors provide a fair degree of discretion for the court to consider health, age, earning capacity, child care costs, needs and resources of the parties and 'all the circumstances of the case'.

Matrimonial property

This is defined under the Act as:

All the property belonging to the spouses or either of them at the relevant date which was acquired by the spouse(s):

(a) before the marriage for use by them as a family home or as furniture or plenishings for such a home, ie the matrimonial home and its contents; or
(b) during the marriage but before the relevant date.

However, the following property is excluded:

(a) property acquired before marriage, within the important exception of property acquired for use as the matrimonial home or its contents;
(b) property acquired by a spouse *after* the relevant date; and
(c) property acquired during the marriage from a third party by way of gift or succession.

Most importantly, matrimonial property includes the portion of any rights or interests of either spouse under life policy or occupational pension scheme which is referable to the period of marriage before the relevant date.

Relevant date

This is the date on which matrimonial property will be valued. It is the earlier of either:

(a) the date on which the parties ceased to cohabit; or
(b) the date of service of the summons of the writ of the action of divorce.

Amendments made to the Family Law (Scotland) Act 1985 by the Pensions Act 1995

Definitions of pension rights as matrimonial property
Section 167 of the Pensions Act 1995 amends s 10(5) of the Family Law (Scotland) Act so that matrimonial property will include: 'The right or interests of either party (a) under a life policy or similar arrangement; and (b) in any benefits under a pension scheme which either party had or may have (including such benefits payable in respect of the death of either party)'. This means that the value of the widow/er's benefit is to be included in the value of pension rights as is any lump sum payable on death in service.

A recognised statutory method is now provided for calculating the relevant value of pension rights. In cases where no action of divorce existed as at 19 August 1996, all pensions will be valued by reference to the Cash Equivalent Transfer Value (CETV) provided by the pension scheme. The court may order 'earmarking of some or all of any lump sum which might become payable under the pension'. This type of order is made under the new s 12A of the Family (Scotland) Act 1985 which is created by s 167 of the Pensions Act. In line with the 'clean break' principle it does not allow such an order to be made against a pension which is already on stream.

The Matrimonial Homes (Family Protection) (Scotland) Act 1981

This Act, which applies to married and cohabiting couples, provides protection for occupancy of the matrimonial home, and power for exclusion orders, arrest and transfer of tenancy. It applies to property which is tenanted or owned and covers property in joint names or in the sole name of one of the spouses or cohabitees.

Civil Evidence (Family Mediation) (Scotland) Act 1995

'An Act to make provision for the inadmissibility as evidence in civil proceedings in Scotland of information as to what occurred during family mediation'.

Section 1

Establishes the basic principle that no information as to what occurred during family mediation shall be admissible as evidence in any civil proceedings. It is not applicable to criminal proceedings. The protection applies to family mediation between:

(1) Two or more individuals relating to:
    (a) residence of a child;

(b) regulations of personal relations and direct contact between child and any other person;

(c) control direction or guidance of a child's upbringing;

(d) guardianship or legal representation of a child or any other matter relating to a child's welfare (includes parties who are not parents of the child concerned).

(2) Spouses and former spouses concerning matters arising out of the breakdown or termination of their marriage—includes all financial disputes.

(3) Parties to a purported marriage concerning the breakdown or annulment of that marriage and between cohabitants or former cohabitants.

(a) information as to when and where the family mediation took place, who was present and any contract which was entered into during the family mediation is admissible;

(b) the protection only extends to family mediation conducted by a person accredited as a mediator in family mediation to an organisation approved by the Lord President of the Court of Session in Scotland.

Section 2

This describes the exceptions to the general rule of inadmissibility. The following exceptions apply:

(a) information as to any *contract* (see below) entered into during family mediation or of the fact that no contract was entered into during mediation;

(b) where any contract is challenged in civil proceedings, information is permitted as to what occurred during family mediation which relates to the subject matter of that challenge;

(c) of information as to what occurred during family mediation if every participant (other than the mediator) agrees that the information should be admitted as evidence; or

(d) of information as to what occurred during family mediation if those civil proceedings are related to children's hearings, adoption proceedings and other proceedings involving children in local authorities or voluntary organisations concerning the child's care or protection.

Contract Legally binding agreement, which mediators do not enter into with parties and which parties do not enter into with each other during the course of mediation.

Participant An individual spouse, former spouse, party to a purported marriage or cohabitant, and where the mediation relates to a child then the definition includes the child who is the subject of such family mediation and who at the time of the mediation was capable of understanding the nature and significance of the matters to which the information which is sought to be admitted as evidence relates.

■ Sheriff Court Rules Relevant to Family Mediation in Scotland

Procedures in Respect of Children

Amendment to Ordinary Cause Rules 1993

33.19.–(1) In a family action, in relation to any matter affecting a child, where that child has:

- (a) returned to the sheriff clerk Form F9, or
- (b) otherwise indicated to the court a wish to express views on a matter affecting him,

the sheriff shall not grant any order unless an opportunity has been given for the views of that child to be obtained or heard.

(2) Where a child has indicated his wish to express his views, the sheriff shall order such steps to be taken as he considers appropriate to ascertain the views of that child.

(3) The sheriff shall not grant an order in a family action, in relation to any matter affecting a child who has indicated his wish to express his views, unless due weight has been given by the sheriff to the views expressed by that child, having due regard to his age and maturity.

Recording of Views of Child

Amendment to Ordinary Cause Rules 1993

33.20.–(1) This rule applies where a child expresses a view on a matter affecting him whether expressed personally to the sheriff or to a person appointed by the sheriff for that purpose or provided by the child in writing.

(2) The sheriff, or the person appointed by the sheriff, shall record the views of the child in writing; and the sheriff may direct that such views, and any written views, given by a child shall:

- (a) be sealed in an envelope marked 'Views of the child—confidential';
- (b) be kept in the court process without being recorded in the inventory of process;
- (c) be available to a sheriff only;
- (d) not be opened by any person other than a sheriff; and
- (e) not form a borrowable part of the process.

Child Welfare Hearing

Amendment to Ordinary Cause Rules 1993

33.22A.–(1) Where:

- (a) on the lodging of a notice of intention to defend in a family action in which the initial writ seeks or includes a crave for a s 11 order, a defender wishes to oppose any such crave or order, or seeks the same order as that craved by the pursuer,
- (b) on the lodging of a notice of intention to defend in a family action, the defender seeks a s 11 order which is not craved by the pursuer, or
- (c) in any circumstances in a family action, the sheriff considers that a child welfare hearing should be fixed

and makes an order (whether at his own instance or on the motion of a party) that such a hearing shall be fixed,

the sheriff clerk shall fix a date and time for a child welfare hearing on the first suitable court date occurring not sooner than 21 days after the lodging of such notice of intention to defend, unless the sheriff directs the hearing to be held on an earlier date.

(2) On fixing the date for the child welfare hearing, the sheriff clerk shall intimate the date of the child welfare hearing to the parties in Form F41.

(3) The fixing of the date of the child welfare hearing shall not affect the right of a party to make any other application to the court whether by motion or otherwise.

(4) At the child welfare hearing (which may be held in private), the sheriff shall seek to secure the expeditious resolution of disputes in relation to the child by ascertaining from the parties the matter in dispute in relation to the child and any information relevant to that dispute, and may:

(a) order such steps to be taken, or

(b) make such order, if any, or

(c) order further procedure, as he thinks fit.

(5) All parties (including a child who has indicated his wish to attend) shall, except on cause shown, attend the child welfare hearing personally.

(6) It shall be the duty of the parties to provide the sheriff with sufficient information to enable him to conduct the child welfare hearing.

Referral to Family Mediation

Amendment to Ordinary Cause Rules 1993

33.22.– In any family action in which an order in relation to parental responsibilities or parental rights is in issue, the sheriff may, at any stage of the action, where he considers it appropriate to do so, refer that issue to a mediator accredited to a specific family mediation organisation.

■ Legal Aid in Scotland

Legal aid in Scotland is administered by the Scottish Legal Aid Board and covers two types: advice and assistance, and civil legal aid. The significant difference between legal aid in Scotland and in England and Wales is that from 1995 for an experimental period, the expenses of voluntary mediation for a person in receipt of legal aid or advice and assistance in a family dispute can be accepted as an outlay, where the mediator or the family mediation service makes a charge.

Terms Relating to Legal Aid

Legal advice and assistance

Commonly referred to as 'the Pink Form'. This is the first type of legal aid usually offered to clients. It will allow the solicitor to give general matrimonial advice and cover an initial meeting and a few letters. It will not cover the cost of raising a divorce action. If a client is on income support no contribution will be payable, otherwise the level of contribution payable is calculated in accordance with the client's disposable income.

Legal aid

This type of legal aid will cover the costs of the client going to court or defending an action. This scheme is also means tested and unless a client is on income support, they will generally have a contribution to pay. The Scottish Legal Aid Board will carry out a detailed investigation of the client's income and outgoings to calculate the contribution and then make an offer of legal aid which does not have to be accepted. The contribution is payable by way of instalments, usually over 12 months.

The statutory charge

If a legally aided person recovers or preserves capital or property worth more than £2,500, then the Scottish Legal Aid Board can recover a proportion of the costs from the client.

Glossary of Scottish Legal Terms

This glossary is based on Duncan, A G M (1982) *Students' Glossary of Scottish Legal Terms*. W Green & Son Ltd.

Agent Person acting on behalf of another, usually a solicitor.

Affidavit Sworn statement from the pursuer and witnesses, possibly also from the other defender and parties involved, only normally needed when divorce is being finalised.

Aliment Support or maintenance of a husband, wife or other relative.

Bar The collective term for members of the Faculty of Advocates in Scotland, who are entitled to represent clients in the highest courts. A number of solicitor advocates have been appointed over the last few years.

Civil action One raised by one party against another.

Cite Summon to court.

Consistorial Actions between husband and wife.

Continue To postpone a decision in judicial proceedings and adjourn them to a later date for further action.

Crave A statement of what is being sought from the court.

Decree The common Scottish technical term for a final judgement *cf* interim order, eg section 11 order under the Children (Scotland) Act 1995 for residence, contact, parental responsibilities or rights.

De facto Physical possession.

Defender Person against whom a civil action is raised.

De jure Following a court order.

Initial writ Document which begins a legal action, containing statement of facts.

Interlocutor An order or decision of the court.

Handbook A

Interdict The judicial prohibition issued by a Scottish court. In an emergency 'interim interdict' can be obtained (on application *'ex parte'* without parties present). The English equivalent is an injunction.

Interim As applied to the ruling of a court, temporary or partial, as for example in matters of interim interdict.

Joint minute Document detailing agreements reached between parties.

Judiciary Judges of the Court of Session and sheriff court.

Matrimonial property All property belonging to the parties or either of them at *the relevant date*, (see below) which was (a) acquired during the marriage (except by gift or inheritance), or (b) acquired before the marriage for use *by them* as a family home or as furniture or plenishings for such home.

Motion An application made in court for some subsidiary purpose during the course of a legal action, eg motion for interim contact.

Process The writs, forms and pleadings from the first step to the judgement, by which an action or prosecution is brought.

Proof A court hearing where evidence is heard to decide the outcome of a case.

Pursuer A person suing in, or raising, an action.

Relevant date Whichever is earlier of: (a) the date of separation or (b) the date an action of divorce was served. It is of great importance in sharing matrimonial property as valuations must be taken as at the relevant date for divorce purposes.

Session, Court of The supreme civil court in Scotland.

Sheriff court The court of the sheriff, in which divorce or other related matrimonial cases can be heard.

Sist To stop or delay a case without limit of time.

Specification of document A court document served upon a party who has failed to produce documentation vouching their financial position.

Sue To raise a civil action.

Warrant Written authority from a court authorising a certain action.

Terms relating to domestic violence

Common law interdict A court order for a person to refrain from threatening, harassing or using violence towards another person.

Exclusion order A court order excluding a person from his house, an extreme measure for a serious case of domestic violence.

Power of arrest A court order attached to an interdict allowing a police officer to arrest a person who has broken the terms of the interdict.

■ Further Reading and References

Bennett, S A (1994) *Divorce in the Sheriff Court*. 4th edn, W Green/Sweet & Maxwell.

Cleland, A and Sutherland, E (1996) *Children's Rights in Scotland*. W Green/Sweet & Maxwell.

Hall Dick, A (1996) *Breaking Up Without Falling Apart: The Essential Guide to Separation & Divorce in Scotland*. B & W Publishing.

Jamieson, G (1995) *Parental Rights & Responsibilities*. W Green/Sweet & Maxwell.

McCulloch, W and Laing, E (1995) *New Ordinary Cause Rules*. CLT Professional Publishing.

McInnes (1990) *Divorce Law Practice in Scotland*. Butterworths.

Nichols, D I (1991) *The Family Law (Scotland) Act 1985*. 2nd edn, W Green/Sweet & Maxwell.

Norrie, K (1996) *Children (Scotland) Act 1995*. W Green/Sweet & Maxwell.

The Scottish Office (1995) *Scotland's Children. A Brief Guide to the Children (Scotland) Act 1995*. HMSO, Scotland.

Thomson, J M (1987) *Family Law in Scotland*. Butterworths.

The Mediation Process

Marian Roberts

'Without some theories about the agreement process in negotiation, about why and in what ways the parties do (or do not) reach agreement, it is difficult to analyse the contribution of the mediator to the resolution of conflict' (Stevens, 1963, p 123).

Two understandings are fundamental to an insight into mediation and the role of the mediator. Firstly, mediation is a way of intervening that is auxiliary to and that serves the process of negotiation. Secondly, we cannot begin to understand what the mediator is doing without a prior understanding of the nature and shape of the negotiation process. In this section this background is described, relying strongly on the work of Stevens (1963) and Gulliver (1977, 1979).

The Negotiation Process and its Relationship to Mediation

The nature of the negotiation process as essentially a process of communication and learning through a series of exchanges of information is described in detail below. This process is not in itself either haphazard or chaotic. If it were, negotiations would be doomed to failure. Whatever the differences in the society, the kind or complexity of the dispute, the length of time needed to reach a settlement, or the framework, the process itself generates an internal structure of its own, a 'succession of stages' that are common to all negotiations, even though no two instances are the same. This intrinsic structure that emerges from and is shaped by the process of negotiation also manifests itself in the rules the parties themselves create, and in the mutual understanding that is a product of the process. Fuller (1971, p 326) adumbrates this further:

> The primary function of the mediator ... is not to propose rules to the parties and to secure their acceptance of them, but to induce the mutual trust and understanding that will enable the parties to work out their own rules. The creation of rules is a process that cannot itself be rule-bound; it must be guided by a sense of shared responsibility and a realisation that the adversary aspects of the operation are part of a larger collaborative undertaking.

Gulliver has described the negotiation process realised through mediation as 'the gradual creation of order and of co-ordination between the parties'. The mediator orchestrates this process in which the parties begin with a degree of assumed knowledge but also, both consciously and unconsciously, with a considerable degree of uncertainty and downright ignorance. That knowledge is tested and altered and refined in the process of interaction. Exchanges of this kind proceed through a series of 'overlapping phases' by means of which progressive and orderly movement towards settlement becomes possible. Each party is engaged in learning—about the other, about him or herself, about the children and about the possibilities and impossibilities of their common situation and possible outcomes. By a process of improved communication and understanding, the parties have the opportunity to learn not only more about all the circumstances, pressures, feelings, perceptions, attitudes and needs that attend the particular dispute, but also how to negotiate. This involves learning how to listen and understand more fully the other's perceptions and interests, how to act rationally and communicate effectively, and how to be open to persuasion rather than coercion or bullying. The cyclical wheels of information exchange and learning that the mediator activates, motivate the negotiation process through its developmental progress towards settlement.

> In negotiation there are two distinct though interconnected processes going on simultaneously: a repetitive, cyclical one and a developmental one. A simple analogy is a moving automobile. There is the cyclical turning of the wheels ... that enables the vehicle to move and there is the actual movement of the vehicle from one place to another (Gulliver, 1979, p 82).

These interlocking developmental and cyclical processes reflect the reality of 'a general overall trend from relative ignorance, uncertainty and antagonism towards increased understanding, greater certainty and co-ordination' (Gulliver, 1979, p 173). What propels this whole process is the basic contradiction between the parties' antagonism (that is, the dispute itself) and their simultaneous need for joint action.

A Developmental Analysis of Negotiation

The staged process outlined below follows Gulliver closely. When a disagreement is precipitated by a crisis into a dispute, one party, or perhaps both, seeks to gain the involvement of others and the issue then enters the public or semi-public domain. Six overlapping phases then follow: the search for an arena; defining the agenda; exploring the field; narrowing differences; bargaining; ritualisation of outcome.

Search for an arena

The arena must be acceptable to both parties, although one may be resistant initially. The arena covers not only the geographical or social location but also who is involved and the ground rules.

Defining the agenda

The search for an arena is also part of the attempt to define the dispute. One party may not know what it is that is in dispute or the issue may have to be clarified and distinguished from other issues or emotional implications.

Exploring the field

In this relatively early phase, the emphasis will be on the differences between the parties. The messages passing between them are intended not to influence or shift the other but to explore the dimensions of the field within which further negotiations are to occur. Initial maximal claims and demands are likely to be set and extreme assertions expressed. The atmosphere is likely to be of competition, even hostility.

Narrowing differences

There is a progressive shift in orientation from difference and animosity towards co-ordination and even co-operation. This may be accomplished by resort to one or more of several strategies, for example by dealing with the less difficult issues first or dealing with each issue separately. If this phase goes well there should be a resolution of some items and the clarification and isolation of any remaining differences.

Bargaining

This may follow on those items which have been most difficult to resolve though they may not be the most important objectively. This is when 'I give in on this if you give in on that' may occur. Sometimes an outcome is reached with an unexpected and arbitrary suddenness when 'agreement *per se* has become more important than the particular point of agreement' (Gulliver, 1979, p 168).

Ritualisation of outcome

If all goes well and agreement is reached, there is a ritualisation of that agreement. This means that the outcome is marked in some way, according to culture, for example by the shaking of hands or by the drawing up and signing of a document. 'The negotiations have been concluded and there may be a good deal of amity. On the other hand, a persisting antagonism and a number of disagreements may remain; the parties may be bitter rivals still. For the moment, however, there is agreement, whether limited or broad, and a mutuality in the achievement of an outcome' (*ibid*. p 169).

The stages of mediation follow these stages of the negotiation process, a process of discovery and clarification, the essence of which is learning through a series of exchanges of information. The process has to be experienced by the parties themselves as negotiators, participating in a dynamic process of exploration, of each other and themselves. This leads finally to the convergence of a joint decision acceptable to both parties, the end of the dispute and the end of negotiations. It is the mediator's job to understand and manage this negotiation process between the parties.

The phases outlined in Gulliver's model have a psychological and social as well as a logical coherence. For example, at an early phase when maximum claims and demands are likely to be made and antagonism will be greatest, the parties are furthest apart in every sense. Intense emotion and harsh language will characterise this distance, for anxiety and insecurity are acute. With the articulation of resentment, the exchange of information and the increase of learning, stress diminishes. Yet this distance between the parties is necessary if subsequent movement is to be apparent.

Actual mediation negotiations are often more complex and variable than is suggested by these analytically distinct phases. Breakdown can occur at any stage. But without a regular pattern of expectations, adjustments and behaviour, negotiations would fail. Without an understanding of this pattern by the mediator, negotiations could be prolonged or damaged if through ignorance, hurry or inexperience short cuts are attempted.

One feature of the mediation process unavailable to judges is its 'procedural flexibility' (McCrory, 1981, p 56). This enables the parties themselves to determine the parameters of their exchanges, freeing them from legal formalities or prohibitions so that they may include those aspects of the dispute that they deem to be pertinent, for example the emotional ramifications of the dispute and private ethical attitudes to fault and fairness. The procedural flexibility of mediation also allows the requirements of full and accurate disclosure necessary for the mediation of financial and property matters to be accommodated. Procedural steps can be inserted at every stage of the process for dealing with the income (gathering, verifying, displaying and sharing), the assets (identifying, understanding, valuing), the options (collating, identifying gaps, dividing etc.) and the outcome (integrating the package, drawing up a Memorandum of Understanding).

Stages of the Mediation Process

© *National Family Mediation*

Stage 1:   *Establishing the Arena*
First contact and reception;
Facilitating communication;
Procedural Step 1: Signing the agreement to mediate and handing out financial information forms;

Stage 2:   *Clarifying the Issues*
Agreeing and defining the agenda;
Facilitating communication;
Procedural Step 2: Working on financial information forms *viz* budget forms, income & assets and liabilities forms;

Stage 3:   *Exploring the Issues*
Managing differences in the early stage;
Managing high conflict;
Facilitating communication;
Procedural Step 3: Displaying the completed budget sheets on flipchart;
Procedural Step 4: Calculation (approximately) of child support;

Stage 4:   *Developing Options*
Facilitating communication;
Further information exchange and learning;
Procedural Step 5: Displaying information on income, assets and liabilities;
Procedural Step 6: Collecting documentation (for verification);
Procedural Step 7: Collating budget and income/asset facts and identifying any gap between need and resources; assisting couples to produce, negotiate about and choose from options;

Stage 5:   *Securing Agreement*
Concluding the session;
Procedural Step 8: Integrating the package;
Procedural Step 9: Drawing up Memorandum of Understanding.

The Framework of Mediation

'For of mediation one is tempted to say that it is all process and no structure' (Fuller, 1971, p 307). What this observation serves to highlight is the difference between the processes involved in mediation and those involved in adjudication. The latter is characterised by institutional rules, formal procedures and clearly demarcated roles and authority (judges, barristers, clerks etc). It is within this formal pattern of due process that any dispute is dealt with.

As we have seen above, no such institutional framework occurs in negotiation processes. The parties seek to sort out their dispute by voluntary exchanges, negotiation and decision-making. But where the parties cannot manage this on their own and so resort to mediation, some structural changes are inevitable. First, obviously a simple bilateral process is transformed into one involving a third party. Secondly, the very presence of this third party imposes the rudiments of a framework upon the encounter, for example who is to participate and where, the time to be made available, and so on. Mediated negotiations require this minimum of rules at least, although cross-culturally mediation processes differ greatly in the way they are organised, the degree of formality (a lack of formality by no means indicating a lack of control), the rigidity of the framework and the number of rules imposed upon the disputants (Roberts, 1983).

This framework within which mediatory processes occur serves two main purposes:

(1) It enables the parties to negotiate together in a way that would not have been possible on their own. Ground rules, for example the right of the mediator to intervene if things get out of hand, embody the values that underpin mediation (such as mutual respect, equity of exchange, and so on) and make rational communication possible.
(2) The framework is designed to secure fairness. Rules of procedure make possible equal opportunities for full and confidential expression, for example the separate meeting with the mediator within the session, and the guarantee that both parties will be able to state their positions without interruption.

Structural Variations or Models of Mediation Sessions

There are a variety of structural arrangements or models that can be used to frame the mediation process. Some examples of these are set out below.

Joint or separate sessions

A joint session involves the presence of both disputants at the same mediation meeting. When the meeting involves the mediator and one party only, this is a separate session and may take place as an early phase within a longer joint session (what Americans refer to as a caucus).

There are powerful arguments why mediation is best conducted in the presence of both parties. Joint meetings enable the mediator 'to observe the parties in their direct relationships with each other' and thereby to gain a clearer understanding of the issues in dispute (ACAS, paras 38, 39). One of the main advantages of mediation in disputes involving children is the opportunity it provides to increase mutual understanding and to facilitate communication and continuing negotiation between the parties. The couple have to manage the many adjustments that are inevitably part of the process of maintaining contact through their children over the years. They have to be able to negotiate together. If there is fear of violence, or if one or both of the parties will not agree even to be in the room together, doubt must be cast on the appropriateness of mediation in those circumstances.

Within the joint session the parties must have an opportunity to express their viewpoint to the mediator in the absence of their former partner. This vital protection should be available not only at the first meeting but at the outset of any subsequent session. It gives the mediator a fuller understanding of the situation and how each party sees it, and gives each party the safety and freedom to state their views and feelings fully. This separate time with each party is not a substitute for pre-mediation screening for unsuitability for mediation.

Shuttle mediation

This refers to the way the mediator may function as a go-between, shuttling between the two parties who remain physically (and possibly temporarily) apart. The mediator may act as a simple conduit passing messages back and forth, or may actively negotiate on behalf of the disputants who obviously cannot negotiate directly. Shuttle mediation is commonly used in international disputes and occasionally in community, environmental and labour relations disputes.

There are three main purposes behind the use of shuttle mediation. First, it aims to avoid confrontation, both for the parties and for the mediator, where the level of conflict is high. Secondly, it allows the parties to disclose confidential information to the mediator that they do not want revealed to one another. Thirdly, it gives the mediator the opportunity to discuss matters that would be uncomfortable to raise if parties were together (Folberg and Taylor, 1984).

In disputes following family breakdown the disadvantages of shuttle mediation outweigh the advantages, except in special circumstances such as illness, extreme stress, or intimidation, where it may be of value as a prelude to joint negotiation. A vulnerable party may feel safer initially communicating at a distance, but it is fair to say that if the level of conflict, anxiety or fear is that high, mediation is probably not appropriate anyway.

Some disadvantages of shuttle mediation are:

(1) The mediator lays him/herself open to charges of partiality. Alliances may more easily arise or be perceived to arise between the mediator and one party. The mediator is placed in the well-nigh impossible position of having to act as spokesperson for each party and yet not to take sides. In the absence of both parties the mediator cannot demonstrate the impartiality that is central to the mediatory role.

(2) The mediator does all the negotiating. The parties are not only denied the information derived from direct experience of each other but they do not learn how to negotiate together.

(3) The power of the mediator and possibilities of manipulating the mediation process are increased. The mediator may find it tempting to exceed the messenger role, especially when negotiations are going badly, as is likely when the parties cannot or will not meet directly together in the first place. The mediator's total control over communication gives opportunities to control the substance of that communication, for example by changing an emphasis, omitting or reframing statements, and so on. Misunderstandings, many of which cause or exacerbate conflict, are often compounded or created in communications between third parties (solicitors' letters, for example). While the role of a mediator in shuttle mediation differs from

that of a solicitor who represents the interests of one party only, the problems arising from third party communications remain the same. Unless everything is out in the open, and seen to be so, the task of the mediator in improving communication is seriously hampered.

(4) The protection of confidential information is problematic. Disputants have no means of knowing whether private information imparted in confidence to the mediator remains protected, especially if the subject crops up spontaneously anyway, for example the intention to move house, change job, end the relationship with a new partner, and so on. This could lead to a loss of trust in the mediator and so undermine his or her efforts.

Co-mediation

This occurs when two mediators, ideally one male and one female, mediate together in a particular case. Co-mediation by two members of the same sex should always be avoided because of the risk of perceived bias, with one party being outnumbered three to one by the opposite sex. Although it may appear to be more expensive, there are distinct advantages in using two mediators in certain cases, eg where there are a number of parties, where there is high conflict or particularly difficult circumstances, or where one mediator alone does not have all the necessary expertise—eg legal, tax or welfare rights (Roberts, 1997).

The advantages of co-mediation are:

(1) Impartiality is enhanced if neither male nor female viewpoint prevails or is perceived to prevail.
(2) Co-mediators can set an example to the disputants in how to negotiate. Of particular value to the disputants is the way the mediators overcome their own (occasional) disagreements. Courteous and considerate behaviour by the mediators sets the tone for relations between the parties.
(3) Co-mediators can share the demanding task of mediating, especially in the longer sessions. They can monitor each other's contributions, offsetting weaknesses, reinforcing messages and providing complementary skills, information and approaches, particularly if they have different professional backgrounds, for example law and psychology or social work.

The disadvantages of co-working are:

(1) The danger of gender bias (actual or perceived) if co-workers are of the same sex. Gender imbalances may be compounded (three to one).
(2) There may be problems of authority/status/control/territory between the workers particularly where they have different professional backgrounds.
(3) Co-working may involve more time, preparation and expense.
(4) The co-working relationship can be problematic—conflicting styles/ philosophy/approaches; confusing signals; working at cross purposes; differences of timing; confusion over division of labour and gender roles.
(5) 'Too perfect' a partnership can intimidate the parties.
(6) Co-working may increase the risks of increasing the pressure that may be exerted on parties for or against certain options and outcomes.

Handbook A

Note

An earlier version of this text first appeared in *Mediation in Family Disputes: Principles of Practice* (2nd edition) by Marian Roberts, published by Arena, Ashgate Publishing Ltd in 1997.

References

Stevens, Carl M (1963) *Strategy & Collective Bargaining Negotiation*. McGraw Hill, New York.

Gulliver, P H (1977) 'On Mediators' in Hamnett, Ian (ed.) *Social Anthropology and Law*. Academic Press, London.

Gulliver, P H (1979) *Disputes & Negotiations: A Cross-Cultural Perspective*. Academic Press, New York.

Fuller, L (1971) 'Mediation—Its Forms and Functions' in *Southern California Law Review*, Vol 44 pp 305–39.

McCory, J P (1981) 'Environmental Mediation—Another Piece For The Puzzle' *Vermont Law Review*, Vol 16, No. 1.

Roberts, S (1983) 'The Study of Dispute: Anthropological Perspectives' in Bossy, J A (ed) *Disputes And Settlements: Law and Human Relations In The West*. Cambridge University Press, Cambridge.

ACAS (no date) *The ACAS Role in Conciliation, Arbitration and Mediation*. ACAS Reports & Publications, London.

Folberg, J & Taylor, A (1984) *Mediation: A Comprehensive Guide to Resolving Conflict Without Litigation*. Jossey-Bass, San Francisco.

Roberts, M (1997) *Mediation In Family Disputes: Principles of Practice*. 2nd edn, Arena, Ashgate Publishing Ltd, Aldershot.

Children and the Mediation Process

Marian Roberts

There has long been a consensus of view that mediation can enhance children's interests. The process and outcome benefits of mediation—collaborative approaches to decision making, improved communication between parents, reduced misunderstanding and conflict, and parents retaining control over the fashioning and content of their own agreements—have recognised advantages for children. Family mediation has also been identified with a greater concentration on the needs and perspectives of children (Davis & Roberts, 1988). Research also highlights the negative consequences for children of the competitive, adversarial approaches of litigation and adjudication which require the disputants (parents in this case) to take up opposing stances in order to achieve their objectives (Lund, 1984; Wallerstein & Kelly, 1980; Maccoby & Mnookin, 1992; Cockett & Tripp, 1994).

Since the 1990s, the convergence of the long practice experience of family mediators, the clarification of the nature of the mediation process that had by then occurred and a fresh climate of thinking about the 'voice' of the child in decision-making (for example the UN Convention on the Rights of the Child 1989 and the Children Act 1989), has resulted in a new appreciation of the distinctive and precise role of children in mediation (National Family Mediation Report, 1994).

In the NFM study the policy question to be resolved was this: 'How can children's perspectives best inform a process in which the parents are the ultimate decision-makers?' The concept of 'consultation' has clarified language use as well as provided the answer to the substantive question; children can be *consulted* as part of their parents' decision-making within mediation. This can take place in two ways:

(1) Indirect consultation by means of the parents themselves bringing their children's views into the process. This is the preferred form of consultation because it encourages parents themselves to consider their children's views and perspectives fully.
(2) Direct consultation with children by the mediator within the process. This is of great assistance, particularly where the perspective of the child may be missing from discussions. Whether children should be consulted directly, how and at what stage, are matters to be agreed jointly by the mediator and the parties.

Training in respect of the consultation of children, direct and indirect, is essential. In addition, children may on occasion need specialist help in coping with the separation of their parents. Counselling, advice-giving, information, assessment and therapy should be available in these cases. These forms of intervention, vital as they may be, should not, however, be confused with mediation or be attempted at the same time by the same person.

Note

An earlier version of this text first appeared in *Mediation in Family Disputes: Principles of Practice* (2nd edition) by Marian Roberts, published by Arena, Ashgate Publishing Ltd in 1997.

References

Davis, G & Roberts, M (1988) *Access to Agreement: A Consumer Study of Mediation in Family Disputes.* Open University Press, Milton Keynes.

Lund, M (1984) 'Research on Divorce and Children' in *Family Law* Vol. 14, pp. 198–201.

Wallerstein, J & Kelly, J R (1980) *Surviving the Break-up.* Grant MacIntyre, London.

Maccoby, E A & Mnookin, R H (1992) *Dividing the Child: Social and Legal Dilemmas of Custody.* Harvard University Press, Cambridge, MA.

Cockett, M & Tripp, J (1994) *The Exeter Family Study: Family Breakdown & Its Impact on Children.* University of Exeter Press, Exeter.

National Family Mediation Report (1994) *Giving Children a Voice in Mediation.* NFM.

Handbook A

All Issues Mediation

Paul Foster

Mediation on financial issues in addition to child focused mediation is offered by the Family Mediators Association (FMA), the Solicitors Family Law Association (SFLA) and a number of National Family Mediation (NFM) and Family Mediation Scotland services. Most, but not all, models involve a lawyer at some stage of the process, and in the case of FMA and SFLA, throughout.

All Issues Mediation is a structured process. There are various ways of depicting the process, but typically the path is as follows:

- induction and engagement;
- signing the agreement to mediate;
- issuing the budget sheets (expert advice may be needed, eg valuation);
- returning the budget sheets duly completed;
- understanding and negotiating the budget sheets;
- displaying the financial data;
- setting objectives (criteria of fairness);
- brainstorming;
- walking through options;
- negotiating (legal advice may be sought throughout);
- reaching acceptable proposals;
- drafting the Memorandum of Understanding;
- approving and signing Memorandum of Understanding (legal advice and ratification of proposals).

(See the same process set out a little differently in Marian Roberts' section 'The Mediation Process' above.)

The use of a flip chart is a crucial element of the process. The chart can be used to display financial data clearly and comprehensibly, record proposals and show calculations. The finished charts need to be carefully marked and stored as an historical record and for use in future sessions. Given their size, storage quickly becomes a problem!

The Agreement to Mediate

The current practice of all member organisations of the UK College of Family Mediators is to use a written Agreement to Mediate. Draft agreements are widely available and should be modified with caution. Interestingly, John Haynes, a leading figure in mediation training, says he doesn't use them (see Haynes, J (1993) *The Fundamentals of Family Mediation*, Old Bailey Press, p28). If employed, the mediator is under a duty to take the couple through the agreement and check out their understanding and full acceptance of the terms. This is not an easy task because the couple are likely to be itching to get on with the substance of the mediation, and paperwork can seem to be no more than a frustrating interruption. Nevertheless, time spent now may help later should problems arise. For example, see later in relation to the unilateral disposal of assets.

Disclosure

It is important that financial information is accurate and verified. The production of up-to-date financial documents allows the mediation to proceed on the basis of sure factual foundations and assists with the trust building process. Income, some items of expenditure, savings, investments, life and endowment policies, overseas assets (eg timeshares) and pensions need to be verified by the production of appropriate documentary evidence.

With experience, family mediators (regardless of their backgrounds) will know what to look for and will feel comfortable interpreting the documents which are produced. It is of course vital that any such disclosure is copied and shared with both clients and (where co-mediating) both mediators. Further, it is always wise to check with both clients that they have an accurate understanding of the meaning of the documents. This can be challenging indeed for the more complex financial assets like stock options, pensions or company accounts. The clients (and the mediators) may well need the assistance of outside experts (see the following section on 'The Lawyer's Role Alongside the Mediation Process'), and should not be afraid to ask the clients to get the help they need. Mediators need to ensure the data produced is current and complete. The mediator can explore with the client whether the data gives an accurate picture. For example, is the pay slip for a typical month? Are there missing bank statements? Do the bank statements reveal transfers to an undisclosed account?

Does this carry with it the danger of turning the mediator into a forensic sleuth? As with nearly all mediation skills, timing and sensitivity are crucial. Very often the most skilled and thorough scrutineer of the paperwork will be the other spouse. He or she will effectively carry out a searching cross-examination of the partner's finances. The mediator should track this process carefully and, as ever, be alert to issues of power balancing, good faith, communication and such like. The mediator is under a duty to ensure that all matrimonial assets have been identified and understood. It is the writer's experience that the legal profession's concerns about the adequacy of All Issues Mediation frequently focus on the question of disclosure. It must be done thoroughly and well. The mediator will, with experience, acquire a repertoire of questioning techniques to explore financial issues without sounding mistrustful or cynical. The mediator needs to bear in mind that clients going through divorce and separation may feel deeply insecure and frightened. Their powerful emotions coupled with well-meaning advice to look after themselves may well lead them to act out of character in relation to money and to attempt to secrete funds or assets. Also, clients may act unilaterally and dispose of or irrevocably convert funds.

Paragraph 2 of NFM's model Agreement to Mediate is typical in providing:

(1) We will make full, frank and true disclosure of finances and provide all supporting documentation.
(2) We will not transfer, charge, conceal nor otherwise dispose of any assets except for the purpose of providing for living necessities and expenses in the ordinary course of business (*sic*).
(3) We will not make any further charges under any charge account for which both of us are legally responsible, unless mutually agreed upon.

It may well pay dividends to spend some time with the couple exploring this clause to ensure it is understood and to discuss in what ways either or both clients might find it difficult to observe. This will reinforce the idea of mediation as a professional discipline with rules—not just a species of chatting, and will provide a reference point for the mediators should problems arise in the future, for example: 'Well John, you remember we talked about not disposing of assets back in May?'.

The mediators will have to make a judgement as to whether or not to continue the mediation if this or similar rules are broken. It is suggested that the sort of factors which should be considered if the rules are broken are:

(a) Has the transgression apparently significantly weakened the financial position of the other party?
(b) Has the action seriously undermined the trust of the other party in the process?
(c) Do the actions indicate a lack of good faith by the client in relation to the mediation process? Is (s/he) engaging in or exploiting mediation?
(d) Is this the first time such things have happened?
(e) Are the couple able to restore the *status quo ante* and negotiate arrangements to prevent a repetition?
(f) Does the client who acted in breach of the rule accept responsibility for (his) actions and give assurances for the future?

Recording

The mediators will acquire a substantial bundle of documents as the mediation progresses. It is good practice to keep this paperwork in a file in an orderly fashion (eg 'his' and 'hers' in date order) and to keep a record of each document produced. For example:

Clients' names	Documents produced in mediation			
Date produced	Produced by	Identity of document	Date of document	Comments

Experiment with the format for recording this information. Such a document:

- acts as an index/*aide memoire*;
- is evidence the mediators have done a professional job;
- can be reproduced as a schedule to the Memorandum of Understanding; and
- can be taken (with the copy documents) to the advising lawyers.

The writer suspects that such relatively minor practices help the couple to feel in safe hands and builds their trust in the process. This schedule can later be included in the Memorandum of Understanding (see below).

Non-disclosure

If a client repeatedly fails to bring promised documentation, the mediators may have to terminate or, at least, suspend the mediation. No doubt most mediators will want to explore the reasons for the failure in some depth and give clear and fair warning of what will happen if next time the material is not produced. However, to proceed in these circumstances is dangerous indeed and probably not in the interests of either client and certainly not in the interests of the mediators.

It can be a useful practice to summarise homework tasks at the end of each session and invite the client to write the tasks down there and then. Clients may need assistance in drafting suitable letters requesting the information, eg from pension trustees, but the mediator should be careful that they do not become the client's agent. The task of getting the information is an important aspect of the mediation process.

Budget forms

Once the Agreement to Mediate has been signed, the mediator may hand out the budget forms and talk them through with the couple. These forms provide a firm basis for the negotiations (when augmented by disclosure—see above), and help the clients to consider the reality of their decision to separate and develop a future focus. A typical display might be:

Peter and Susan in mediation with PF			12.5.97
Income	*Peter*	*Susan*	
Earnings			
Investment income			
Child benefit			
One parent benefit			
Capital	*Peter*	*Susan*	*Joint*
Matrimonial home			
etc.			
Expenses	*Peter*	*Susan*	
Accommodation			
Utilities			
Loan repayments			
Insurance			
Food			
Transport			
Clothes			
Leisure			
Other			
Children			
Totals			
Joint total			
Income – Joint total = **The Gap!**			

Both clients need to fill out a form. If one client fills out both forms this should give the mediator cause for concern. Failures to wholly or partly complete the form should be discussed. What was difficult? When can it be done by? What does the client need to get the form filled out? Again each mediation association has its own preferred form. These documents are under constant review. As a generalisation, the writer suspects the trend is towards developing the forms to provide more specific detail about assets and rather less about expenditure where a 'broad brush' approach may be sufficient. It is, however, important that expenditure forms are detailed enough to produce a good picture of likely living costs. They also help the client who has not hitherto been responsible for housekeeping to think about what it will entail.

The budget forms done well can be a fairly gentle first leg of the 'walk into the future' which is mediation. When the forms are completed, the mediator goes through the forms collecting, verifying, sharing and displaying the data. The data is displayed on a flip chart. In practice, it may be necessary to use two or three A2 charts and to display these on the walls using pins or Blu-Tack in subsequent sessions.

Memorandum of Understanding

When acceptable proposals have been negotiated, the mediator prepares the Memorandum of Understanding. Before doing so, it is vital that the terms are noted by the mediator in the presence of the couple and that they accept the accuracy of the mediator's understanding. The Memorandum of Understanding should be written in ordinary language not the mediator's. It is the clients' document not the mediator's. It should, in the writer's view, be written in the first person plural, eg 'We have decided that Melanie should live with Sue and spend every other weekend with Bob'. It is a privileged document, and should be marked 'Without Prejudice'.

The College is actively reviewing the format and content of Memoranda of Understanding. Therefore, it is not proposed to pre-empt that valuable work by specifying their content here. However, some general guidance may be useful. We suggest, as a minimum, a well-drafted Memorandum of Understanding will contain:

(1) An introduction. This will describe where the mediation took place, its primary objectives and the general principles which informed the mediation.
(2) Background information such as the names, dates, ages, etc. The mediator should remember to check this information at the conclusion of the final session.
(3) Supplied information. It is helpful to set out a list of documentation produced by the clients during the mediation. This might be set out in a schedule, for example:

Document	Date of document	Date produced	Comments
Pension transfer value	12.5.97	25.6.97	Shown to X&Co financial advisors

(4) A summary of assets at the start of the mediation, and as they will be if the proposals contained in the Memorandum of Understanding are

implemented. Again, this may be supplied in a schedule. Effectively, this will be a reproduction of the flip-chart summary of capital assets.

(5) A description in an appropriate level of detail of the proposals for the arrangements for the children.

(6) A clear statement of the financial arrangements proposed. This must deal with each of the assets in non-legal language. It is suggested that the reasoning behind the proposals can usefully be included in addition to the substance, eg 'Sue will receive £75,000 from the net sale proceeds of 37 Bathwick Way. This will enable her to buy a new property for around £50,000 and make contributions to her pension. It will also enable her to have an emergency fund'. If things are to be done it is important that it is clear who is to do them and within what timescale. If processes (eg how a house is to be marketed) have been agreed, these should be recorded.

(7) Frequently an agreement to return to mediation in the event of further dispute.

The Memorandum of Understanding will be sent in draft to each client. To send it in duplicate would be a useful gesture. It is anticipated they in turn will consider it carefully, possibly (and desirably) with their solicitors before returning one copy amended or approved. If there are significant differences between the couple, they would then be offered another session. Otherwise, the Memorandum of Understanding will be fair copied and sent to each client. They will then be able to instruct their respective lawyers to prepare a separation agreement or application for a matrimonial consent order and subsequently implement the proposals.

Family mediators can usefully research as part of their 'knowledge bank' what agreements can be made the subject of court orders and what cannot be ordered. Agreements that cannot be ordered have to be either the subject of a side agreement, or promised to the court by the client giving what is known as an undertaking. For example, the court can, upon divorce or judicial separation, transfer a capital asset (commonly a matrimonial home) from one party to the other. It cannot order one party to take out a policy of insurance.

It is also important for the mediator to be very clear, both during the mediation and in the Memorandum of Understanding, whether or not the couple have agreed a clean-break, and if so whether as to capital, income or both. Mediators need to understand and explain the final and irrevocable nature of these orders. If the couple are proposing payment of spousal maintenance for a limited term (eg five years) will this be an absolute limit or will the recipient have the option of applying to the court to extend the duration of the payments?

Issues of Child Support

The proposals for child support will of course be set out under 'financial arrangements'. It may be that the couple have agreed a figure for child support between themselves. If that is the case, mediators can suggest that the couple consider with their legal advisors whether or not this agreement should be incorporated in a court order and the extent to which (whether or not it is incorporated) it may subsequently be varied or cancelled by the Child Support Agency.

A thorny issue which has been much considered by members of the UK College of Family Mediators is whether mediators should do child support calculations (based upon the formula in the Child Support Act) during the mediation. The writer would not presume to offer a dogmatic opinion on this issue, but mediators should carefully consider whether doing such a calculation is consistent with their role, and be aware that an inaccurate calculation would be worse than none. The mediator may well wish to suggest to the clients that they find out what a likely assessment might be. A well-drafted Memorandum of Understanding will state that the mediation service/mediators are not liable for the accuracy of any child support calculations relied upon by the clients. However, family mediators should be familiar with the basics of the formula.

All Issues Mediation and Children

In All Issues Mediation the focus of planning for those clients who are parents, when settling child issues alone, is the short- and long-term plans for their children's future.

Confidentiality and Privilege in Mediation

Marian Roberts and Stephen Wildblood

Confidentiality is integral to the relationship between the mediator and the parties and is one of the four fundamental and universal characteristics of mediation (McCrory, 1981). It is the cornerstone of the relationship of trust that must exist between the mediator and the parties, and of the free and frank disclosure that is necessary if obstacles to settlement are to be overcome. It is crucial to the voluntariness of participation of the parties and to the impartiality of the mediator. The parties must not feel that they might be disadvantaged by any disclosure that may be used in legal proceedings, or in any other way. They need to know they have nothing to lose by resorting to mediation.

Therefore, for mediation to be successful it is necessary for the parties to mediation to speak frankly upon the issues that they are seeking to address. Their ability to do so would be undermined if they felt that every word that they said could be used in court (possibly out of context) if the issues between them fell to be litigated. This is a very real problem where the parties involved in mediation are involved at the same time in litigation (eg on issues relating to the breakdown of a marriage).

Confidentiality Between the Mediator and the Parties

Mediators have a duty to make clear to the parties at the outset that communications between them and the mediator are made in confidence and that the mediator must not disclose any statements made or information received (to the court, solicitors, court welfare officers, social workers, doctors or anyone else) without their joint and express consent or an order of the court.

The issue of child protection in particular, highlights the need to define the limits of confidentiality in mediation. Confidentiality is, of course, not absolute as it is always subject to the requirement that the law of the land shall be complied with (*Parry-Jones v Law Society* [1969] 1 Ch 1 p9). The limits are those pertaining in all confidential or professional communications, whether between doctor and patient, priest and penitent, or journalist and informant. Therefore, the promise of confidentiality does not prevent the mediator from disclosing information in the exceptional circumstances where there is substantial risk to the life, health or safety of children, the parties, or anyone else.

All communications made in the course of mediation, whether between the parties themselves, or between the parties and the mediator(s), or between mediators or the parties' solicitors are confidential subject to certain exceptions and will not be disclosed. In addition to the child protection exceptions already referred to, another exception relates to factual disclosures made in the course of mediation on financial or property issues. Factual data of this kind may be disclosed in any subsequent legal proceedings.

Confidentiality of Communications Between the Parties and Third Parties Outside the Process

While confidentiality can be promised by the mediator, confidentiality belongs to the parties and it is a matter of their own discretion, that is, it is their choice as to what information they impart to their solicitors or anyone else. These matters should all be clearly stated at the outset, as should the fact that the court will be very reluctant to allow confidential exchanges between the parties to be used as evidence in any subsequent proceedings (see below).

Confidentiality in Relation to Legal Proceedings (Privilege)

Public policy has always favoured the settlement of disputes—that it is in the public interest that disputes be settled and litigation reduced to the minimum. The privilege of 'without prejudice' negotiation (that is, without prejudice to the legal rights of the maker of the statement) has long been a principle of English law. It attaches to statements and offers of compromise made by the parties and their legal advisers in negotiations for settling disputes. These disclosures may not be used in subsequent legal proceedings without the consent of both parties. The policy of the law has also been in favour of enlarging the cloak under which negotiations may be conducted without prejudice (Cross, 1985).

In 1971, a Practice Direction on Matrimonial Conciliation issued by the President of the Family Division of the High Court, provided that both reconciliation and conciliation negotiations should be legally privileged. The Booth Committee recommended that conciliation in court proceedings be absolutely privileged (para 4.60). There is in fact no legislation, and until 1993 there was no case law, to clarify the issue of privilege in mediation where reconciliation was not an issue. The case of *Re D (Minors) (Conciliation: Privilege* [1993] 1 FLR 934CA, Sir Thomas Bingham) is such a landmark. This case establishes for the first time that in mediation where reconciliation is not the purpose of the negotiations, discussions in relation to disputes involving children are privileged. The Court of Appeal had to decide this issue: 'To what extent, if at all, may evidence be given in proceedings under The Children Act 1989 of statements made by one or other of the parties in the course of meetings held or communications made for the purpose of reconciliation, mediation or conciliation?'. That issue arose in this case where the mother wished to file evidence from a psychologist who had mediated between the mother and the father.

The Court of Appeal held that evidence may not be given in proceedings under the Children Act 1989 of statements made by one or other of the parties in the course of mediation/conciliation save in the very unusual case where a statement is made clearly indicating that the maker has in the past caused, or is likely in the future to cause, serious harm to the well-being of a child. This decision was based upon the 'substantial and unquestioned line of authority [that] establishes that where a third party receives information in confidence with a view to conciliation, the courts will not compel him to disclose what was said without the parties' agreement'. Even within that narrow exception, the trial judge would admit the statement only if, in his/her judgment, the public interest in protecting the child's interest outweighed the public interest in preserving confidentiality.

This Court of Appeal decision is significant in three further respects. First, the privilege of exchanges relating to the resolution of disputes over children exists as an independent head of privilege. It is based on the public interest both in sparing children unnecessary suffering by encouraging the settlement of issues over them, and in reducing the burden of the cost and delay of litigation. Second, their Lordships stated explicitly that mediation did not form part of the legal process, though as a matter of practice, it was becoming an important and valuable tool in the procedures of many family courts. Third, the Master of the Rolls stated that the privilege belongs to the parties themselves and that they may, if they so choose, waive it. In such circumstances the implications are clear. The mediator may be compelled to testify.

Notwithstanding this limitation, the judgment of the Court of Appeal in *Re D (Minors)* is a valuable clarification of the legal position in relation to the confidential exchanges that occur in family mediation. The decision is confined to the circumstances of the case, that is, to matrimonial disputes over children in proceedings under the Children Act 1989. The privilege of 'without prejudice' negotiations still attaches, it may be assumed, to mediated negotiations relating to finance and property issues. This 'without prejudice' privilege is subject to three limitations when applied to mediation (Cross, 1985):

(1) The privilege belongs to the parties jointly, and not to the mediator or the process. It can therefore be waived by both parties expressly or otherwise in legal proceedings and then the mediator could be compelled to testify.
(2) The cloak of the privilege does not cover statements that are not sufficiently related to the dispute which is the subject of negotiation.
(3) A binding agreement that results from privileged negotiations is not itself privileged. It is important therefore that the status of any mediated agreement be clear to all concerned (see below).

The court is unlikely in practice to allow either party to make use of evidence derived from failed negotiations. Agreements are encouraged by the court which will not wish either party to be disadvantaged by prior attempts to reach agreement. Although, for example, no privilege exists as a matter of law to protect confidential communications (except between lawyers and their clients and in proceedings under the Patents Act 1943) these are in practice frequently protected. The judge has a discretion to disallow questions concerning them and witnesses are not in fact pressed to disclose confidential information.

Privilege and Agreements

What happens where a couple reach an agreement in mediation but later one of them decides to break the agreement and to seek to achieve a different solution? Can the court be informed of the agreement that was reached in mediation, or is the agreement itself confidential? It must be at least doubtful that, in those circumstances, one of the parties could be prevented from telling the court about the agreement, unless it had been specifically agreed that the agreement would remain confidential in all circumstances. This arises from the rule that negotiations that are made 'without prejudice' lose the protection of confidentiality if the negotiations result in a concluded agreement.

Prior Agreement

It is always advisable for the people involved in mediation to be asked to agree formally at the outset of any course of mediation that things said in mediation will remain privileged, unless revelations are made in the course of the mediation that require protective measures to be initiated in relation to the children. If an agreement is reached and the parties wish the agreement to remain confidential, the agreement should itself record that it is so to remain. In that way, there is no scope for misunderstanding or misuse of the mediation process.

Abusive Behaviour and Disclosure

Where revelations of abusive behaviour are made during mediation, the mediator will be left in a position of some delicacy and difficulty. If the information is to be passed on to a third party, who should be responsible for this, the mediator or the other party? This must surely be one of the most difficult matters that the mediator would have to address within mediation. If the mediator accepts the task of passing the information on to a third party, that places a very heavy responsibility on the mediator. It is plainly necessary to have an established system for dealing with such revelations, and in most instances it is sensible for the mediator to discuss matters with another mediator or a supervisor. It is obviously important to get the facts of the abuse right if those facts are to be repeated to third parties. Further, it is important that both parties to mediation should have known from the start that revelations of child abuse would not remain confidential. Once third parties are told that the abuse has occurred, it may make the continuation of mediation doubtful.

Full and Frank Disclosure

The need for a full and frank discussion of the issues that bring the parties to mediation is obvious. However, that level of discussion can never take place unless both parties make full and frank disclosure of relevant facts that are known to them. If there is to be financial mediation, there has to be a full and frank disclosure of the financial circumstances of both parties (eg if one party has £100,000 in a secret account, any financial agreement is likely to be unfair and unsustainable). In mediation concerning children, it is also necessary to know the full facts of each party's position (eg that the mother has a cohabitee that the child will meet). The courts expect that duty of full and frank disclosure to be observed in cases concerning children and in cases concerning the redistribution of the financial assets following the separation of a married couple. Once disclosure is imparted within the mediation process, it will remain known to both parties to mediation. Although that sort of information may well be regarded as confidential in the light of the decision in *Re D (Minors)*, once it is known to both parties it will often not take much for that same information to be unearthed in any court proceedings (eg if the husband admits to having an account in a building society, the wife may call upon him to produce details of the account in any subsequent proceedings). Thus the cloak of confidentiality may be technical rather than real in some cases.

Privilege in Scotland

Unlike the rest of the UK which relies on case law for clarifying the privilege of mediation, in Scotland it is defined by statute (see 'Family Mediation and the Law in Scotland' above).

Note

An earlier version of Marian Roberts' contribution to this text first appeared in *Mediation in Family Disputes: Principles of Practice* (2nd edition) by Marian Roberts, published by Arena, Ashgate Publishing Ltd in 1997.

■ References

McCrory, J P (1985) 'The Mediation Process', paper delivered at the Bromley Conference, organised by South-East London Family Mediation Bureau.

Booth Committee (1985) *Report of the Committee on Matrimonial Cases*, HMSO, London.

Cross, R (1985) *Cross on Evidence*, 6th edn. Butterworths, London.

McCrory, J P (1988) 'Confidentiality in Mediation of Matrimonial Disputes' in *Modern Law Review*, Vol. 51, No. 4.

The Lawyer's Role Alongside Mediation

Paul Foster

The Lawyer's Role

Probably all family lawyers would benefit from an understanding of the mediation process. Mediation training teaches communicating and negotiating skills which enhance the lawyer's effectiveness as a lawyer. In addition, any referrals to mediation can be made more sensitively and knowledgeably if the lawyer has some understanding of what the client will experience during mediation and what the mediator will be hoping to achieve. Here, however, we are concerned with the lawyer's role during, but *outside,* the mediation process. It is likely that lawyers will increasingly be instructed to advise clients who are undertaking mediation on all issues. How should the lawyer respond? This is a skill in development and what follows is not intended to be an exhaustive guide; rather a collection of thoughts derived from practical experience to date.

(1) Remember you have been instructed as a lawyer. Your duties to your client remain the same. Give your advice fearlessly and if need be, robustly. Your client has presumably consulted you to understand her options. She needs to know the boundaries of what she might hope to achieve in court and, of course, a realistic assessment of the likely costs of going to court.

(2) Seek to acquire a good understanding of the process of All Issues Mediation as it is practised in your local mediation service and by the Family Mediators Association (FMA). Get in touch with local mediators. If they have not done so, encourage them to give a talk with a role play. This will illuminate your understanding of your client's experiences.

(3) Try to grasp the hopes, expectations and fears which have led your client to mediation. Aim to be a supporter and guide as she travels through the process. Try to avoid undermining her trust in the process.

(4) Understand in particular how disclosure is dealt with in mediation and get sight of the disclosed material if you can.

(5) Consider the adequacy of the disclosure with your client. If the mediation is continuing, any deficiencies may be remedied in future sessions. If the client brings a Memorandum of Understanding that reveals deficiencies, the lawyer may either advise the client that it is dangerous to proceed to implement the Memorandum of Understanding without further information, or seek to limit his liability by writing the usual sort of disclaimer letter.

(6) Do not treat the Memorandum of Understanding as a draft consent order or separation agreement. It is not. It is the couple's personal expression of the outcome of their negotiations, even if inevitably Memoranda acquire a structural similarity as good practice emerges and is copied around the country. Accordingly, use the red pen sparingly. It is often preferable to take a further copy of the Memorandum of Understanding and make any amendments on the copy. It is of course vital that any amendments are understood by the client. The lawyer's role is to empower the client in *her*, the client's, negotiations. It will not assist the client in the next session to find

herself saying: 'My lawyer says I cannot agree. It is something to do with pensions but I don't know what'.

(7) A client who chooses All Issues Mediation is making a profound statement about his or her wish to have responsibility for managing the ending of their relationship. The advising lawyer does well to be sensitive to this wish and to frame his or her advice accordingly while honouring the 'golden rule' of best advice.

(8) Lawyers should also understand that All Issues Mediation is not a cheap way of reaching the same decision a court would impose. Couples in mediation are striving to negotiate their own unique preferred solutions to the joint problems they bring to the mediation. This, in the author's view, is a fundamentally different task to that of a judge who is seeking to apply abstract rules to a specific set of facts even if those same rules admit of a large discretionary element. Accordingly, the proposals in a Memorandum of Understanding may look very different from the anticipated court solution without being 'wrong'. Having said that, the client needs to clearly understand the differences between the proposals in the Memorandum of Understanding and the likely court decision and the costs and benefits that flow from these differences.

Other Advisors' Role

It is for the couple to determine with the assistance of the mediator what additional information and advice they need from external resources to assist them negotiate their proposals. Typical examples are:

- the use of independent valuers to value a former matrimonial home;
- the use of an accountant to value a business;
- the use of an accountant to advise on the ability of a business to raise capital in order to finance a divorce settlement;
- the use of a pensions advisor to advise a wife on the cost of providing an adequate pension.

In every case, the mediator can suggest a timely enquiry and maybe assist the couple frame helpful questions which they may wish to commit to writing and take with them to the expert. The basic rules still hold good. The couple supply the content. The mediators run the process. Control should not be ceded to outside professionals. Equally well, such professionals are a valuable resource which, used wisely, can move the mediation forward, and can often be essential if the proposals eventually reached are to be built upon adequate foundations.

Cost

Mediation is a professional skill. To mediate well requires aptitude, training, time and commitment. This investment deserves to be rewarded. If mediators are not paid at appropriate rates, there will inevitably over time be a dilution of the quality of mediators and a corresponding diminution in the value of mediation as perceived by the general public. 'You get what you pay for.'

Mediation is also a business. Like any other it must at least break even over time if it is to survive. Individual services and mediators if self-employed need to consider what income they must generate to stay in business. What return must be achieved to make mediating a preferred activity to doing other things with one's time? The clients must then be charged at either a sessional or unit (ie whole mediation) cost. It is good practice to raise the question of costs at the outset. Clients need to be given accurate information, preferably in writing, before they make a commitment. Thereafter, the costs need to be collected regularly. There must be a sanction for non-payment.

Partnership

The professional trust and respect between mediators and advising solicitors creates a secure foundation whether settling all or some issues in mediation. It is a partnership that repays effort spent upon it.

Useful Statistical Information for Mediators

Fiona McAllister

Marriage and Divorce

Marriage rates in the UK remain relatively high compared to other countries in the EC. In 1994, the UK had the third highest marriage rate in the Community following Denmark and Portugal. However, the latest figures show that the numbers getting married are continuing to fall. In 1995, there were 283,000 marriages in England and Wales.

In 1994, the UK divorce rate was the highest in the European Community. In England and Wales, the divorce rate (the number of couples who divorced per 1,000 married couples) stood at 13.4 per 1,000. The numbers divorcing each year in England and Wales have recently declined. In 1996, 154,000 couples obtained a divorce, the third successive annual fall—1,000 fewer than 1995 and 4,000 fewer than in 1994. Provisional figures for England and Wales in 1996, indicate that the average age at divorce has fallen for the first time in ten years, standing at 37.4 for men and 35.3 for women (compared to 39.6 and 37.0 respectively in the previous year). In 1995, divorce rates were highest for men aged 30–34 and women aged 25–29, reflecting the tendency for women to marry men older than themselves.

Estimates suggest that 41 per cent of current marriages in England and Wales will end in divorce. Of the 155,000 divorces in 1995, 86,000 involved at least one child under the age of 16. Updated calculations show that if divorce rates remain constant at 1994/5 levels, 7.5 per cent of children will see that parents divorce by their fifth birthday; nearly one in five children will experience parental divorce before they are 10 years old and by age 16, 28 per cent of children will have divorced parents. This represents an overall rise in the proportion of children experiencing divorce. In calculations based on the situation in 1988/9, 24 per cent of children were projected to experience their parents' divorce by age 16. These figures do not include children whose parents separate informally or whose cohabiting relationship breaks down, and so the proportion of children who experience family disruption is larger than that relating solely to parental divorce.

Cohabitation

Trends in marriage and divorce are affected by the growing popularity of cohabitation. The majority of couples now live together before getting married, a practice which has influenced the later average ages at marriage today and the lower rates of marriage (couples getting married as a proportion of those eligible to do so) observed in recent years. Although premarital cohabitation is the most common form of living together, divorced people as a group are more likely to cohabit than single people.

The growth in cohabitation is also one important reason for the rise in the number of births outside marriage and the corresponding fall in marital fertility. In 1995, 34 per cent of births occurred outside marriage, an increase of almost 2 per cent on 1994. The evidence suggests that many births outside marriage are to cohabiting couples: about 80 per cent of such births were jointly registered by both parents in 1995, and four-fifths of these parents were registered at the same address.

For many, cohabitation remains a transitory phase before marriage or break up. Nonetheless, the reported duration of cohabitation is increasing and the average is now over two years. Data from the British Household Panel Study (1991–94) shows that of women cohabiting in 1991, 16 per cent married in the next three years, while in 13 per cent of cases the cohabitation broke down.

At any one time, the proportions of people in specific groups who are cohabiting are quite small: only 6 per cent of couples with dependent children were found to be cohabiting in a recent analysis of General Household Survey (GHS) data. Overall, 25 per cent of non-married women aged 18–49 were cohabiting according to the latest GHS of 1995–6. This proportion has doubled since 1981. A range of studies have suggested that the breakdown rates of cohabiting couples exceed those for married couples.

The Family Law Act: A New Process of Divorce

The Family Law Act of 1996 carries a range of implications for the process of divorce. The system of petitioning on grounds for divorce will be replaced by a staged process, allowing opportunities for reflection and possible reconciliation. The structure of the new process means that there will be a minimum period of eighteen months between the initiation of the divorce process and the granting of divorce for those with children under 16, and a minimum period of one year for childless couples seeking divorce. It has been estimated that this will increase the duration of the divorce process for 90 per cent of parents and 80 per cent of childless couples, compared to the time taken to divorce under the current system.

Since the passing of the Family Law Act, a number of pilot projects have been set in motion to test out various models for the compulsory information meeting at the beginning of the new divorce process, and the context and practice of mediation services (see Sarah White's article *Legal Aid Board Family Mediation Pilot Project* above). The new law includes specific measures to encourage couples into mediation so that financial matters and access to children can be discussed in advance of divorce, and the possibility of reconciliation explored where appropriate. The pilot research into mediation services will provide much-needed knowledge concerning client profile and outcomes achieved in a range of settings. The first results should appear later in 1998.

Fiona McAllister writes from the Family Policy Studies Centre.

Sources

Social Trends 27. The Stationery Office, London.

Christopherson, O (1997) 'Population Review of 1996; England and Wales' in *Population Trends 90*.

Haskey, J (1997) 'Children who experience divorce in their family' in *Population Trends 87*.

Taxation and Benefits

Stephen Wildblood and Daniel Leafe

Taxation

When dealing with financial issues in mediation, it may well be necessary to understand the tax consequences of any proposal. The most frequent problems arise over capital gains tax. However, it is also necessary to have some understanding of the implications of income tax on maintenance payments. As will be seen, two of the main disadvantages of cohabitation from the point of taxation are that, unlike marriage:

(a) the exemption in relation to capital gains tax that applies to married people is not available to cohabitees; and

(b) the married couple's income allowance is also not available to cohabitees.

Capital Gains Tax

Capital gains tax (CGT) is a tax that is payable on the gain made following the disposal of a capital asset. The tax is payable by the person who makes the disposal (ie not by the person who receives the asset following its disposal). In order to calculate the gain, the original price is identified and is then increased by what is called 'indexation' to allow for the effects of inflation. The indexed purchase price is then compared with the price at disposal in order to calculate the gain. Thus, if a holiday home was bought by a husband in January 1984 for £20,000 and was sold by him in December 1995 for £50,000, the original price would be 'indexed' to £34,700, making the gain for the purposes of CGT £50,000 – £34,700 = £15,300.

Allowances

There are a number of specific allowances that apply to capital gains tax. The following are some of the main ones:

(1) CGT will not be payable on transfers between spouses where they have not separated. Therefore, if during the subsistence of the marriage a husband were to transfer to his wife an asset, no CGT would be payable. Similar exemption from CGT will apply where the transfer between spouses occurs during the tax year of the separation. Otherwise, once the spouses have separated, transfers between them will attract CGT. This allowance would not apply to people who were not married.

(2) A person's principal place of residence is exempt from CGT on its disposal (which is why we do not have to pay CGT each time we move home). However, this exemption would not apply to a second home. The Inland Revenue has agreed that, where spouses separate and one of them remains in a matrimonial home, the party who left may rely upon this exemption if he transfers the home to the other spouse later, as long as he has not elected to treat another property as his principal place of residence (eg the husband leaves in 1994 and moves into rented accommodation; the wife remains in the home; the husband transfers the home to the wife in 1997. No CGT will be payable).

(3) Each person has an annual tax allowance (in 1997/98 it is £6,500; it was £6,300 in 1996/97). Sometimes disposals can be spread over the tax years (eg one on 1 April 1997 and one on 1 May 1997) so that each disposal will attract the allowance.

Examples

Therefore, where parties separate, CGT may well be payable where assets are transferred between them. CGT most frequently arises where people separate and then transfer shares, business interests (eg a husband and wife are in partnership and the wife transfers her partnership share to the husband) and second homes.

Accountants

When dealing with financial issues where CGT arises, it will be necessary to identify the liability first and then to identify upon whom that liability will fall. This is usually a job for the accountants. An accountant will often need to be asked by one or both of the parties to advise upon:

(a) the amount of CGT that may arise;
(b) the party who is likely to have to bear that CGT;
(c) when the CGT will be payable;
(d) the steps that might be taken to reduce or avoid the liability.

Once the liability has been identified and quantified, the parties will need to consider who should be responsible for the tax. It is possible for one party to agree to indemnify the other against any liability to CGT, either in whole or in part. Any such agreement needs to be formally recorded.

Common errors

Common areas for error are:

(a) overlooking CGT entirely; this can make an enormous difference to one or both of the parties;
(b) trying to guess the amount of CGT without the help of an accountant;
(c) failing to record accurately or completely where the burden of any CGT should lie.

Mesher/Martin arrangements

Sometimes it is proposed in cases concerning married or formerly married people that a family home should be held under what has become known as a 'Mesher' order. This usually means that the house remains unsold until the first of the following events:

(i)   the death or remarriage of the wife (it being presumed for these purposes that the wife is the spouse that will remain in occupation);
(ii)   the parties agreeing to the sale of the property;
(iii)   the wife vacating the property;
(iv)   the youngest child attaining the age of 18 (or some other stipulated age);
(v)   a further order of the court.

Alternatively, a 'Martin' order might be agreed. This is the same as the Mesher order, save that the clause in paragraph (iv), above (that relates to the children) is left out. At the end of the period of deferment of the sale (eg when the wife remarries) the house is sold and the proceeds are divided in the way specified in the order or agreement (eg 50/50 or 60/40, etc). Where a Martin or Mesher type order is proposed, it might be achieved in one of two ways:

(a) the house could stand in the joint names of the parties until sale; or
(b) the house could stand in the name of the spouse that occupies it and could be subject to a charge in favour of the other spouse (eg it is transferred into the sole name of the wife, subject to a charge in favour of the husband for 33 per cent of the net proceeds of sale of the property).

If a Mesher or Martin type arrangement is proposed, it may well be that the occupying spouse will prefer an arrangement whereby the house is transferred into her name, subject to a charge in favour of the other spouse. This may allow the spouse in occupation to feel that the house is 'hers'. However, there may be some capital gains tax implications for the non-occupying spouse under such an arrangement where a charge is granted (as opposed to where the property stands in the parties' joint names. Where the spouse is granted a charge under such an arrangement (rather than a continuing share of the house) he may have to pay some capital gains tax when the charge is realised (ie when he gets his share of the house under the order or arrangement). He would be less likely to pay capital gains tax if the Mesher or Martin arrangement is on the basis of the house remaining in joint names.

Income Tax

Income tax is no stranger to most people. Issues may arise on the separation of a couple that require some basic understanding of income tax. Particular complications over income tax used to arise in cases where a previously married couple separated and maintenance was paid by one to the other. Although the tax treatment of maintenance payments is now much more straightforward, it may still be necessary to consider other aspects of the liability for this tax.

Tax rates

Income tax is payable at a lower rate, a basic rate and at a higher rate, after various allowances have been taken into account. Each year the personal allowances for income tax vary. For the year 1997/98 (ie as from 6 April 1997) the tax rates are as follows (the 1996/97 figures are given in brackets):

- Lower rate: 20 per cent on the first £4,100 of taxable income (£3,900);
- Basic rate: 23 per cent on taxable income from £4,101 to £26,100 (24 per cent on taxable income from £3,901 to £25,500);
- Higher rate: 40 per cent on taxable income over £26,100 (£25,500).

Personal allowances

The figures for personal allowances change annually. The personal tax allowances that were announced in the budget of 26 November 1996 (and which will apply from 6 April 1997) are as follows (the 1996/97 figures are given in brackets):

Single person
Under 65: £4,045 (£3,765)
65–74:   £5,220 (£4,910)
75+:   £5,400 (£5,090)

Married couple (restricted to tax relief at 15 per cent)
Under 65: £1,830 (£1,790)
65–74:   £3,185 (£3,115)
75+:   £3,225 (£3,155)

Restrictions apply to higher age allowances if the total income exceeds £15,600 (for 1996/97 the figure was £15,200). Single parent families may also claim the additional person's allowance of £1,830. There is also a blind person's allowance of £1,280 (£1,250 in 1996/97).

Income tax and maintenance

Maintenance used to be paid out of gross income. The payer would be entitled to claim tax relief on the whole of the maintenance payment, subject to a number of exceptions. The income tax rules in relation to maintenance payments have been simplified since 15 March 1988. The rules concerning maintenance relate to 'qualifying payments'. Qualifying payments are payments:

(a) under a United Kingdom court order, a legally enforceable written agreement made in the United Kingdom or an assessment by the Child Support Agency;

(b) which are made by one divorced or separated spouse to another (or to the DSS, where the payments are treated as made by the spouse or former spouse to the other spouse or former spouse);

(c) where the payer has not remarried;

(d) for the maintenance of the other spouse or of a child aged under 21 where the child is either the child of the parties or has been treated as such.

Qualifying payments will now be made out of net income. However, the payer will be entitled to claim tax relief at 15 per cent on a maximum of £1,830 of the qualifying maintenance payment (the figure of £1,830 represents the amount of the married person's tax allowance for the year 1997/98; it was £1,790 in 1996/97). If the maintenance payments are less than that figure of £1,830, the payer will only be able to claim relief on the actual amount of the payments (eg if the payments are £1,500, the payer will only be able to claim tax relief on the £1,500).

The 'old' income tax rules apply to maintenance payments where:

(a) the order was made prior to 15 March 1988;

(b) the order was applied for prior to 15 March 1988 and was made by 30 June 1988

(c) they are made pursuant to an agreement that was made before the 15 March 1988 and a copy of the agreement was received by the tax office by 30 June 1988.

(d) the original order or agreement was made in accordance with (a), (b) or (c) above and has subsequently been varied.

Old orders will attract tax relief that is pegged to the level of relief that was being claimed during the tax year that ended on 5 April 1989. It is rare now to meet such orders.

Mortgage interest tax relief

As matters currently stand, mortgage interest tax relief is available in relation to loans up to £30,000. To qualify for the relief, the loan must be for a fixed amount and must be for the purchase of property, a large caravan or a houseboat. The relief is given in respect of the interest payments made under the loan. The property etc that has been bought must be in the United Kingdom or the Republic of Ireland and must be used as the main or principal place of residence of the borrower. The rate of relief is 15 per cent and will fall to 10 per cent in 1998.

Partnerships

Complications over income tax will often arise where the couple have been working in a trading partnership together. In most circumstances it will be essential to have the help of an accountant as to the best way to deal with the income tax complications that may arise on the dissolution of a partnership. Any agreement between a couple that are separating and are dissolving a trading partnership will need to consider:

(a) who will be liable for any past income tax;
(b) who will be liable for future income tax;
(c) on what date will the partnership be dissolved (there may well be tax implications that arise out of the choice of the date);
(d) should a 'continuation election' be made (by which the business will be treated for tax purposes as a continuing concern, notwithstanding the dissolution of the partnership);
(e) should a reserve be set aside to ensure that funds are available to meet identified tax liabilities.

Inheritance Tax

With the abolition of capital transfer tax in 1986, issues concerning inheritance tax are less likely to arise on divorce or separation. Liability to inheritance tax may still arise where the transferor dies within seven years of the transfer. Therefore, if a couple come for mediation where one or both of them is very elderly or ill, it may be necessary to consider obtaining advice about inheritance tax. Transfers of money or property pursuant to court orders in proceedings for divorce or nullity will in general be exempt from inheritance tax (this arises by reason of an agreement that was made with the Inland Revenue in 1975). Therefore, where the parties agree financial terms and there is a risk of inheritance tax, there may well be advantages in obtaining an order of the court that embodies those agreed terms.

■ Welfare Benefits

Welfare benefits can be divided into those that are means tested and those that are not. The main means tested benefits are:

(a) income support;
(b) job-seeker's allowance;
(c) family credit;
(d) disability working allowance;
(e) housing allowance.

Income Support

Under the relevant legislation, everyone over the age of 18 (and in some specified circumstances, people over the age of 16) who has no income or who has an income that is less than the specified amount, is entitled to income support. The rates for income support vary from year to year. The rules governing the entitlement to income support are lengthy and complex; they are not set out here. The April 1998 rates are:

Single person

Under 18 (usual rate)	£30.30
Under 18 (higher rate payable in specific circumstances)	£39.85
18–24	£39.85
25 or over	£50.35
Lone parent (under 18)	£30.30
Lone parent (18 or over)	£50.35

Couple

Both under 18	£60.10
One or both over 18	£79.00

Dependent children

Birth to Sept following 11th birthday	£17.30
From Sept above to Sept following 16th birthday	£25.35
From Sept above to day before 19th birthday	£30.30

Dependent children with protected rates

Age 11 before 1 April 1997	£24.75
Age 16 before 1 April 1997	£29.60
Age 18 before 1 April 1997	£38.90

Premiums

Family	£11.05
Family (one parent rate)	£15.75
Pensioner (single)	£20.10
Pensioner (couple)	£30.35
Pensioner (enhanced single)	£22.35
Pensioner (enhanced couple)	£33.55
Pensioner (higher single)	£27.20
Pensioner (higher couple)	£38.90
Disability (single)	£21.45
Disability (couple)	£30.60
Severe disability (single)	£38.50
Severe disability (couple, one qualifies)	£38.50
Severe disablility (couple, both qualify)	£77.00
Disabled child	£21.45
Carer	£13.65

If a claimant has capital this may affect his or her entitlement to income support. Capital up to £3,000 is ignored. Capital between £3,000 and £8,000 is deemed to produce £1 for each £250 over £3,000. If capital exceeds £8,000 (excluding the value of the home), there is no entitlement. Entitlement to income support brings automatic entitlement to housing benefit and council tax benefit.

Job-Seeker's Allowance

This is a new benefit available from 7th October 1996 which replaces unemployment benefit and income support for those who are unemployed and able to actively seek work. In effect, it runs parallel to income support rather than entirely abolishing it. Again the rules of entitlement are complex and are not, for that reason, set out here. In any event it will not usually be necessary for the mediator to determine which of the two benefits is applicable because the rates and restrictions are essentially identical to those set out above in relation to income support. It is, however, worth noting that the normal rates are reduced if the claimant is penalised for failing to accept the work opportunities properly presented to him.

Family Credit

This benefit is paid to top up the wages of people who work and have children. The claimant must be working for 16 hours or more each week. The entitlement to benefit arises if the net income of the claimant and any partner of the claimant is equal to or less than the 'applicable amount'. The applicable amount from April 1998 is £79.00. If the income exceeds the applicable amount, 70 per cent of the excess is deducted from the family credit. The same rules as to capital apply as they do to income support. The rates of family credit as from April 1998 are:

Claimant (if working 30 hours or more)	£10.80
Child claimant (under 11)	£12.35
Child claimant (11–15)	£20.45
Child claimant (16–17)	£25.40
Child claimant (18)	£35.55

Housing Benefit and Council Tax Benefit

Housing benefit is available to help with the housing costs of people who are not owner/occupiers. Council tax needs no explanation, save that it is not payable by people under the age of 18. The main rates for these benefits are:

Claimant (16–24)	£39.85
Claimant (25 or over)	£50.35
Lone parent (under 18)	£39.85
Lone parent (18 or over)	£50.35
Couple (both under 18)	£60.10
Couple (one or both over 18)	£79.00
Dependent children (ignoring protected rates)	
birth to Sept following 11th birthday	£17.30
from Sept above to Sept following 16th birthday	£25.35
from Sept above to Sept before 19th birthday	£29.60

Disability Working Allowance

This is paid to top up low wages for the disabled. Capital may affect entitlement to this benefit. Capital of less than £3,000 is disregarded and capital of £3,000 to £16,000 is deemed to produce income of £1 for each £250 over £3,000. The rates for this allowance as from April 1998 are:

Claimant (if working 30 hours or more)	£10.80
Adult allowance (single)	£50.75
Adult allowance (couple/lone parent)	£79.40
Child allowance (under 11)	£12.35
Child allowance (11–15)	£20.45
Child allowance (16–17)	£25.40
Child allowance (18)	£35.55

Non-means Tested Benefits

The following is a list of some of the main non-means tested benefits at the rates that apply from April 1997:

Child benefit

Only/elder/eldest for whom child benefit is payable (couple)	£11.45
Only/elder/eldest for whom child benefit is payable (lone parent)	£17.10
Each subsequent child	£9.30

Incapacity benefit

Long-term Incapacity Benefit	£64.70
Short-term Incapacity Benefit (under pension age)	
lower rate	£48.80
higher rate	£57.70
Short-term Incapacity Benefit (over pension age)	
lower & higher rate	£62.05
Increase of Long-term Incapacity Benefit for age	
higher rate	£13.60
lower rate	£6.80
Invalidity Allowance (transitional)	
higher rate	£13.60
middle rate	£8.60
lower rate	£4.30

Invalid care allowance

Claimant	£38.70

Maternity allowance

Lower rate	£50.10
Higher rate	£57.70

One parent benefit

Nil

Severe disablement allowance

Basic rate	£39.10
Adult dependent, extra	£21.95
Age-related additions (from Dec 1990)	
higher rate	£13.60
middle rate	£8.60
lower rate	£4.30

Statutory maternity pay

Earnings threshold	£64.00
Higher rate (first six weeks)	90 % of average earnings
Lower rate (next 12 weeks)	£57.70

Statutory sick pay

Earnings threshold	£64.00
Standard rate	£57.70

Widow's benefit

[For deaths before 11 April 1988 refer to age points in brackets.]

Widow's benefit (lump sum)	£1,000.00
Widowed mother's allowance	£64.70
Widow's pension	
standard rate	£64.70
age-related	
age 54 [49]	£60.17
age 53 [48]	£55.64
age 52 [47]	£51.11
age 51 [46]	£46.58
age 50 [45]	£42.06
age 49 [44]	£37.53
age 48 [43]	£33.00
age 47 [42]	£28.47
age 46 [41]	£23.94
age 45 [40]	£19.41

Handbook
A

Family Mediators Association

Ruth Smallacombe

The Family Mediators Association was founded in 1989 by a group of six professionals who, through their collective experience in family law and mediation, created a new model for professional practice. This became known as the co-working approach and was designed to both blend the expertise and knowledge of mediators from legal and therapeutic professions working together, and to provide the first model in All Issues or comprehensive mediation in the UK. This meant that, for the first time, couples could bring all issues in dispute—whether concerned with arrangements for their children, finance or property—into the mediation arena. Co-mediation offers couples an informed, sensitive and balanced forum for resolving their difficulties. This comprehensive approach is now firmly embodied in family mediation practice nationally across all organisations and, with the passing of the Family Law Act 1996, into statute.

From this small group of professionals in 1989, FMA membership has grown to nearly 500 members in 1997. All have been trained in the co-working model. FMA's Foundation Training now encompasses all models of mediation—co-working and sole and anchor practice. Further training for FMA and other mediators includes a range of professional interest and policy development topics, updates and refresher courses and supervision/consultancy training. FMA, therefore, offers a range of functions to professional family mediators, principally:

- recruitment, selection and training of family mediators who meet the Association's criteria for entry into training;
- professional and administrative support to the membership including professional practice consultancy, and route to accreditation
- post-qualifying opportunities to develop knowledge and skills in family mediation practice;
- support to mediators in Legal Aid Board mediation pilots and to other members in establishing and developing their practice standards.

FMA is uniquely placed as the founding training agency offering All Issues Mediation training to qualified and experienced professionals drawn from a range of backgrounds, including family law and interpersonal and therapeutic practice with families. The Association is a registered charity and is self-supporting. Legal Aid Board funding is envisaged during 1998 to strengthen the support to the significant number of FMA members in the pilot scheme.

Management

The association is managed by a Board which is elected from and by the membership at the annual general meeting. For 1997/98 the officers of the Board of Management are: Ruth Smallacombe (Chair), Simon Pigott (Vice Chair), Beverley Sayers (Secretary) and Jeremy Abraham (Treasurer). The Board also appoints from within its membership representatives to head working parties in specific areas (eg marketing and PR, training and professional development, UK College policy and membership). Angela Lake-Carroll is FMA's Director of Training and Professional Development and Martin Couchman is the Administrator, based in the national office. Plans to increase the staff structure are underway, in line with the needs of the members and development of the profession during 1998 and beyond.

As a registered charity, FMA trains individual family mediators who will then become members of a regional group. The association currently has 45 regional groups, based in the main town/city areas of England and North and South Wales. Each regional group has a co-ordinator who is responsible for dealing with mediation enquiries and referring the work on to local mediators, in addition to organising meetings for the region on a regular basis. With FMA's growing and widespread membership network, the role of the regional co-ordinator provides a vital link between the Board of FMA and the Association's membership. A Regional Council meets every three months, and the Chair of the Council is an *ex officio* member of the Board.

FMA Professional Development

The Board of Management aims:

- to continue to respond to the needs of the members of the Association and to build on FMA's professional image and strengths;
- to have regard to national developments in practice and to respond appropriately;
- to ensure best practice standards and continuing professional development for members, ensuring a quality-assured family mediation service;
- to ensure access to accredited professional practice supervision and consultancy for members.

Further training (CPD) is therefore seen as important for all FMA members and other mediators. A continuing training programme is offered in a range of areas including:

- sole and anchor practice models;
- co-working mediation practice;
- issues concerning children and mediation;
- family law—appropriate to mediation practice;
- issues of domestic violence and screening for domestic violence;
- constructing and drafting summaries/Memoranda of Understanding;
- finance and mediation practice;
- preparing for franchise and marketing mediation;
- professional practice supervision and consultancy.
  (FMA courses carry CPD points.)

The last of these, professional practice supervision and consultancy, is an important component for FMA in all family mediation practice, and the Association has a training and mentoring programme for experienced and accredited mediators who wish to become professional practice supervisor consultants. FMA is currently able to offer a national network of professional practice supervisor consultants who offer professional practice support in All Issues family mediation.

Professional Standards

FMA keeps under review all standards in policy and practice, and with the years of experience it has, believes it is able to respond to the needs of its members and to changing times in family mediation practice. The

Handbook A

Association is committed to a code of practice and is also co-author of the UK College of Family Mediators' professional standards and mediation practice guidelines.

Representation and Provision of Consultancy and Training Services

The Association is currently represented on UK College Governorship, Management, Publicity and PR and Professional Standards committees. It has an input into various other professional and statutory bodies, including the National Council for Family Proceedings, The Law Society, the Relate Quality Partnership and the Legal Aid Board. FMA provides education for family lawyers in family mediation in order to assist them to support their clients appropriately through family mediation. FMA provides training and professional practice consultancy to other organisations on request.

The Association's Commitment

FMA believes that family mediation is a professional service provided to those contemplating separation or divorce. Our fees are set to reflect the standards, expertise and professionalism demonstrated by our members. The association currently recommends a charging rate of £60 per hour per person. Mediators in each region may vary the charge to suit the needs of their local area, and flexible arrangements are available in many of our geographical regions, designed to assist, wherever possible, access to high-quality standards of family mediation practice. Although our training is charitably based (and is self-financing), our mediators operate, for the most part, within the private sector at present, with a significant and increasing number being part of Legal Aid Board mediation pilots.

If you would like further information about any of our services, training or promotional material, please contact FMA's National Office at 1 Wyvil Court, Wyvil Road, London SW8 2TG Tel 0171 720 3336; Fax 0171 720 7999.

▥ FMA Regional Groups

Bath District Family Mediators Association
Bedford Family Mediators Association
Birmingham Family Mediators Association
Bristol Family Mediators Association
Cambridge Family Mediators Association
Cornwall Family Mediators Association
Coventry and South Warwickshire Family Mediators Association
Derbyshire Family Mediators Association
Devon Family Mediators Association
Essex Family Mediators Association
Family Mediation in Norfolk
Family Mediators South Wales Ltd
Greater Manchester Family Mediators Association
Hampshire and Isle of Wight Family Mediators Association
Hereford & Worcester Family Mediators Association
Herts & Bucks Family Mediators Association

Jersey Family Mediators Association
Kent Family Mediators Association
Lancashire Family Mediators Association
London North & Central Family Mediators Association
London South & Central Family Mediators Association
London South & West Family Mediators Association
Mediation East Anglia
Merseyside Family Mediators Association
Milton Keynes Family Mediators Association
North Wales Family Mediators Association
Northants, Bucks and Leics Family Mediators Association
Nottinghamshire Family Mediators Association
Oxford Family Mediators Association
South Yorkshire Family Mediators Association
Shropshire Family Mediators Association
Somerset Family Mediators Association
South Midlands Family Mediators Association
Southampton Family Mediators Association
South West Region Family Mediators Association
Surrey & North Hampshire Family Mediators Association
Sussex Family Mediators Association
Thames Valley Family Mediators Association
The Hertfordshire Comprehensive Mediation Service
West Yorkshire Family Mediators Association
Wiltshire Family Mediators Association
York Family Mediators Association

Handbook A

Family Mediation Scotland

Maureen Lynch

Family Mediation Scotland (FMS) is the co-ordinating body for 12 local affiliated family mediation services located across Scotland.

Local FMS Services

Family mediation affiliated services provide family mediation as their core activity, free to all separating and divorcing parents who jointly seek solutions for their children. Six services provide mediation on All Issues, allowing agreement to be sought in relation to finance and property as well as children. Mediation usually takes place in the premises of the local family mediation service. However, in the more rural areas of Scotland, mediation may be provided in other premises nearer to the clients' homes. While the process itself is a formal and controlled one, couples will usually sit round a coffee table in an informal way. Some of the services provide toys, books and other facilities for children in their waiting rooms. The individual intake interview is an essential part of the mediation services offered in local areas. It provides each parent with the opportunity for an individual session which will help them to decide whether or not to enter mediation; its other main purpose is to screen for domestic violence.

All the services are independent charities with their own boards of management from the local community. A wide spectrum of the local community is represented on them, including sheriffs, solicitors and child-care professionals. The services are managed by a co-ordinator or a manager and, where the co-ordinator is not also a mediator, a supervisor will be provided to oversee local standards of practice. As well as providing mediation, a number of local family mediation services offer facilities directly for children. Three services offer the opportunity for direct counselling for children and young people; one service provides access to children's groups for children between the ages of 8 and 11 who are experiencing difficulties because of their parents' separation and divorce. Three services provide contact centres where parents who no longer live with their children may spend time with them.

Partnership

Two of the local family mediation services in Scotland are based on partnerships with NCH Action for Children. The Western Isles service is offered in partnership with Marriage Counselling.

FMS's Volume of Work

FMS services currently complete mediation for over 1,000 couples per year. Almost 70 per cent of children whose parents use FMS services are under the age of ten. A substantial proportion of the services' clients are not married. Parents may be referred to local services from the court through a rule of court. Mediation in this circumstance remains voluntary and the mediation service makes no report to the court. Parents may decide not to proceed with mediation, having undertaken an initial interview. FMS services act as a telephone information service to an average of 2,000 callers a year.

Fees

Family mediation services make no charge for mediation on children's issues alone. The work of the local services is financed through government and local authority grants, and awards from charitable trusts. Some services which offer mediation on All Issues apply charges on a sliding scale. Two to three mediation sessions are usually required for issues related to children, with at least four to five sessions being required in All Issues Mediation.

FMS Staff

The staff of FMS comprises a Director, Elizabeth Foster; a Training Officer, Fiona Garwood; a Publicity Officer, Gay Cox; an Education Officer, Maureen Lynch; and a Contact Centre Development Officer, Pauline Linn. There are three secretaries. The organisation is accountable to an Executive Committee which represents the local services. In matters of day-to-day management, the officers are accountable to a Management Committee chaired by Hugh Donald. The Patron of FMS, Elaine C Smith, plays an active role in its events.

FMS's Management and Professional Standards

Local services in Scotland have to meet the FMS affiliation criteria, renewable every year. The criteria cover the service's own management structure, uniform standards of selection, training, supervision and evaluation of mediators. All trainee mediators attend the FMS National Training Course, following selection by local services, according to national selection procedures. The National Training Course covers four training weekends and four practice skills days, evaluation and observed and recorded mediation roleplays and lasts for ten months. Towards the end of this time the trainees undertake supervised mediation practice. FMS has an equal opportunities policy which underpins selection, training and service provision. FMS provides continuing professional development for practising mediators, service co-ordinators, supervisors and training staff. Mediators are expected to attend at least one CPD event per year. Six FMS services currently provide All Issues Mediation, for which FMS provides a specialist five day training course.

FMS's Parent Information Programme

FMS is currently piloting and developing a Parent Information Programme to support parents who separate or divorce. It provides a two-and-a-half hour group information session backed up with a booklet, 'Parents Apart' . The main focus of the programme is the effects of parental separation on children and the ways in which parents may offer support. The options available to parents for resolving disputes are also explored, with an emphasis on the benefits of mediation. Parent information sessions will become a significant component of the provision available through FMS in the future.

Family Mediation Scotland can be contacted at 127 Rose Street, South Lane, Edinburgh EH2 4BB Tel 0131 220 1610; Fax 0131 220 6895.

FMS Family Mediation Services

Family Mediation Borders
Family Mediation Central Scotland
Family Mediation Grampian

Family Mediation Lothian
Family Mediation Orkney
Family Mediation Service (Highland)
Family Mediation Service Western Isles
Family Mediation Shetland
Family Mediation Tayside
Family Mediation (West of Scotland)
NCH Action for Children Dumfries & Galloway Family Mediation Service
NCH Action for Children Family Mediation Fife

National Family Mediation

Thelma Fisher

National Family Mediation is an association of 70 local family mediation services in England, Wales and Northern Ireland.

Local NFM Services

NFM affiliated services provide family mediation as their core activity on a not-for-profit basis. They especially help separating and divorcing parents jointly to seek solutions for their children that protect them from the conflict and loss inherent in the breakdown of a marriage. Mediators meet couples on their own specialised premises designed to create a safe, impartial, professional and family-friendly setting for mediation. Couples will usually talk around a coffee table and there are books, toys and other facilities for children. Children may, in particular circumstances, be consulted within the mediation process. Twelve services also offer counselling for children and many have links with local contact centres. Forty services provide mediation of all issues, integrating finance and property decisions with those about children. More services are training to provide this, using interdisciplinary teams of mediators, some from local law firms.

Each service employs a manager or co-ordinator who runs the day-to-day business of the service and a supervisor trained by NFM who is responsible for local standards of practice. Both partners are given a prior separate appointment, which includes screening for domestic violence, to help them decide whether to enter mediation. Almost every service is an independent charity, overseen by trustees from the local community. These include the local district judge, local magistrates, the legal profession and health and community professionals and representatives.

Partnerships

More than two-thirds of NFM services have partnership arrangements with other organisations. NFM's partners include the Probation Service, NCH Action for Children and Relate with whom there are regular meetings at national as well as local level. Many NFM services also have service agreements under the Children Act 1989 with their local Social Services departments.

NFM Regions

NFM services maintain regional links within six regions (North East, North West, Midlands, East, West and London/South) which foster regular meetings and professional seminars.

NFM's Volume of Work

NFM services currently complete mediation for over 6,000 couples per annum. Experienced services are used by over 10 per cent of the divorcing population. Twenty per cent of NFM's clients are not married and a proportion come to NFM after legal proceedings are completed. Twenty per cent are referred from courts, usually at a directions hearing and with the help of the local family court welfare service. NFM services act as the first telephone port of call to a further 8,000 callers.

Fees

NFM services are committed to providing mediation to all, regardless of their ability to pay, and use charitable donations, grants and contracts to subsidise those clients who cannot pay. As the Family Law Act comes in, an increasing number of services are in receipt of Legal Aid Board franchises to cover the fees of the legally aided client. Otherwise, most services charge clients on a sliding scale. The mediation of the arrangements for children usually takes about three hours and All Issues about 12 hours.

NFM's National Staff

NFM has a Director, Thelma Fisher OBE; two Assistant Directors, Marian Roberts (Professional Practice) and Sheena Adam (Services), and a Finance Director (Rupert Wiles). There is a training manager and three secretaries and the office receives many calls from the public. During the run-up to the implementation of the Family Law Act, five part-time staff are working on projects, funded by the government, to assist local services to prepare for the Act. The officers are accountable to an elected Management Committee chaired by John Shaw CB. An active part is played by the President, Dame Brenda Hale DBE, and by the Patron, Lord Habgood.

NFM's Management and Professional Standards

To gain affiliation, local services have to meet NFM's quality assurance management standards and use NFM's selection and training procedures. To achieve quality standards, services are audited by NFM's specially trained teams of auditors.

NFM mediators are selected on the basis of aptitude and the relevance of their background and in accordance with NFM's equal opportunities policy. They are then trained in the core skills of mediation over a six month period. Training includes small group sessions, individual supervision and attendance at a national training event at Nottingham University for expert presentations on such topics as the latest research into children's experience of divorce and changes in family law. Additional training modules are provided to services for:

- All Issues Mediation;
- direct consultation of children in the mediation process;
- screening for domestic violence;
- supervision;
- cross-cultural mediation.

Local services recruit in relation to client demand to ensure that mediators gain practical experience during and after training. Services recruit from a range of professional backgrounds. Those services offering the mediation of all issues (AIM) have interdisciplinary teams of mediators, including lawyer mediators and legal consultants. Many of NFM's mediators have been mediating for ten or 15 years and therefore have considerable experience of a range of client needs. Accreditation is granted upon the completion of 75 hours of face-to-face mediation and upon the demonstration and independent assessment of competence. NFM trains local supervisors and NFM's team of trainers are all drawn from local services.

Research into NFM's Work

NFM's work has been independently researched several times, including:

(1) In 1988 by Marian Roberts and Professor Gwynn Davis of the University of Bristol. This reported positively on the successful work of the South-East London Family Mediation Bureau.

(2) In 1985–9 by the Conciliation Project Unit at the University of Newcastle, commissioned by the government. This reported favourably on the mediation of children's arrangements in a range of NFM services, showing an average 68 per cent agreement rate, agreements that lasted well and parents valuing the unpressured environment. Disputes about finance and property often, however, continued unresolved.

(3) In 1990–93 by the University of Newcastle into the mediation of all issues in five services. This project was set up by NFM to introduce the mediation of finance and property into NFM practice. The researchers reported that in All Issues Mediation cases 39 per cent agreed all issues and 41 per cent agreed some issues—80 per cent overall compared with 63 per cent in child focused mediation.

(4) In 1996 by the University of Newcastle—a follow-up study of the 1990–3 clients. The benefits of All Issues Mediation were found to be that clients were :

    (a) more likely to feel that mediation had helped them to end the marital relationship amicably, reduce conflict, maintain good relationships with their ex-spouses and carry less bitterness and resentment into their post-divorce lives;

    (b) more content with existing child-care arrangements and less likely to have disagreements about child contact;

    (c) less likely to have sought help from outside the family with problems experienced by children;

    (d) able to reach agreements which had survived the test of time;

    (e) glad that they had used mediation.

The researchers concluded overall that it is *the process of reaching agreement* that couples most value and which is associated with the reduction of conflict and bitterness. NFM mediators find that the clients who use mediation for children's arrangements are likely to be in dispute, whereas those who use mediation for all issues are more likely to be seeking to prevent disputes.

National Family Mediation can be contacted at 9 Tavistock Place, London WC1H 9SN Tel 0171 383 5993; Fax 0171 383 5994.

NFM Local Services

African Caribbean Family Mediation Service
Berkshire Family Mediation
Birmingham District Family Mediation
Bradford Metropolitan Family Mediation Service
Bristol Family Mediation Service
Cambridge Family & Divorce Centre
Cheshire Mediation Service
Chiltern Family & Mediation Centre
Cleveland Family Mediation Service
Coventry & Warwickshire Family Mediation Service

Cumbria Family Mediation Service
Derbyshire Family Mediation Service
Divorce Mediation & Counselling Service
Dorset Family Mediation Service
Durham Family Mediation
Exeter & District Family Mediation Service
Family Mediation (Central Middlesex)
Family Mediation Cardiff
Family Mediation Service (Greater Manchester)
Family Mediation Service (Northumberland & Tyneside)
Family Mediation Service (North-West Yorkshire)
Family Mediation Service—Institute of Family Therapy
Family Mediation Service: Barnet Haringey & Hertsmere
Gloucestershire Family Mediation
Gwent Mediation Service
Hampshire Family Mediation
Herefordshire Family Mediation Service
Kent Family Mediation Service
Lancashire Family Mediation Service
Lincolnshire Family Mediation Service
Mediation Advisory Service for Stafford and North Staffordshire
Mediation for Families (East London & City)
Mediation in Divorce
Merseyside Family Mediation Service
Mid-Essex Family Mediation Service
Milton Keynes Family Mediation
NCH Action for Children Eye to Eye Mediation
Norfolk Family Mediation Service
North Devon Family Mediation Service
North East London Family Mediation Service
North Wales Mediation Service
Northamptonshire Family Mediation Service
Northern Ireland Family Mediation Service
Nottinghamshire Children & Families Mediation Service (FAME)
Oxfordshire Family Mediation Service
Peterborough & District Family Mediation Service
Plymouth Mediation
Salisbury & District Family Mediation Service
Scarborough & District Family Mediation Service
Shropshire Family Mediation Service
Somerset Family Mediation Service
South East London Family Mediation Bureau
South Essex Family Mediation Service
South Staffordshire Family Mediation Service
South Yorkshire Family Mediation Service
Suffolk Family Mediation Service
Sunderland and South Tyneside Family Mediation Service
Surrey Family Mediation Service
Sussex Family Mediation Service
Swindon Family Mediation Service
Thames Valley Family Mediation
West Essex Family Mediation Service
West Yorkshire Family Mediation Service
Worcestershire Family Mediation
York Family Mediation Service

LawGroup UK's Family Mediation Register

Stephen Madge

LawGroup UK was launched in 1990 to provide training, marketing and support services to firms of solicitors nationwide which meet LawGroup's quality standards. In order to join LawGroup UK, firms have to undergo a quality control review. There are currently over 80 LawGroup member firms in more than 180 locations across the UK.

LawGroup UK's Family Mediation Training

LawGroup UK has developed an initiative taken by Devon & Exeter Law Society in 1995 and by LawNet in 1996 to train experienced family lawyers in the model of sole family mediator, as well as in co-mediation. Its prime mover in Devon, Jeremy Ferguson, was one of the first solicitors outside London to train with the FMA in 1989. LawGroup UK now provides this training in association with Devon & Exeter Law Society, LawNet, Liverpool Law Society and ILEX. LawGroup UK's training in family mediation is offered at introductory and advanced levels to family lawyers who meet LawGroup UK's criteria and entry requirements. The great majority are members of SFLA and there is a rigorous application and selection procedure. The training is not exclusive to LawGroup UK member firms.

Main objectives of LawGroup UK's family mediation training and Family Mediation Register

- to provide a programme of family mediation training which builds on the knowledge and expertise of experienced family lawyers and enables them to acquire additional skills in making the transition to the different role of family mediator;
- to develop the model of the sole lawyer mediator as one of the models available to separating and divorcing couples, with co-mediation as another option;
- to provide a challenging and enjoyable programme of core training linked with a structured programme of practical training and mandatory continuing training, up to and following accreditation;
- to develop an assessment procedure for entry to LawGroup UK's Family Mediation Register and systems of quality control to maintain standards of mediation practice;
- to provide marketing and support services for members of the Register to help them establish their family mediation practice— producing publicity material, organising launches of new services to increase public awareness, issuing press releases.

Requirements for LawGroup UK's family mediation training

(a) applicants must be solicitors, barristers or members of the Institute of Legal Executives with at least three years' post-admission experience (preferably five) involving a substantial amount of matrimonial and family work;
(b) a current practising certificate or equivalent;
(c) a statement of reasons for wishing to train as a family mediator and the qualities and skills the applicant considers most important for a family mediator;

Handbook A

(d) two references—one from a judge or barrister and one from a solicitor of at least five years' standing, practising as a family lawyer in another firm;

(e) an individual interview before and/or during foundation training.

LawGroup UK's Trainers

LawGroup UK's trainers are accredited family mediators, among the most experienced in the country. As well as drawing on their very substantial experience as practitioners of All Issues Mediation, they have extensive experience as trainers, especially in training family lawyers for sole mediation and for co-mediation.

LawGroup UK's Director of Family Mediation Training, Lisa Parkinson, is known in this country and overseas as a leading authority on family mediation. Lisa was NFM's first training officer and a co-founder and the first director of FMA. She is also Director of Mediation Training with CALM (Comprehensive Accredited Lawyer Mediators) in Scotland, all of whom are accredited as mediators through the Law Society of Scotland. Lisa continues to practise as a co-mediator with Bristol Family Mediators Association Ltd, which holds a franchise under Phase 1 of the Legal Aid Board's Family Mediation Pilot Project. Sweet & Maxwell published her book, *Family Mediation*, in November 1997.

Lisa's co-trainers include Elizabeth Allen, Robert Clerke and Andrew Don. Andrew is head of the family law department at Blandy & Blandy. He is a member of the FMA and conducts mediations on a regular basis. Robert Clerke also trains for SFLA. Additional trainers lecture on specialist aspects of family law practice and mediation. Lisa works with LawGroup UK's Director of Training, Stephen Madge and with Tim Nightingale, Public Relations and Marketing Consultant in developing training and practice initiatives for Members of LawGroup UK's Register. A hardworking administrative team based at LawGroup UK's headquarters at Caterham supports them.

Assessing the Competence of Family Mediators

The assessment of mediators' competence is a very topical subject in the UK and in other countries. The USA-based Academy of Family Mediators has embarked on a two-year study of mediators' qualifications and competence. LawGroup UK's trainee mediators must complete their core training satisfactorily, with written assignments, and must obtain a positive recommendation from trainers and assessors before they may proceed to the next stage of practical training. Full members of LawGroup UK's Register have all reached this second stage. Associate members may co-mediate with a full member but they may not offer sole mediation under LawGroup UK auspices.

LawGroup UK's assessment procedure identifies the essential level of understanding and competencies that family mediators need to have and seeks demonstrable evidence of this understanding and competencies. The Legal Aid Board is piloting a broadly similar approach to the assessment of mediators' competence in franchised services. LawGroup UK aims to work with the UK College in developing a reliable assessment procedure that will meet the Legal Aid Board's requirements.

Admission to LawGroup UK's Family Mediation Register

In addition to LawGroup UK-trained mediators, LawGroup UK's Register also includes mediators who have trained with FMA, SFLA and LawWise and who wish to join the Register for the purpose of obtaining practical/continuing/advanced training, PPSC and assistance in marketing mediation services. Attendance at a conversion or refresher course may be required, depending on the date and content of previous training. Members of the Register who are not already Associate or Full Members of the College must undertake stage 2—Practical training in receipt of PPSC. This is organised via regional panels of full members of the Register. Many of these panels include experienced mediators who are already Associate Members of the College, or full Members. They assist in providing opportunities for practical training through co-mediation with an experienced mediator. LawGroup UK provides PPSC.

PPSC—Professional Practice Supervision and Consultancy

PPSC takes place in the regions using UK College-approved supervisors working to recognised national standards. Consultancy on urgent matters is also available by telephone, fax or E-mail.

Continuing Professional Development in Family Mediation

LawGroup UK was one of the first national training providers to make Continuing Professional Development (CPD) in family mediation a mandatory requirement. To avoid a long gap between initial training courses and follow-up training, LawGroup UK has developed a CPD programme in family mediation, organised regionally. Regionally based CPD offers the considerable advantages of accessibility and lower travel costs. It also assists the development of regional networks, which are useful for referring clients for mediation or for legal advice. The current requirement for members of LawGroup UK's Family Mediation Register is a minimum of 12 hours' CPD annually. This generally involves attendance at a training day at six-monthly intervals. LawGroup UK courses are recognised by the Law Society. Current topics include:

- Advanced communication skills for family mediators;
- What family mediators need to know about prolonged parental conflict and its associations with children's post-divorce adjustment ;
- Issues concerning children's direct involvement in mediation;
- Impasse strategies;
- Issues of domestic violence in mediation;
- Obtaining and operating under a family mediation franchise.

CPD to accreditation level involves a total of at least 180 hours, including practical training, over two years. Accreditation may be applied for at the end of this period, provided all the requirements for accreditation have been met.

Geographical Coverage

There are currently about 150 members of LawGroup UK's Family Mediation Register and the number is growing steadily, after full assessment for admission. LawGroup UK is extending the availability of family mediation to many urban and rural areas where it was previously almost non-existent. There are now strong regional groups in the Home

Counties and also in Devon and Cornwall, Cheshire, Hull, Kent and Sussex, Lincoln.

Further information about LawGroup UK's Training and Family Mediation Register may be obtained from: Stephen Madge, Head of Training, LawGroup UK, Orbital House, 85 Croydon Road, Caterham, Surrey CR3 6PD Tel 01883 341 341; Fax 01883 340 066; Mobile 0585 54 33 74; E-mail S.Madge@BTInternet.com

Recent Developments — LawGroup UK's Family Mediation Video

Many family mediators in the UK have learnt a great deal from watching John Haynes' mediation tapes. There is also need for British video material showing models of family mediation in this country, in the context of our legal system. In 1997 LawGroup UK produced a video showing a sole lawyer mediator working with a recently separated couple who are most convincingly played by two solicitors, drawing from their experience of advising divorcing clients. This video has been very well received and copies are now available for sale, with accompanying notes for trainers and to assist in public presentations on mediation.

LawWise Legal Education & Training Services Ltd

Alastair Logan

LawWise was founded in 1995 by Alastair and Pat Logan. It was founded in response to the need to provide training for lawyers as sole mediators in All Issues Mediation. Alastair and Pat Logan trained as family mediators and as trainers and supervisors with Dr John Haynes who is widely regarded as the founder of family mediation. He combines an extensive mediation practice with a worldwide and unequalled reputation as a mediation trainer both of lawyers and the judiciary. Dr Haynes founded the Haynes Mediation Training Institute and has trained in many different legal jurisdictions in Europe, North America, Australia and New Zealand. He is currently training judges in Singapore. For 12 years Dr Haynes was Professor of Social Welfare at the State University of New York where he taught Social Policy and Conflict Management and was the founding President of the Association of Family Mediators. As a trainer he has trained more than 20,000 professionals in mediation and conflict management, including more than 500 in the UK. His training has formed the core of family mediation training in this country. Dr Haynes is the Director of Studies of LawWise training.

LawWise's philosophy of training is that the best training can be obtained by using small groups and an intensive five-day basic course followed later by advanced training over three days. By keeping the group size small, LawWise ensures that the full quality of training is available to each participant. By being clear about the needs of lawyers in relation to family mediation training and practice, LawWise is able to provide the right training and the right support for lawyers wishing to train as sole family mediators.

LawWise was the first independent training body to receive approval for its family mediation training from the UK College of Family Mediators. LawWise training is designed to train lawyers to be family mediators and to date it has trained over 250 lawyers in courses which have been well-received around the country. LawWise offers initial and further training in family mediation in sole practice and professional practice supervision/consultancy. Its courses therefore offer a range of skills to professional family mediators, principally in the areas of recruitment, selection and training of lawyers who meet LawWise's criteria for entry into training and the profession, as family mediators.

LawWise has its own Code of Practice which is approved by the UK College of Family Mediators and provides accreditation through its panel of accredited mediators to those who have trained to the standard required by the UK College. LawWise provides all of the professional practice supervision/consultancy that is necessary for family mediators to comply with the requirements of the UK College of Family Mediators and the Legal Aid Board Franchise Specification.

LawWise also provides administrative support to the mediators that LawWise has trained, with a focus on opportunities to develop knowledge and skills in family mediation and practice. We have developed disks that provide the family mediator with all the documentation required to be a family mediator and to apply and maintain a franchise from the Legal Aid Board in family mediation. LawWise keeps under review its standards in relation both to training, policy and practice. It works closely with other family mediation organisations and with the UK College itself, and with other bodies, notably the British Association of Lawyer Mediators, the Legal Aid Board, The Law Society, the General Council of the Bar and the Lord Chancellor's Department.

LawWise can be contacted at: The Shooting Lodge, Guildford Road, Sutton Green, Guildford, Surrey GU4 7PZ. Tel 01483 235000; Fax 01483 237004.

The Solicitors Family Law Association's Mediation Programme and Training

Members of the Solicitors Family Law Association, formed in 1982, believe that aggressive solicitors and reliance on the court process can add to distress and anger on the breakdown of a family relationship. SFLA members abide by a Code of Practice designed to promote a conciliatory atmosphere in which matters are dealt with in a sensitive, constructive and cost-effective way. SFLA provides support, guidance and training for its members and is actively involved in law reform, both initiating improvements and responding to proposals for change.

Family lawyers have played a major role in the development of All Issues Mediation in the UK. Until the commencement of the pilot scheme in All Issues Mediation ('Solicitors in Mediation') in 1985, family mediation was limited mainly to dealing with children's issues, while financial issues were dealt with by lawyers in the legal process. When this pilot scheme resulted in 1988 in the launch of the Family Mediators Association with its co-mediation model, both the SFLA and The Law Society supported that launch and were represented on the Board of FMA. All the solicitors who co-founded FMA were also members of the SFLA.

In 1995 the SFLA decided to establish its own family mediation practice and training programme for sole lawyer mediators who wished to mediate as part of their practice. It commissioned two of its members, who had both been members of Solicitors in Mediation and founder members of FMA, to assist it in this task. A training faculty of lawyers and experienced mediators from other disciplines was established to run training courses nationally. The first course ran in May 1996 and since then over 250 lawyers, drawn from practising family solicitors and Fellows of the Institute of Legal Executives, have been trained.

SFLA mediation follows the principles of established practice while recognising that parties negotiate 'in the shadow of the law'. Its theoretical perspective may be summarised as comprising a structured, comprehensive framework bounded by a body of ethical and practice rules and defined stages, within which it allows for creativity and flexibility appropriate to the parties' needs and issues. The SFLA has adopted The Law Society's recommended Family Mediation Code of Practice which it helped to create and which went through an extensive consultation process. This Code provides a sound ethical base, which is supplemented by ensuring that mediators have an appreciation of the principles and values underlying the Code, so that they can work not only within its letter but also its spirit.

The SFLA also follows The Law Society's recommended mediation training standards. SFLA mediators attend an 8-day training programme. This provides a theoretical understanding of mediation and its process; sound communication and other mediation skills; an ethical appreciation as previously outlined; an understanding of the emotional issues facing couples in mediation, and the integration of existing expertise and practice with new ways of working. The course gives attention to couple and mediator dynamics, to financial issues arising on separation and divorce, and to the position and needs of children in mediation and divorce. It enables practitioners to make the transition from lawyers, representing one party, to impartial and non-directive mediators, helping couples with their communications, negotiations and the resolution of their issues. Based on sole mediation, it also covers co-mediation so that practitioners are able to co-mediate when they consider this appropriate. After satisfactory completion of training, mediators can commence mediation practice, but the accreditation process will ordinarily take two years. During this time they will be expected to undertake mandatory further relevant education, have peer group communications, use the available consultancy facilities and maintain a prescribed minimum level of mediation practice.

Consultancy arrangements established by the SFLA are in two parts. One involves each mediator having a Designated Consultant, who will support the mediator as required during and after the accreditation process. The other lies in the SFLA's Helpline facility, through which mediators can obtain emergency advice, help and support on the phone from a team of Helpline consultants. The SFLA is pleased to have joined the UK College of Family Mediators and to have established full approved body status. It shares many values, ideas and aspirations with the College and its other members and looks forward to developing these constructively. As with any new professional body, it acknowledges that there are also some areas where organisational members of the College have differences of view and approach, but strength lies in diversity. It is anticipated that these are likely to be bridged as a process of harmonisation takes place.

In the coming years there will be many challenges for professionals working in the field of marriage breakdown. The Family Law Act will introduce not only new procedures, but new concepts of approach. Not all aspects of the legislation have been fully thought through, and some strains are probably inevitable. For mediators, the Act provides opportunities and also concerns, as some of the principles of the process are supported and others potentially undermined, for example, where mediators are required to report back on 'suitability' for mediation in ways that might affect legal aid entitlement. Legal aid pilot schemes and practice arrangements are in the process of development and some aspects still cause concern, but hopefully will be addressed. Other new schemes are being tested, including for example, the Ancillary Relief Pilot Scheme, with its Financial Dispute Resolution procedure, which offers yet another way of avoiding long, costly and contentious family litigation. The inter-relationship between counselling, mediation and the legal process will continue to be developed.

Continuing inter-disciplinary co-operation will be necessary in this new environment. The SFLA expects to play its part in consultation with other practitioners, and meanwhile it will continue to provide traditional legal services and offer an effective, sensitive and economic resource to the public through its mediation practice.

For more information about the SFLA contact Mary I'Anson, PO Box 302, Orpington, Kent BR6 8QX or telephone 01689 850227.

Glossary of Terms

Marian Roberts

Mediation is a form of intervention in which an impartial third party, the mediator, assists the parties to a dispute to negotiate over the issues which divide them and to reach their own mutually acceptable joint decisions.

Negotiation (bilateral or multiparty) involves processes of communication, information exchange and learning which lead to adjustments of expectations and demands between two or more parties.

Bargaining refers to a series of offers and counter offers, demands and counter demands, a 'trading' of concessions. Bargaining stages may take place at a late and final phase of the negotiation process.

Arbitration involves an appeal to a third party to impose a decision because the parties themselves cannot agree. The parties invite the arbitrator to make this decision and agree to honour the decision even though it is not legally binding.

Adjudication involves a third party, the judge, imposing a decision, not by invitation of the parties as in arbitration, but by virtue of the office from which s/he derives authority. Adjudication usually follows a hearing attended by formal rules and procedures, and the parties are represented by professional advocates. The order made by the judge is in favour of one of the parties who is regarded as the winner. The loser is legally bound by the order, the implementation of which carries the authority and sanction of the court.

Lawyer Representation is a bilateral process of negotiation in which professional advisers (solicitors or barristers) act on their clients' behalf. The parties are not present and do not therefore participate in the negotiations, the pace, substance and tone of which is controlled by the lawyers.

All Issues Mediation (AIM) covers all the issues (including financial and property, as well as issues over children) that may require decision-making following family breakdown.

Advice Giving is inseparable from a partisan relationship with the client. It includes evaluation and the recommendation of a particular course (or courses) of action.

Information Giving involves maintaining a relationship of impartiality with the client(s). It involves setting out information as a resource without recommending which course of action/option to choose.

The Agreement to Mediate is a contract setting out the terms of participation in mediation for the parties and the mediator. It includes a declaration for full, frank and open disclosure and the right for either party and the mediator to withdraw from mediation at any time.

The Memorandum of Understanding is a record of the parties' proposals agreed during mediation. These are not legally binding and are recommended to be subject to the advice of solicitors. They may be converted into a legally binding agreement or a consent order.

A Parenting Plan sets out agreed arrangements relating to children in a businesslike format. This may be a formal document or a less formal one according to preference, and as well as practical details, may include explanations for children and statements of commitment to them.

Useful Names and Addresses

I. Family Mediators

Family Mediation Scotland (FMS)

127 Rose Street, South Lane, Edinburgh EH2 4BB

Tel 0131 220 1610; Fax 0131 220 6895

Family Mediation Scotland is the co-ordinating body for 12 affiliated family mediation services. Each of the local services is independent and managed locally. By affiliating to FMS, they accept FMS's affiliation criteria, Code of Practice and standards for training supervision, accreditation and registration. A number of services provide mediation on all issues; some services provide support for parents who are experiencing divorce, and support and counselling for children. FMS is approved by the Lord President of the Court of Session as a family mediation organisation. Therefore, the confidentiality of family mediation in Scotland is protected by law.

Family Mediators Association (FMA)

1 Wyvil Court, Wyvil Road, London SW8 2TG

Tel 0171 720 3336; Fax 0171 720 7999

The Family Mediators Association was founded in 1989 to offer co-mediation, drawing on and combining the skills of family law practitioners with those who possess qualifications in either counselling, family and children's social work, or family therapy. FMA has over 400 members and 39 regional groups in England and Wales which offer a comprehensive mediation service to couples about to separate or divorce. FMA members have access to post-qualification training and professional practice supervision/consultancy. FMA adheres to the UK College Code of Practice.

National Family Mediation (NFM)

9 Tavistock Place, London WC1H 9SN

Tel 0171 383 5993; Fax 0171 383 5994

National Family Mediation is the longest standing body of family mediators in the UK. It has about 70 local Family Mediation Services in England, Wales and Northern Ireland which specialise in family mediation in separation and divorce. Each local service is independently and locally managed as a charity; selection, training and accreditation are carried out nationally by NFM. Services work to NFM quality standards, mediators are supervised by trained supervisors and work to the College Code of Practice. Mediators are drawn from a range of relevant disciplines. Many services provide All Issues Mediation and all focus upon children's issues. Committed to equal opportunity.

The Solicitors Family Law Association (SFLA)

PO Box 302, Orpington, Kent BR2 6EZ

Tel 01689 850227; Fax 01689 855833

The SFLA is an association of family solicitors who work to achieve fair and amicable divorces. They work to a Code of Practice. The SFLA now trains some of its members to mediate and is developing standards in conjunction with The Law Society and the UK College of Family Mediators. A lawyer mediator cannot mediate in a situation where he or she, or his or her firm, is advising one of the parties.

BALM (The British Association of Lawyer Mediators)

The Shooting Lodge, Guildford Road, Sutton Green, Guildford, Surrey GU4 7PZ

Tel 01483 235000; Fax 01483 237004

BALM is an association of lawyers who also mediate. They may also mediate in fields other than family law. LawWise is the training arm of BALM and can be contacted at the same address.

LawGroup UK

Orbital House, 85 Croydon Road, Calerham, Surrey CR3 6PD

Tel 01833 341341; Fax 01833 340066

LawGroup provides training, marketing and support services to firms of solicitors. In family mediation it offers training, PPSC, continuous professional development and a Family Mediation Register.

CALM (Comprehensive Accredited Lawyer Mediators)

42 Carden Place, Aberdeen AB1 1UP

Tel 01224 621 622; Fax 01224 621 623

CALM is the Scottish equivalent to BALM. It has been established for longer and specialises in family mediation.

Alone in London

3rd Floor, 188 Kings Cross Road, London WC1X 9DE

Tel 0171 278 4486; Fax 0171 837 7943

Offers mediation for the homeless young to re-establish family contact.

Post Adoption

Centre 5, Torriano Mews, Torriano Avenue, London NW5 2RZ

Tel 0171 284 0555

Offers mediation on contact and other matters in open adoptions.

Mediation UK

Alexander House, Telephone Avenue, Bristol BS1 4BS

Tel 0117 904 6661; Fax 0117 904 3331

An umbrella body for community mediation schemes which deal with community and neighbour disputes.

Irish Family Mediation Service

Irish Life Centre, Lower Abbey Street, Dublin, Ireland

Tel 00 353 1 872 8277

Mediators' Institute Ireland

c/o 13 Royal Terrace West, Dun Laoghaire, Dublin, Ireland

Tel 00 353 1 284 5277; Fax 00 353 1 280 0259

Umbrella body for mediators working in different fields in Ireland.

National Association of Family Court Welfare Officers

Court Welfare Office, East House, 9 East Street, Swindon SN1 5BU

Family court welfare officers are court officers who work within the framework of the Children Act 1989 specifically to focus on the interests of the child. They are professionally trained social workers. They devise and work to Home Office standards. Many probation departments assist NFM services. Their main activities are to resolve disputes at court, write welfare reports, supervise family assistance orders and talk to children at the request of judges. In places they provide contact centres (see Community Help below). Local addresses can be obtained from county probation services.

2. Legal Services

(a) England and Wales

The Solicitors Family Law Association (SFLA)

(See above for address.) Will supply lists of solicitor members and is an association of family lawyers committed to good practice.

The Family Law Bar Association

Secretary, Queen Elizabeth Building, Temple, London EC4Y 9BS

Tel 0171 797 7837

The Law Society

113 Chancery Lane, London WC2A 1PL

Tel 0171 242 1222

The Law Society governs the professional standards of solicitors. Its Family Law Committee meets the UK College regularly.

The Legal Aid Board

85 Gray's Inn Road, London WC1X 8AA

Tel 0171 813 1000

The Legal Aid Board franchises family solicitors to provide publicly-funded legal advice and representation. When the Family Law Act is enacted there will be legal aid for mediation via franchises which are being piloted.

Handbook A

The Citizens' Advice Bureau

The Citizens' Advice Bureau keeps a list of local family solicitors and family mediators and of local services. It also provides advice (particularly on welfare benefits) and debt counselling.

Divorce and Family Courts

Most divorces are handled by district judges. Applications can be made to any county court or to The Principal Registry of Family Division, Somerset House, The Strand, London WC2R 1LP

Children's Legal Centre

University of Essex, Wivenhoe Park, Colchester CO4 3SQ

Tel 01206 873 820 (helpline)

Gives free and confidential information and advice by letter and phone on all aspects of law and policy affecting children and young people

(b) Scotland

The Family Law Association

Dorothy McGhie, Chairman, Family Law Association, Fordyce & Co, 1 Glenview Place, Main Street, Alexandria

Tel 01389 759811

This organisation can supply a list of solicitors who specialise in family law.

The Law Society of Scotland

26 Drumsheugh Gardens, Edinburgh EH3 7YR

Tel 0131 226 7411; Fax 0131 225 2934

The Law Society of Scotland governs professional standards for solicitors in Scotland. It can provide a list of solicitors in any area of Scotland and information about solicitors' fees.

The Scottish Legal Aid Board

44 Drumsheugh Gardens, Edinburgh EH3 7SW

Tel 0131 226 7061

The Scottish Legal Aid Board franchises family solicitors to provide publicly-funded legal advice and representation.

The Citizens' Advice Bureau

The Citizens' Advice Bureau keeps a list of local family solicitors and family mediators and of local services. It also provides advice (particularly on welfare benefits) and debt counselling.

Divorce and Family Courts

Most divorces are handled by the sheriff court. An initial writ should be lodged in the sheriff court which is nearest to the partner starting the action.

Scottish Child Law Centre

Cranston House, 108 Argyle Street, Glasgow G2 8BH

Business Line 0141 226 3434; Fax 0141 226 3043
Advice Line (for adults): 0141 226 3737
Freephone No. (for under-18s only): 0800 317 500

Gives free confidential information and advice on law and policy affecting children and young people. Free confidential helpline for under-18s.

3. Community Help

There is a wide range of agencies in the community to help people with family changes. Imaginative schemes have grown as more and more people become aware of the pressures and overload on families. There are groups providing help for marriage, parenting, direct services to families and to children. Sometimes these are professional services, sometimes helplines staffed by trained volunteers, sometimes clubs and courses and information providers.

(a) Special concern for separation and divorce

(i) Contact

Network of Access and Child Contact Centres

St Andrew's with Castle Gate United Reform Church, Goldsmith Street, Nottingham

NG1 5JT Tel/Fax 0115 948 4557

There are 200 centres which provide places for children to meet parents, usually on Saturdays and Sundays. They have staff on hand, toys and games and resources for preparing food and drink. These can be invaluable for parents who do not live with their children and do not have accommodation that can easily adapt to the needs of children. NACCC publishes a directory of centres and is open to provide information on Mondays, Tuesdays and Wednesdays from 10 am to 3 pm.

Network of Access & Contact Centres in Scotland

Pauline Linn, Scottish Access & Contact Centre Development Officer, Family Mediation Scotland, 127 Rose Street South Lane, Edinburgh EH2 4BB

Tel 0131 220 1610; Fax 0131 220 6895

Thomas Coram Foundation

40 Brunswick Square, London, WC1N 1AZ

This long-established children's charity provides a contact centre (and a mediation service) in central London.

(ii) Support and action

National Council for the Divorced and Separated

PO Box 519, Leicester LE2 3ZE

Tel/Fax 0116 2700595

A national network of social clubs for the separated and divorced.

Stepfamily (National Stepfamily Association)

Chapel House, 18 Hatton Place, London EC1N 8RU

Tel 0171 209 2460; Helpline 0990 168 388

Stepfamily is a membership body which provides a range of services, books and newsletter for adults and children. Its helpline is very well used.

Stepfamily Scotland

5 Coates Place, Edinburgh EH3 7AA

Tel 0131 225 8005

National Council for One Parent Families

255 Kentish Town Road, London NW5 2LX

Tel 0171 267 1361

This long-established body runs an information line, produces valuable literature and publicly represents the concerns of lone parenthood.

One Parent Families Scotland

13 Gayfield Square, Edinburgh EH1 3NX

Tel 0131 556 3899

Reunite

PO Box 4, London WC1X 3DX

Tel 0171 404 8356

Self-help for parents whose children have been abducted.

Fairshares

14 Park Road, Rugby, Warwickshire CV21 2QH

Tel 01788 570585

A group which campaigns about pensions on divorce.

MATCH (Mothers Apart from their Children)

c/o BM Problems, London WC1N 3XX

Links together mothers living apart from their children.

Families Need Fathers

Postal address: BM Families, London WC1N 3XX
Office: 134 Curtain Road, London EC2A 3AR

Tel 0171 613 5060; Helpline 0181 886 0970

Advice, support and representation for parents (particularly non-resident parents) following separation and divorce. It produces a magazine called Access .

Gingerbread

16–17 Clerkenwell Close, London EC1R OAA

Tel 0171 336 8183

A support organisation for lone parents and their families, with over 275 groups in England and Wales. It also publishes advice and information leaflets.

Gingerbread Scotland

19 Chester Street, Edinburgh EH3 7RF

Tel 0131 220 1585

Rights of Women

52–54 Featherstone Street, London EC4Y 8RT

Tel 0171 251 6577

Provides free legal advice to women.

(b) Counselling services for married and unmarried couples

Relate

Herbert Gray College, Little Church Street, Rugby CV21 3AP

Tel 01788 573 241; Fax 01788 535 007

Marriage Counselling Scotland

105 Hanover Street, Edinburgh EH2 1DJ

Tel 0131 225 5006; Fax 0131 220 0639

Marriage Care (formerly Catholic Marriage Guidance)

Clitheroe House, 1 Blythe House, Blythe Road, London W14 0NW

Tel 0171 371 1341

Scottish Catholic Marriage Care

113 Whitehouse Loan, Edinburgh EH9 1BB

Tel 0131 440 2650

London Marriage Guidance Council

76a New Cavendish Street, London W1M 7LB

Tel 0171 580 1087

Jewish Marriage Council

23 Ravenhurst Avenue, London NW4 4EE

Tel 0181 203 6314 (Advisory Service); 0181 203 6211 (Helpline); 345 581999 (Crisis Helpline)

Asian Family Counselling Service

74 The Avenue, London WC13 8LB

Tel 0181 997 5749

One Plus One

14 Theobald's Road, London WC1X 8PF

Tel 0171 831 5261; Fax 0171 831 5263

Produces research information and literature to help couples identify early signs of difficulty.

Tavistock Institute of Marital Studies

The Tavistock Centre, 120 Belsize Lane, London NW3 6BA

Provides couple and marriage therapy.

Marriage Enrichment

Inquiries to: Churches Together in England, Interchurch House, 35–41 Lower March, London SE1 7RL

Tel 0171 620 4444

FLAME (Family Life and Marriage Education)

All Saints Vicarage, 20 Burcot Lane, Bromsgrove, Worcestershire B60 1AE

(c) Direct services for children involved in separation and divorce

(i) Children's counselling

National Family Mediation

9 Tavistock Place, London WC1H 9SN

Tel 0171 383 5993; Fax 0171 383 5994

Over 12 NFM services provide a counselling or listening service for children who have experienced separation and divorce. Some also work in groups in schools.

Relateen in Northern Ireland

Relate, 76 Dublin Road, Belfast BT2 7HP

A counselling service for teenagers whose parents separate or divorce. Referrals can come from parents, teenagers or professionals. The range of provision includes one-to-one counselling for teenagers, family counselling for families with younger children and group work for teenagers.

Family Mediation Scotland

127 Rose Street South Lane, Edinburgh EH2 4BB

Tel 0131 220 1610; Fax 0131 220 6895

Three family mediation services provide counselling and support for children whose parents separate or divorce.

(ii) Services for children—children's charities

NCH Action for Children

85 Highbury Park, London N5 1UD

Tel 0171 226 2033

NCH Action for Children Scotland

17 Newton Place, Glasgow G3 7PY

Tel 0141 332 4041

NCH Action for Children is actively concerned about children in separation and divorce. It manages several Family Mediation Services within the NFM and Family Mediation Scotland framework in England, Wales and Scotland. Its family mediation services are also likely to manage counselling services for children.

Barnardo's

Tanners Lane, Barkingside, Ilford, Essex IG6 1QG

Tel 0181 550 8822

Barnardo's Scotland

235 Corstorphine Road, Edinburgh EH12 7AR

Tel 0131 334 9893; Fax 0131 316 4008

Barnardo's is a large, nationwide charity with no special focus on separation and divorce, although it has a focus on children and therefore this includes a large number of children whose parents are separated or divorced. It provides one mediation project (Chilston).

Children First (RSSPCC)

41 Polwarth Terrace, Edinburgh EH11 1NU

Tel 0131 337 8539

NSPCC

67 Saffron Hill, London EC1N 8RS

Tel 0171 825 2500

NSPCC is large and has a preventative and protection focus. It has no specific focus on separation or divorce but provides family centres and advocacy for children, work with survivors of abuse and perpetrators of abuse, provides helplines, training for listening to children and preparation for parenthood.

Children's Society

Edward Rudolf House, Margery Street, London WC1X OJL

Tel 0171 837 4299

The Children's Society identifies the same areas of work as Barnardo's, although it becomes involved in 'moral debates' because of its link to the established church. It builds school links for education for parenthood.

Young Minds

102–108 Clerkenwell Road, London EC1M 5SA

Tel 0171 336 8445; Helpline 0345 626376

Telephone service offering advice and information for parents concerned about children or young people.

(iii) Services for Children—Children's Rights

The Children's Rights Development Unit

235 Shaftesbury Avenue, London WC2H 8EL

Tel 0171 240 4449

The National Children's Bureau

8 Wakley Street, London EC1V 7QE

Tel 0171 843 6000

The groups above are concerned that English law should not be in breach of the UN Convention, article 12, ratified by the UK, nor of the European Convention (Strasbourg).

The Association of Lawyers for Children

c/o Ronald Prior & Co, 163–165 Hoe Street, Walthamstow, London E17 3AL

Tel 0181 520 5632

IRCHIN (Independent Representation for Children in Need)

1 Downham Road South, Heswall, Wirral, Merseyside L60 5RG

Tel 0151 3427852

Many 15 to 16 year olds contact IRCHIN for help on a helpline. IRCHIN works towards a comprehensive information, advice and representation service for children.

(d) Help for families and parents

The following list of organisations that offer help to families is mainly drawn from a report by the Family Policy Studies Centre of work sponsored by the Department of Health, called 'The Parenting Initiative' begun at the end of the International Year of the Family. They are here set out alphabetically.

Black Fathers

Moyenda Project, National Parenting Development Centre, Exploring Parenthood, 4 Ivory Place, 20A Treadgold Street, London W11 4PB

Tel 0171 221 4471

The Moyenda Project, run by Exploring Parenthood, runs groups that focus on black fathers and their particular cultural experience.

Child Poverty Action Group

Citizens Rights Office, 4th Floor, 1–5 Bath Street, London EC1V 9PY

Tel 0171 253 3406

Produces valuable information about benefits and poverty in families.

Family Rights Group

The Print House, 18 Ashwin Street, London E8 3DL

Tel 0171 923 2628

Especially concerned about the rights of children within the family, it provides high quality information and direct initiatives to help children in care.

Family Welfare Association

501-505 Kingsland Road, London E8 4AU

Tel 0171 254 6251

Publishes useful information and offers direct social work help to families. The association focuses on poverty issues.

Family Service Unit

207 Old Marylebone Road, London NW1 5QP

Tel 0171 402 5175

Operates in some urban areas, offering direct help to families.

Grandparents' Federation

Room 3, Moot House, The Stow, Harlow, Essex CM20 3AG

Tel 01279 444964

This organisation links grandparents and provides volunteers to help children out of care.

Home-start UK

2 Salisbury Road, Leicester LE1 7QR

Tel 0116 233 9955

Home-start UK offers local direct help with managing the overloads of family life to families in their own homes.

Newpin

Sutherland House, Sutherland Square, Walworth, London SE17 3EE

Tel 0171 703 6326

Offers seminars and groups for fathers.

Parent Link Scotland

15 Saxe Coburg Street, Edinburgh EH3 5BR

Tel 0131 332 0893

(e) Domestic violence

Women's Aid Federation

PO Box 391, Bristol BS99 7WS

(Helpline) 0345 023468

Support and advice for any woman worried by violence, whether physical or mental. Provides temporary secret refuge for women and children. There is a helpline, access to legal advice and in the refuges there are workers with a special focus on children.

Northern Ireland Women's Aid

129 University Street, Belfast BT7 1HP

Tel 01232 249041

Scottish Women's Aid

13–19 North Bank Street, The Mound, Edinburgh EH1 2LP

Tel 0131 2210401

Welsh Women's Aid

38–48 Cruwys Road, Cardiff CF2 4NN

Southall Black Sisters

52 Norwood Road, Southall UB2 4DW

Tel 0181 571 9595

Counselling and advice for Asian and black women experiencing domestic violence. The advice also covers immigration, housing and matrimonial questions.

UK COLLEGE OF FAMILY MEDIATORS

STANDARDS AND CODE OF PRACTICE

JANUARY 1998

The following abbreviations are used throughout the Standards and Guidelines:
PPSC   Professional Practice Supervisor/Consultant
ppsc   professional practice supervision/consultancy
cpd   continuing professional development

Standards for Mediators

A. In order to satisfy the requirements for *entry* on the Register of the College, mediators must demonstrate:

For Associates: that they have been selected and have completed a training course approved by the College, are practising mediation and in receipt of approved professional practice supervision/consultancy (ppsc), and

For Members: that they have also been Recommended for Membership of the College Register by an Approved Body and/or a professional practice supervisor/consultant (PPSC)

according to the following standards:

1. SELECTION FOR MEDIATION PRACTICE (before, during or after training)

(a) Successful demonstration of aptitude for mediation, namely:
> personal qualities
> interpersonal skills
> intellectual capacity
> professional ethical behaviour

(b) Commitment to continuing professional development

(c) Evidence of professional and other relevant qualifications and experience

For guidance see Guidelines2(a)-(g), pages 8-9

2. TRAINING

(a) Successful completion of family mediation training approved by the College which will include a minimum of 10 hours mediation practice (in receipt of ppsc approved by the College) within an 18 month period (subject to discretion in exceptional circumstances) and covers the requisite mediation knowledge, principles, values and skills. Applications to become an Associate can be submitted at the end of an Approved Training Course, but the Associateship cannot be renewed after 18 months if there has been no mediation practice.

See Guidelines 3(f)ii page 11

See Guidelines 3(f)i pages 9-11

(b) Achievement of satisfactory evaluation/assessment throughout and on completion of training.

3. PROFESSIONAL PRACTICE SUPERVISION/ CONSULTANCY (ppsc)

The receipt of ppsc must include all of the three following components:

i.   accountability/management functions; involving quality control of professional standards

ii.   a professional development function; involving training and continuing professional education

iii. support; for a stressful and difficult occupation.

See Guidelines 4(f)ii, page 13

See Guidelines 4i page 12

See Guidelines 6b, page 15

Completion of the required level of ppsc which includes observation of the mediator's practice and consists of a minimum of 10% of the face to face mediation hours to the satisfaction of a PPSC approved by the College, or 5% after achievement of Membership of the Register. From 1998 the PPSC must be approved by the College, have received approved training in the ppsc of family mediation, and maintain a minimum level of mediation practice consistent with Membership of the Register.

4. DEMONSTRATION OF COMPETENCE

Competence as a mediator in values, principles, skills and knowledge to the satisfaction of an assessment panel approved by the College and a minimum of 75 hours of mediation practice (transitional arrangements apply—1998, 30 hours).

As set out in Guidelines 3(f)i, pages 9-11
See Guidelines 5(e)ii(9), page 14

5. ETHICS & EQUALITY

The mediator abides by a Code of Practice approved by the College.

6. PAYMENT OF A FEE

Associates and Members must pay the annual fee and apply each year to renew their Associateship or Membership of the Register.

B. In order to satisfy the requirements for *maintaining* membership of the Register:

Associates need to demonstrate:

i.   a minimum of 10 hours mediation practice p.a. within a 3 year period

ii. 4 hours individual ppsc p.a. or 10% of face to face mediation hours, whichever is the greater

iii. 7 hours continuing professional development approved by the College

iv. appropriate Professional Indemnity Insurance

v.   payment of the fee.

Members need to demonstrate:

i.   a level of continuing mediation practice (15 hours p.a.) subject to discretion in exceptional circumstances

ii. ppsc amounting to a minimum of 2 hours individual ppsc or 5% of face to face mediation hours whichever is the greater

iii. evidence of continuing professional development (minimum of 7 hours p.a.) approved by the College

iv. that they are recommended for continuing Membership by approved PPSC

v.   appropriate Professional Indemnity Insurance

vi. payment of the fee.

See Guidelines 6.a.i
page 15

Non Practising (Special) Members

1.   Those who are unable to maintain a level of continuing mediation practice (15 hours per annum) as a result of exceptional circumstances shall be known as Non Practising Members or Associates.

2.   The exceptional circumstances are:
     (a) illness OR
     (b) pregnancy OR
     (c) geographical isolation OR
     (d) lack of practice opportunities beyond the control of the individual mediator, eg

          (i)   closure of the Service
          (ii)   disbanding of the regional group
          (iii) Practice withdrawing its mediation facility

3.   Where there are exceptional circumstances, membership or associate membership can be maintained for a period of 12 months only.

4. At the end of the 12 months period, when membership has been maintained in these exceptional circumstances,the mediator must, on again reapplying to maintain membership

    (a) have resumed practice at the required level (15 hours per annum)
    (b) have undertaken a College approved re-entry course of 5 hours training in addition to the requirement of 7 hours CPD
    (c) have obtained PPSC approval before returning to full practice
    (d) have recorded a minimum of 2 hours ppsc or 5 % of face-to-face mediation practice, whichever is the greater
    (e) have appropriate Professional Indemnity Insurance.

5. If, at the point of applying for renewal for normal membership status, less than 15 hours of practice have been completed, the Membership Committee will decide over what period the special circumstances will be deemed to have run, and at what point renewal is to be accepted.

6. In the case of Associate Members where the above exceptional circumstances apply, an additional year's grace will be allowed for completion of the requisite 10 hours face-to-face mediation or for the 18 months in which to complete training, provided that the Associateship fee and the other conditions of Associateship are maintained.

Non Practising (General) Members

1. Those who have not maintained practice from personal choice, but wish to remain members of the College shall be known as Non Practising (General) Member.

2. At the point of renewal for practising membership status:

    (a) They should have resumed practice at the required level (15 hours per annum).

    (b) They should have undertaken a College approved re-entry course, in addition to the requirement of 7 hours CPD, of
    (i)   5 hours training, after 1 year's break in practice
    (ii)   10 hours training, after 2 years' break in practice
    (iii)   15 hours training, after 3 years' break in practice

       (iv)   20 hours training, after 4 years' break in practice

(c) After more than 4 years' break in practice it will be considered necessary to apply for retraining on the Foundation Training Programme at the Associate level and thereafter make a fresh application to the College.

(d) They should have recorded a minimum of two hours ppsc in the 12 preceding months.

(e) They should have proof of appropriate Professional Indemnity Insurance.

On application, Members in this category must be reassessed as competent to resume practice by a College approved PPSC. The PPSC will need to provide justification for his/her recommendation according to the Mediator's

- length of experience
- length of time away from practice
- demonstrated commitment to CPD

TRANSITIONAL ARRANGEMENTS FOR JOINING AND MAINTAINING MEMBERSHIP OF THE REGISTER FOR 1998

Associates
- completion of an approved training programme
- ppsc to the level of 10% of practice or a minimum of 4 hours p.a.
- 7 hours cpd (encouraged but not yet mandatory)

Members
- completion of an approved training programme
- completion of 30 hours practice (including that acquired during training)
- ppsc to the level of 5% of practice or a minimum of 2 hours p.a.
- 7 hours cpd (encouraged but not yet mandatory)

Standards for Approved Bodies

Approved Bodies must meet the standards as set out below:

1. RECRUITMENT

Provide evidence that their policies and procedures for recruitment provide the widest possible access to information about entry and demonstrate consideration of gender, geographical and cultural factors in line with current legislation and the likely demand for mediation.

2. SELECTION FOR MEDIATION PRACTICE (before, during or after training)

(a) Provide demonstrable, objective procedures for assessing potential mediators for aptitude for mediation (personal qualities, interpersonal skills, intellectual capacity, professional ethical behaviour)
(b) Ensure commitment to professional development
(c) Provide evidence of the requirement for professional and other relevant qualifications and experience.

3. TRAINING

See Guidelines
3(f)ii(2), page 11

As set out in
Guidelines 3(f)i,
pages 9-11

(a) Provide training in family mediation approved by the College (to include a minimum of 10 hours mediation practice in receipt of professional practice supervision/consultancy (ppsc) and which covers mediation knowledge, principles, values and skills.
(b) Provide training delivered by trainers authorised by the Approved Body.

4. PROFESSIONAL PRACTICE SUPERVISION/ CONSULTANCY (ppsc)

(a) Authorise Professional Practice Supervisors/Consultants to provide ppsc which comprises all the following three components:

  i.   accountability/management functions: involving quality control of professional standards

  ii. a professional development function: involving training and continuing professional education

  iii. support; for a stressful and difficult occupation.

(b) Ensure that PPSC's are approved by the College, have received training in ppsc of family mediation and maintain a minimum level of practice consistent with being a Member of the Register.

5. RECOMMENDATION FOR MEMBERSHIP

Approved Bodies must provide evidence that they have a procedure for:

(a) The recommendation of individuals for Membership of the Register based on demonstrated competence as a mediator to the satisfaction of an assessment panel in the following areas:

  • Successful completion of College approved training
  • Completion of 75 hours mediation practice (after the termination of the transitional arrangements—30 hours for 1998) in receipt of ppsc
  • An outcome measure approved by the College
  • Some direct observation of mediator's practice

(b) Competence must be assessed

(c) Criteria of competence must be demonstrated

6. ETHICS & EQUALITY

(a) Demonstrate an equal opportunities policy approved by the College

(b) Satisfy the College that the responsibilities for training and Recommendation for the Register are carried out independently of each other.

7. COMPLAINTS AND DISCIPLINE

Have a Complaints & Disciplinary procedure approved by the College.

8. APPEALS

Have a written appeals procedure approved by the College available for all responsibilities.

See Guidelines 5(d), page 14
See Guidelines 5(e)(i)(2), page 14

See Guidelines 5(e)(ii)(9), page 14
See Guidelines 5(e)(i)(3), page 14
As set out in Guidelines 5(a)-(e)(i), pages 13-14
As set out in Guidelines 5(e)(ii), page 14

Guidelines to the Standards

These are expectations of quality which may be met by Individuals or Approved Bodies in ways different from those set out here, at the discretion of the College.

1. Recruitment Policies and Procedures

Approved Bodies show evidence that their policies and procedures for recruitment ensure:

(a) the widest possible access to information about entry
(b) the use of job descriptions, personnel specifications, conditions of service and other relevant information
(c) consideration of gender, geographical and ethnic factors in line with current legislation and the likely demand for mediation.

2. Selection for Mediation Practice

Potential mediators show evidence that they have been selected by an Approved Body according to the following standards:

(a) Provision in written form of selection procedure to be used.
(b) The use of a selection procedure for all applicants.
(c) A statement of aims of the selection procedure which includes:
   i. the provision of evidence of professional and other relevant qualifications and experience required by the Approved Body
   ii. the demonstration of identified personal qualities indicating:
     • aptitude for mediation
      —personal
      —interpersonal
      —intellectual capacity
      —professional and ethical behaviour
     • commitment to professional development
(d) Best Practice requires selectors to:
   i. be trained and authorised by an Approved Body to carry out the procedure adopted
   ii. be Members of the Register or persons approved by the College as suitable to select applicants
   iii. have knowledge of the relevant mediation training and context (geographical and professional).

(e) A procedure in accordance with best practice includes:
  i.   content which is specific to mediation (see 3.f.i. below)
  ii. a range of methods to include:
    • written application, references and personal statement, and/or
    • police checks for applicants being selected to undertake face to face consultation with children (if relevant), and/or
    • personal interview, and/or
    • additional exercises to identify aptitude for mediation, and/or
    • rating and recording of decisions reached by the selectors.
(f) Regular evaluation and review of selection procedure.
(g) Efficiency of procedure, e.g. timetables; ratio of selectors to applicants; timing of selection in relation to training.

3. Training

Mediators show evidence that they have been trained according to the following standards:
(a) Detailed provision in written form of training programme.
(b) Requirement that trainees must complete the whole programme (e.g. a trainee contract).
(c) A statement of aims including adherence to the College's Equal Opportunities Policy and a commitment to an Equal Opportunities perspective permeating the whole training programme.
(d) A requirement for trainers to be trained by an Approved Body or a trainer authorised by the Approved Body to carry out the training programme. (Criteria to be devised by the College.)
(e) A programme approved by the College including a minimum of 10 hours in receipt of ppsc and which covers mediation knowledge, practice principles, values and skills. *As set out in (f)i below*
  The College would not expect this to be covered in less than 105 hours (see below).
(f) A programme designed to provide quality training in the principles, knowledge and skills of family mediation.
  i.   *Core Content*
    (1) *Induction consisting of pre-course reading, information and observation*
    (2) *Principles & Values:*
       focus on needs of children
       no compulsion

Best practice for a training course would comprise induction, observation, reading, a taught course, including role play, and a minimum of 10 hours mediation practice linked to the course by ppsc.

---

joint decision-making by the parties
clarity of the process
confidentiality and privilege
impartiality of the mediator
fairness
freedom from pressure
available to all in accordance with an equal
    opportunity policy
availability at all stages of separation and divorce
issues appropriate for mediation
procedural flexibility
sufficient time for parties to use the process.

(3) *Knowledge:*

mediation theory
negotiation theory
conflict theory and management
needs of children
cultural diversity
communication theory
appropriate knowledge of family law & legal
    processes, namely:

- current legislation concerning families, family breakdown and financial support following separation and divorce, court process; rules of court (Scotland)
- Family Law Act 1996, and its changes to divorce legislation, or family law legislation in Scotland;
- legal aid legislation and its likely impact on access to and levels for legal aid;
- the range of orders relating to children contained in the Children Act 1989 and the Children (Scotland) Act 1995;
- legislation relating to pensions and divorce, the Pensions Act 1995, and any subsequent alterations and how this works in practice;
- the Child Support Act 1991, and the recent changes to it, in particular how clean break settlements are dealt with, and where the Act may not apply;
- issues regarding domestic violence, and Part IV of the Family Law Act 1996;
- knowledge of the law relating to maintenance and capital settlements;
- the Civil Evidence (Family Mediation) (Scotland) Act 1995. Evidential rules (Scotland).

family transition & psychological and social processes
    of separation and divorce

power and gender issues
dispute resolution
child protection procedures
indicators of possible child abuse
domestic violence
organisational context within which the mediator
works
College Standards & Code of Practice
(4) *Skills:*
ensuring informed participation
listening
acknowledging
managing the process
managing the conflict
questioning
summarising
communicating clearly
power balancing
facilitating the exchange of information including
option development
drafting
co-mediating where appropriate
consulting with children
recognising domestic violence
being aware of cultural diversity
self monitoring and the use of ppsc.

ii. *Practice Component*
Best training practice would comprise:
(1) links between theory and practice to assist their
integration
(2) training to include a minimum of 10 hours face-to-
face practice in receipt of ppsc, approved by the
College, within 18 months of the taught, non-
practising component of the course.
(3) ppsc by a College approved PPSC
(4) co-mediation with an experienced mediator
throughout training.
(5) practice in a quality assured setting
(6) direct observation of practice by the approved PPSC
(this can be by audio tape, video tape, live
supervision, observation by the PPSC or co-
mediating with a mediator who is approved by the
College) over a period of no less than 3 hours
comprising more than one case.

iii. *Methods of training include a mix of:*
(1) formal and appropriate expert input
(2) experiential training, i.e.
• trainer demonstration and simulation
• active experimentation (including role play and
feedback)

- structured observation
(3) audio-visual material
(4) reading
(5) written work.
(g) Regular evaluation and review of training programme.
(h) An assessment procedure of trainees which includes at least three of the following:
   i.   written work
   ii. supervisor/trainee evaluation
   iii. trainer/trainee evaluation
   iv. an approved method of peer evaluation.
(i) A contract for ppsc after training. Training should clarify the purpose of post-training ppsc as an opportunity for development.
(j) Organisational and administrative efficiency, e.g.:
   i.   high quality material
   ii. reasonable timing with good advance notice of training events
   iii. access to texts
   iv. a physical environment conducive to training.

4. Professional Practice Supervision/Consultancy

After training, mediators require ppsc from an Approved Body or ppsc approved by the College.
i.   The minimum of ppsc after training is, an average of 4 hours individual ppsc (Associates), or 2 hours (Members), or 10% (Associates) of time spent in face to face mediation, or 5% (Members).
ii. Ppsc must be maintained even if the mediator is not practising. Ppsc can combine with continuing education to ensure the maintenance of skills and understanding.
iii. Access to emergency ppsc must be available as and when required.

PPSCs must meet the following standards:
(a) Written contracts for ppsc detailing all the standards set out below with a joint expectation of commitment by both mediator and PPSC.
(b) An expectation that ppsc after training is mandatory and of a duration as set out at 4.i above and of a standard as set out at (d) below.
(c) Equal Opportunities Perspective:
   i.   PPSCs will possess knowledge, experience and skills in anti-discriminatory practice
   ii. PPSCs have a responsibility to educate themselves to ensure that they are promoting anti-discriminatory practice and not condoning discriminatory practice
   iii. training of PPSCs will include an anti-discriminatory perspective.

(Criteria for the training of PPSCs to be devised by the College)

(d) A Statement of Aims for ppsc which include that quality ppsc is an opportunity for professional development coinciding with the College's and Approved Body's concern for standards.

PPSCs will be seeking for evidence and assisting the development of:

   i.   acquisition of core family mediation skills and knowledge
   ii.   application of core family mediation skills and knowledge
   iii.   understanding of family mediation principles and values
   iv.   the ability to make the transition to the role of family mediator
   v.   the ability to cope with a range of family mediation issues
   vi.   professional development.
   vii.   positive use of ppsc.

(e) PPSCs will either belong to an Approved Body or otherwise be approved as a PPSC by the College. They will:

   i.   be Members of the Register
   ii.   have received approved training in ppsc of family mediation
   iii.   maintain a minimum level of practice consistent with retaining membership of the Register.
   iv.   if not members of an Approved Body, be approved by the College as a PPSC who can recommend mediators for Membership of the Register.

(f) *A range* of approved methods of ppsc.

   i.   Ppsc must consist of individual ppsc.
   ii.   Ppsc of each mediator requires a minimum of 3 hours direct observation of mediation practice, including more than one case, before Recommendation for Membership of the Register on the basis of competence.
   iii.   Ppsc includes monitoring of the records kept by the mediator according to the Approved Body's quality assurance standards.
   iv.   Group ppsc is recommended in addition.
   v.   Ppsc of pair working is additionally recommended.

5. Recommendation for Membership on the basis of competence

Approved Bodies or PPSCs who are approved by the College who wish to recommend mediators for Membership on the basis of competence will:

(a) Produce written descriptions of their assessment of competence procedure and its requirements leading to the recommendation for Membership of the Register.

    (b) Make known the implications of Membership of the Register.

    (c) State how the assessment procedure ensures equality of opportunity in line with the College policy (e.g. anonymity of candidate).

    (d) Appoint or ensure the use of a panel of assessors of which:
       i. 3 is the minimum number
       ii. the majority are Members of the Register and who are independent:
- from the mediator
- from the mediator's PPSC

The College will monitor the work of Assessment Panels.

    (e) Make recommendations to the College by providing assessments of individuals who comply with the standards given below:
       i. Preconditions.
         (1) Completion of College-approved training.
         (2) Completion of 75 hours in receipt of ppsc (following the implementation of Part III of the Family Law Act in England and Wales, transitional arrangements apply).
         (3) Direct observation of mediator's practice.
       ii. Criteria for Family Mediation Competence.
       Written material produced jointly by the mediator and supervisor jointly demonstrating:
         (1) acquisition and application of core mediation principles and values
         (2) acquisition and application of core mediation knowledge
         (3) acquisition and application of core skills
         (4) transition to role of mediator
         (5) capacity to deal with a range of cases
         (6) responsibility for professional development
         (7) positive use of ppsc
         (8) body of work totalling a minimum of 75 hours face to face mediation (following the implementation of Part III of the Family Law Act in England and Wales, transitional arrangements apply).
         (9) evidence of at least 8 recorded case outcomes, of which a minimum of 50% should show evidence of some agreement, or whatever outcome measure the Approved Body devises to the satisfaction of the College.
         (10) proof of the requisite ppsc.

    (f) Make clear the requirement that Membership of the Register must be maintained and be re-applied for if mediation practice lapses for more than 4 years.

    (g) Evaluate and review their assessment procedure and submit it for inspection by the College when required.

(h) Ensure administrative efficiency in:
   i.   carrying out the assessment procedure
   ii. submitting regular recommendations to the College for membership on behalf of mediators applying to them, with a minimum of delay (no longer than 3 months).
(i) Carry out any other such measures required by the College to ensure consistency of standards between Approved Bodies and between PPSCs who are Members of the Register and approved as PPSC by the College.

6.a. Maintenance of Associateship

Associateship must be maintained by:
i.   a minimum of 10 hours face to face mediation practice p.a. (subject to review). This is distinct from the 18 months to complete training.
ii.   a minimum of 4 hours ppsc p.a. or 10% of face-to-face mediation practice whichever is the greater.
iii. 7 hours of continuing professional development approved by the College.
iv.   receipt of continuing ppsc
v.   proof of appropriate Professional Indemnity Insurance

The College may make exceptions in particular circumstances.

6.b. Maintenance of Membership

Membership must be maintained by:
i.   15 hours face-to-face mediation practice p.a.
ii.   a minimum of 2 hours ppsc p.a. or 5% of face-to-face mediation practice whichever is the greater.
iii. 7 hours continuing professional development over the year.
iv.   recommendation of continuing Membership by an approved PPSC
v.   proof of appropriate Professional Indemnity Insurance.

The College may make exceptions in particular circumstances at its discretion.

7. Review of Standards and Guidelines

The Standards and Guidelines will be subject to regular review with a view to raising them as more work becomes available.

UK College of Family Mediators Code of Practice

1. DEFINITIONS

1.1 This Code of Practice applies to all family mediation conducted or offered by mediators registered by the UK College of Family Mediators.

1.2 Family mediation is a process in which an impartial third person assists those involved in family breakdown, and in particular separating or divorcing couples, to communicate better with one another and reach their own agreed and informed decisions concerning some or all of the issues relating to the separation, divorce, children, finance or property.

1.3 This Code applies whether or not there are or have been legal proceedings between any of the participants and whether or not any or all of them are legally represented.

1.4 In this Code, "mediation" means the family mediation to which this Code applies, "mediator" means any person offering such mediation, and "participant" means any family member taking part in it. The "College" means the "UK College of Family Mediators".

2. AIMS AND OBJECTIVES

2.1 Mediation aims to assist participants to reach the decisions which they consider appropriate to their own particular circumstances.

2.2 Mediation also aims to assist participants to communicate with one another now and in the future and to reduce the scope or intensity of dispute and conflict within the family.

2.3   Mediation should have regard to the principles that where a marriage or relationship has irretrievably broken down and is being brought to an end it should be brought to an end in a way which minimises distress to the participants and any children, promotes as good a relationship between the participants and any children as possible, removes or diminishes any risk of violence to any of the participants or children from the other participants, and avoids unnecessary cost to the participants.

2.4   By virtue of the Children (Scotland) Act 1995, mediators in Scotland are required to have regard to the principles contained in Part 1 of that Act on Parental Rights and Responsibilities.

2.5   By virtue of the Family Law Act 1996, mediators in England and Wales are required to have regard to the general principles set out in section 1 of that Act when exercising functions under or in consequence of it.

3. SCOPE OF MEDIATION

3.1   Mediation may cover all or any of the following matters:

   i.   options for maintaining the relationship between the adult participants and the consequences of doing so;

   ii.   with whom the children are to live; what contact they are to have with each parent and any other person such as grandparents;
         and any other aspect of parental responsibility, such as schooling and holidays;

   iii. what is to happen to the family home and any other property of the adult participants and whether any maintenance is to be paid by one to the other either for that adult or for the children;

   iv.   how any adjustments to these arrangements are to be decided upon in the future.

3.2   Participants and the mediator may agree that mediation will cover any other matters which it would be helpful to resolve in connection with any breakdown in relationships between the participants and which the mediator considers suitable for mediation.

4. GENERAL PRINCIPLES

Voluntary Participation

4.1   Participation in mediation is always voluntary. Any participant or mediator is free to withdraw at any time. If a mediator believes that any participant is unable or unwilling to participate freely and fully in the process, the mediator may raise the issue with the participants and may suspend or terminate mediation. The mediator may suggest that the participants obtain such other professional services as are appropriate.

Neutrality

4.2   Mediators must at all times remain neutral as to the outcome of mediation. They must not seek to move the participants towards an outcome which the mediator prefers, whether by attempting to predict the outcome of court proceedings or otherwise. They may, however, inform participants of possible solutions, their legal and other implications, and help participants to explore these.

Impartiality

4.3   Mediators must at all times remain impartial as between the participants. They must conduct the process in a fair and even-handed way.

4.4   Mediators must seek to prevent manipulative, threatening or intimidating behaviour by any participant. Mediators must conduct the process in such a way as to redress, as far as possible, any imbalance in power between the participants. If such behaviour or any other imbalance seems likely to render mediation unfair or ineffective, the mediator must take appropriate steps to try to prevent this, terminating mediation as necessary.

Independence and Conflicts of Interest

4.5   Mediators must not have any personal interest in the outcome of the mediation.

4.6   Mediators must not mediate in any case in which they have acquired or may acquire relevant information in any private or other professional capacity.

4.7   Mediators who have acquired information in the capacity of mediator in any particular case must not act for any participant in any other professional capacity in relation to the subject matter of the mediation

4.8   Mediation must be conducted as an independent professional activity and must be distinguished from any other professional role in which the mediator may practise.

Confidentiality

4.9   Subject to paragraphs 4.11 and 4.14 below, mediators must not disclose any information about, or obtained in the course of, a mediation to anyone, including a court welfare officer or a court, without the express consent of each participant or an order of the court.

4.10   Mediators must not discuss or correspond with any participant's legal adviser without the express consent of each participant. Nothing must be said or written to the legal adviser of one, which is not also said or written to the legal adviser of the other(s).

4.11   Where a mediator suspects that a child is in danger of significant harm, or it appears necessary so that a specific allegation that a child has suffered significant harm may be properly investigated, mediators must ensure that the local Social Services (England and Wales) or Social Work Department (Scotland) is notified.

Privilege and Legal Proceedings

4.12   Subject to paragraph 4.14 below, all discussions and negotiations in mediation must be conducted on a legally privileged basis. Participants must agree that discussions and negotiations in mediation are not to be referred to in any legal proceedings, and that the mediator cannot be required to give evidence or produce any notes or recordings made in the course of the mediation, unless all participants agree to waive the privilege or the law imposes an overriding obligation upon the mediator.

4.13   Participants must, however, agree that any factual disclosure made with a view to resolving any issue relating to their property or finances may be disclosed in legal proceedings.

4.14   In Scotland, admissibility as to what occurred during family mediation is protected by the Civil Evidence (Family Mediation) (Scotland) Act 1995 in any subsequent civil proceedings. Mediators must be aware of the exceptions to the general rules of inadmissibility, including where there are civil or criminal proceedings related to the care or protection of a child.

Welfare of Children

4.15   Mediators have a special concern for the welfare of all the children of the family. They must encourage participants to focus upon the needs of the children as well as upon their own and must explore the situation from the child's point of view.

4.16   Mediators must encourage the participants to consider their children's own wishes and feelings. Where appropriate, they may discuss with the participants whether and to what extent it is proper to involve the children themselves in the mediation process in order to consult them about their wishes and feelings.

4.17   If, in a particular case, the mediator and participants agree that it is appropriate to consult any child directly in mediation, the mediator should be trained for that purpose, must obtain the child's consent and must provide appropriate facilities.

4.18   Where it appears to a mediator that any child is suffering or likely to suffer significant harm, the mediator must advise participants to seek help from the appropriate agency. The mediator must also advise participants that whether or not they seek that help, the mediator will be obliged to report the matter in accordance with paragraph 4.11.

4.19   Where it appears to a mediator that the participants are acting or proposing to act in a manner likely to be seriously detrimental to the welfare of any child of the family, the mediator may withdraw from mediation. The reason for doing so must be outlined in any summary which may be sent to the participants' legal advisers, who may be recommended that it would be appropriate for a court welfare officer's (or other independent) report to be obtained.

Violence within the family

4.20   In all cases, mediators must discover through a screening procedure whether or not there is fear of violence or any other harm and whether or not it is alleged that any participant has been or is likely to be violent towards another. Where violence is alleged or suspected mediators must discuss whether any participant wishes to take part in mediation and information about available support services should be provided.

4.21 Where mediation does take place, mediators must uphold throughout the principles of voluntariness of participation, fairness and safety and must conduct the process in accordance with paragraph 4.4 above. In addition, steps must be taken to ensure the safety of all participants on arrival and departure.

5. QUALIFICATIONS AND TRAINING

5.1 Mediators must have successfully completed such training as is approved by the College to qualify them to mediate upon those matters upon which they offer mediation.

5.2 Mediators must be an Associate or Member of the College. They must therefore have successfully demonstrated personal aptitude for mediation (Associate and Member) and competence to mediate (Member).

5.3 Mediators must satisfy the College that they have made satisfactory arrangements for regular supervision /consultancy in relation to their professional practice with a supervisor or consultant who is a Member of or approved by the College.

5.4 Mediators must agree to maintain and improve their skills through continuing professional development courses approved by the College.

5.5 Mediators must not mediate upon any case unless they are covered by professional indemnity insurance.

5.6 Mediators must abide by the complaints and disciplinary procedures and the ethical and equality requirements as laid down by the College.

5.7 Mediators registered by the College must adhere to this Code of Practice.

6. CONDUCT OF MEDIATION

6.1 Participants must be clearly advised at the outset of the nature and purpose of mediation and of how it differs from other services, such as marriage counselling, therapy or legal representation. In particular, they must be informed of the general principles above, of the extent of the disclosure which will be required particularly in cases relating to their property and finances, of the nature and limits of the principles of confidentiality and privilege and of the mediators' special concern for the welfare of the children of the family. Each participant must be supplied with written information covering the main points in this Code and given an opportunity to ask questions about it.

6.2 Mediators must keep the possibility of reconciliation under review throughout the mediation.

6.3 The terms upon which mediation is to be undertaken should be agreed in advance. Such agreement should preferably be in writing and must be in writing where finance and property issues are involved. Such agreement must include the basis upon which any fees are to be charged and should if practicable indicate the anticipated length of the mediation. Participants must be advised to notify any legal advisers acting for them of the appointment of a mediator.

6.4 Mediators must assist participants to define the issues, identify areas of agreement, clarify areas of disagreement, explore the options and seek to reach agreement upon them.

6.5 Mediators must ensure that participants make their decisions upon sufficient information and knowledge. They must inform participants of the need to give full and frank disclosure of all material which is relevant to the issues being mediated and assist them where necessary in identifying the relevant information and any supporting documentation.

6.6 Mediators must not guarantee that any communication from one participant will be kept secret from the other(s), except that they may always agree not to disclose one participant's address or telephone number to the other(s). They may see participants separately if both agree, but if any relevant information emerges which one participant is not willing to have disclosed to the other(s), mediators must consider whether or not it is appropriate to continue with mediation.

6.7   Mediators must ensure that each participant is given the opportunity to make further enquiries about the information disclosed by any other participant and to seek further information and documentation when required. Mediators must promote the participants' equal understanding of such information before any final agreement is reached.

6.8   Mediators must make it clear that they do not themselves make further enquiries to verify the information provided by any participant; that each participant may seek independent legal advice as to the adequacy of the information disclosed before reaching a decision; that in any court proceedings a sworn affidavit, written statement or oral evidence will be required; and that authoritative calculations of liability under the Child Support Act can only be made by the Child Support Agency.

6.9   Mediators must where appropriate inform participants of the benefits of seeking the help of other professionals, including counsellors, accountants, valuers, pensions consultants and other financial advisers.

6.10   Mediators may inform participants about the court proceedings which are available, the procedures applicable to these, the nature and extent of the financial disclosure which would be required, the nature and finality of the court orders which might be made, and the broad principles of law applicable to the matter in dispute. They must not give legal or other advice. They must not predict the outcome of court proceedings in such a way as to indicate or influence the participants towards the outcome preferred by the mediators.

6.11   Mediators must inform participants of the advantages of seeking independent legal advice whenever this appears desirable during the course of the mediation. Mediators must advise participants that it is desirable in their own interests to seek independent legal advice before reaching any final agreement and warn them of the risks and disadvantages if they decide not to do so.

6.12   Whenever appropriate or required by the participants, mediators must prepare a written summary of the factual outcome of the mediation.

6.13   Mediators must ensure that agreements reached by participants are fully informed and freely made. Participants must have as good an understanding as is practicable of the consequences of their decisions foe themselves, the children of the family and other family members.

DIRECTORY

Groups/Services by Region

This section provides a listing by region of the regional groups and services of some of those organisations which make up the UK College of Family Mediators. The regions are listed in the following order: London, South East, South West, South, Midlands, East Anglia, North East, North West, Scotland, Wales and Northern Ireland. The information in this section was supplied by the individual groups and services, some of which have taken the option of providing additional details about the background and history of the group or service.

African Caribbean Family Mediation Service

Manager / Co-ordinator of Regional Group / Service: Arnold Gordon

Suite 71, Eurolink Business Centre, 49 Effra Road, Brixton, London SW2 1BZ
Telephone 0171 737 2366, Facsimile 0171 737 0637

Affiliation body: National Family Mediation

| | Year Trained | Areas of Practice | | |
		Finance	Children	All Issues
Members				
Aggrey Simela	1992	✓	✓	–
Associates				
Evangeline Bankole-Jones	1996	–	–	–
Alice Johnson-Buchanan	1995	✓	✓	–
Simeon Grosset	1996	–	–	–

Divorce, Mediation & Counselling Service

Manager / Co-ordinator of Regional Group / Service: Meredith Yates

38 Ebury Street, London SW1W 0LU
Telephone 0171 730 2422

Affiliation body: National Family Mediation

| | Year Trained | Areas of Practice | | |
		Finance	Children	All Issues
Members				
Una Cottingham	1989	–	✓	–
Sally Bentley	1996	–	✓	–
Amanda Checkley	1996	–	✓	–
Meredith Yates	1990	–	✓	–

Family Mediation (Central Middlesex)

Manager / Co-ordinator of Regional Group / Service: Jo Gillard

Civic Centre Complex, Station Road, Harrow HA1 2XH
Telephone 0181 427 2076

Affiliation body: National Family Mediation

| | Year Trained | Areas of Practice | | |
		Finance	Children	All Issues
Members				
Mary Egan	1988	–	✓	–
Ruth Fine	1995	–	✓	–
Jo Gillard	1992	–	✓	–
Stella Hutchison	1995	–	✓	–
Vinnette Melbourne	1995	–	✓	–
Jennifer Peiser	1988	–	✓	–

LAWGROUP UK
FAMILY MEDIATORS REGISTER

- ◆ LawGroup UK provides introductory, foundation and advanced training courses in family mediation throughout England and Wales.
- ◆ LawGroup UK is an Approved Body within the UK College of Family Mediators and its training is also recognised by the Law Society
- ◆ LawGroup's trainers are amongst the most experienced family mediation trainers and practising mediators in the UK.
- ◆ LawGroup's Director of Family Mediation Training, Lisa Parkinson, is known internationally as a pioneer in the field of Family Mediation.

Full members of LawGroup's Family Mediators Register:

- ◆ are experienced family lawyers in current practice as solicitors, barristers or as Members of ILEX (not necessarily in LawGroup member firms)
- ◆ have met LawGroup's criteria for family law mediators
- ◆ have successfully completed LawGroup's foundation training in family mediation, which involves formal assessment prior to admission to the Register **or**
- ◆ have successfully completed comparable mediation training with another training provider with short refresher and/or conversion training as required
- ◆ receive practical support and training from LawGroup in setting up and developing their family mediation practice and in applying for a family mediation franchise
- ◆ adhere to the UK College's Code of Practice for Family Mediators
- ◆ may offer sole or co-mediation, depending on the issues and nature of the conflict
- ◆ receive professional practice supervision and consultancy (ppsc) from experienced mediation supervisors recognised by the UK College
- ◆ undertake CPD to develop further specialist mediation skills and extend their knowledge base
- ◆ have opportunities to attend specialist lectures and workshops given by nationally known experts. These are organised by LawGroup regionally as well as in London.
- ◆ may apply for accreditation through LawGroup after meeting the requirements and standards for accreditation recognised by the UK College

Associate members of LawGroup's Family Mediators Register include family mediators (non-lawyers) with background training in counselling, family court welfare or social work and experience in family work involving children. They co-mediate with lawyer mediators on all issues, including finance and property.

Associate membership of LawGroup's Family Mediators Register is also available to those who do not meet, or do not yet meet, the requirements for full membership.

LawGroup's video, "Mediating in the Millennium" is the first British video showing a family law mediator working through different stages of the mediation process with a recently separated couple (in role-play).

For further information please contact Stephen Madge,
Head of Training:

LawGroup UK

Orbital House   Tel: 01883-370029
85 Croydon Road   Fax: 01883-370066
Caterham   DX: 36806 Caterham
Surrey CR3 6PD   E-mail: smadge@prof-group.com

Family Mediation Service: Barnet, Haringey & Hertsmere

Manager / Co-ordinator of Regional Group / Service: Val Crane

267 Ballards Lane, London N12 8NR
Telephone 0181 383 9899, Facsimile 0181 445 2446

Affiliation body: National Family Mediation

| | | Areas of Practice | | |
	Year Trained	Finance	Children	All Issues
Members				
Gloria Simmons	1988	–	✓	–
Evelyn Kennedy	1984	–	✓	–
Ines Weyland	1985	–	✓	–
Associates				
George Dawson	1995	–	✓	–

Facilities: 5 mediation rooms; separate waiting rooms; facilities for seeing children; disabled access on site

Geographical area covered: Barnet, Haringey, Hertsmere, Enfield

Areas of practice: Children Issues

Additional training undertaken by members: consultation with children; domestic violence

Languages spoken: Spanish

Experience of working with different cultures: Black Carribean; Black African; Jewish; Hindu; Moslem; Black Other; Sikh

Family Mediation Service – Institute of Family Therapy

Manager / Co-ordinator of Regional Group / Service: Alison Norton

24-32 Stephenson Way, London NW1 2HX
Telephone 0171 391 9150, Facsimile 0171 391 9169

Affiliation body: National Family Mediation

| | | Areas of Practice | | |
	Year Trained	Finance	Children	All Issues
Members				
Irene Gee	1986	✓	✓	✓
Margaret Adcock	1986	✓	✓	✓
Rose Leigh	1995	✓	✓	✓
Wendy Crisp	1988	✓	✓	✓
Di Elliott	1986	✓	✓	✓
Alan Morris	1986	✓	✓	✓
Dominic Raeside	1986	✓	✓	✓
Huguette Weiselberg	1995	✓	✓	✓
Anthony Slingsby	1993	✓	✓	✓

Facilities: 5 mediation rooms; separate waiting rooms; facilities for seeing children; disabled access on site; induction loop facilities

Geographical area covered: London and South East England

(cont'd)

Areas of practice: Finance Issues; Children Issues; All Issues

Areas of specialism: consultation with children; high income

Courses provided: conflict resolution skills; impact of divorce on children; information for solicitors; observation slots

Additional training undertaken by members: consultation with children; domestic violence; initial information giving and/or assessment; mediator trainer training; Professional Practice Supervision/Consultancy

Languages spoken: Hebrew; French

Interpreters available ✓

Experience of working with different cultures: Jewish; French speaking

The Family Mediation Service was founded in 1984 by family therapists at the Institute of Family Therapy in London, who were aware that the problems presented by many of the children in the families we were seeing related to their parents' separation. The service has developed into a multi-disciplinary, mixed-gender team of family solicitors and family mediators, with professional backgrounds in child guidance, law, guardian ad litem, probation and welfare rights. All are fully trained and experienced mediators, who have worked together for many years. We offer mediation over the whole range of issues that couples may bring: helping couples come to terms with the end of the marriage; child centred mediation – helping parents focus on the children's needs when planning the future for their children and themselves; direct consultation with children; financial mediation: family home, property, capital, maintenance. We are situated in central London, a minute's walk from Euston Station, in a modern building with disabled access. The Institute has well-appointed interview rooms that are comfortable and welcoming and there are separate waiting areas for those who prefer it.

■ London South & Central Family Mediators Association

Manager / Co-ordinator of Regional Group / Service: Hazel Wright

Columbia House, 69 Aldwych, London WC2 4RW
Telephone 0171 242 0422, Facsimile 0171 831 9081, DX 250 LDE
LONDON/CHANCERY LANE

Affiliation body: Family Mediators Association

		Areas of Practice		
	Year Trained	Finance	Children	All Issues
Members				
Jeremy Abraham	1992	✓	✓	✓
William Ackroyd	1990	✓	✓	✓
Kim Beatson	1989	✓	✓	✓
Elisabeth Cliff	1991	✓	✓	✓
Judy Cunnington	1992	✓	✓	✓
Stuart Delve	1992	✓	✓	✓
Elisabeth Edwards	1994	✓	✓	✓
Pauline Fowler	1992	✓	✓	✓
Irene Gee		✓	✓	✓

(cont'd)

	Year Trained	Areas of Practice		
		Finance	Children	All Issues
Peter George	1992	✓	✓	✓
Rosemary Guest	1992	✓	✓	✓
Irena Hill	1991	✓	✓	✓
Frances Hughes	1989	✓	✓	✓
Rhiannon Lewis	1991	✓	✓	✓
Simon Pigott	1989	✓	✓	✓
Dominic Raeside	1990	✓	✓	✓
Sara Robinson	1991	✓	✓	✓
Ruth Smallacombe	1991	✓	✓	✓
Anne-Lise Wall	1992	✓	✓	✓
Eileen Walsh	1989	✓	✓	✓
Colin Webb	1995	✓	✓	✓
Hazel Wright	1992	✓	✓	✓
Associates				
Paul Butner		✓	✓	✓
Geraldine Mushett		✓	✓	✓
Patrick Quinn	1995	✓	✓	✓
Clare Renton	1995	✓	✓	✓

■ London South & West Family Mediators Association

Manager / Co-ordinator of Regional Group / Service: Elizabeth Muirhead

11b Colbeck Mews, London SW7 4LX
Telephone 0171 835 1292, Facsimile 0171 373 5088, DX 11704
CHELSEA 2

Affiliation body: Family Mediators Association

■ Mediation for Families (East London & City)

Manager / Co-ordinator of Regional Group / Service: Hazel Chowcat

2nd Floor, 74 Great Eastern Street, London EC2A 3JL
Telephone 0171 613 1666, Facsimile 0171 613 1666

Affiliation body: National Family Mediation

	Year Trained	Areas of Practice		
		Finance	Children	All Issues
Members				
Leasa Lambert	1992	–	✓	✓
Myrna Lazarus	1992	–	✓	✓
Gail Neill	1993	–	✓	–
Linda Peffer	1992	–	✓	✓
Aggrey Simela	1993	–	✓	–
Eldred Williams	1992	–	✓	✓

▪ Mediation in Divorce

Manager / Co-ordinator of Regional Group / Service: Jane Mallinson

13 Rosslyn Road, East Twickenham, Middlesex TW1 2AR
Telephone 0181 891 6860/3107

Affiliation body: National Family Mediation

	Year Trained	Areas of Practice		
		Finance	Children	All Issues
Members				
Gill Cashdon	1986	✓	✓	✓
Margaret Crabtree	1996	✓	✓	✓
Patricia Gunningham	1991	✓	✓	✓
Ann Milroy	1992	✓	✓	✓
Caroline Morcom	1989	✓	✓	✓
Margaret Pendlebury	1993	✓	✓	✓
Christopher Richards	1989	✓	✓	✓
June Smale-Adams	1986	✓	✓	✓

▪ NCH Action for Children Eye to Eye Mediation

Manager / Co-ordinator of Regional Group / Service: Vicky Leach

231 Camberwell New Road, London SE5 0TH
Telephone 0171 701 1114/703 2532, Facsimile 0171 703 6129

Affiliation body: National Family Mediation

	Year Trained	Areas of Practice		
		Finance	Children	All Issues
Members				
Vicky Leach	1984	–	✓	–
Fred Gibbons	1978	–	✓	–
Irena Hill	1990	–	✓	–
Gail Neill	1993	–	✓	–
Michael Williamson	1995	–	✓	–
Javed Ali	1995	–	✓	–
Saeeda Short	1995	–	✓	–
Lorraine Schaffer	1995	–	✓	–
Katherine Stylianou	1995	–	✓	–
Arthur Charlton	1996	–	✓	–
Colin Webb	1996	–	✓	–
Anthony Phillips	1996	–	✓	–
David Walker	1997	–	✓	–

Facilities: 3 mediation rooms; separate waiting rooms; facilities for seeing children; off site disabled access arrangements can be made; induction loop facilities; emergency alarm system

Geographical area covered: All inner London boroughs

Areas of practice: Children Issues

Areas of specialism: consultation with children; 'Child's Eye' service

Courses provided: conflict resolution skills; impact of divorce on children; information for solicitors; children's service

(cont'd)

Additional training undertaken by members: consultation with children; domestic violence; initial information giving and/or assessment; Professional Practice Supervision/Consultancy; child protection; equal opportunities; ADP; States of Mind – The Dynamics of Divorce

Languages spoken: French; Greek; Italian; Urdu

Interpreters available ✓

Experience of working with different cultures: Black Carribean; Black African; Black Other; Moslem; Arabian; Multi-cultural mediation team

'Eye to Eye' Mediation was first established as a partnership between NCH Action for Children and Inner London Probation Service in 1994. We provide child-focused mediation services for the families of inner London.

'Eye to Eye' recognises that every family is unique. Our service is committed to the interests of children and parents, in particular, to respecting their dignity, needs, privacy, culture and beliefs. We are a Legal Aid Pilot franchised service.

'Eye to Eye' Mediation provides a safe, confidential and neutral place where parents and other family members in conflict can meet to discuss issues relating to children. We assist clients to work out their own solutions in the best interests of their children, and ensure equality of opportunity to all service users. Anti-discriminatory practice is an integral part of our work. We operate a consumer complaints and representation policy.

'Eye to Eye' employs 14 experienced mediators drawn from a diversity of ethnic backgrounds The project manager is an accredited mediator. All practitioners have completed NFM/FMA training. We specialise in 'child focused' mediation, and offer a specialist child counselling service, 'Child's Eye'. We anticipate offering an 'All Issues' service in 1998/99.

North & Central London Family Mediation Service

Manager / Co-ordinator of Regional Group / Service: Jane Butler

(for correspondence only), 26A Edis Street, London NW1 8LE
Telephone 0171 813 5943

Affiliation body: Family Mediators Association

		Areas of Practice		
	Year Trained	Finance	Children	All Issues
Members				
Ruth Bross	1990	✓	✓	✓
Henry Brown		✓	✓	✓
Wendy Crisp	1988	✓	✓	✓
Felicity Crowther	1989	✓	✓	✓
David Du Pre	1992	✓	✓	✓
Anna Henderson	1991	✓	✓	✓
Mary Kane	1988	✓	✓	✓
Simone Katzenberg	1993	✓	✓	✓

(cont'd)

London Marriage Guidance

Working with Couples

THE SERVICE FOR COUPLES

We provide counselling for couples or individual partners, both married and unmarried, who are:-

◇   trying to maintain their relationship/marriage
◇   going through difficulties in their relationship
◇   considering separation/divorce
◇   considering co-habitation/marriage

For more information or a preliminary session telephone 0171 580 1087

Appointments are available in the West End within 1-3 weeks

THE TRAINING FOR COUNSELLORS

◇   **Foundation Course***
       in Psychodynamic Marital and Couple Counselling   2 terms
                                                            (Jan - June)

◇   **Diploma Course***
       in Psychodynamic Marital and Couple Counselling   3 years
                                                            (September)

           * Accredited by BAC
           * Validated by Roehampton Institute

Short courses can be designed to suit specific requirements

For more information on all courses, please contact Heather Williamson
on 0171 637 1318

London Marriage Guidance Council
76a New Cavendish Street London W1M 7LB
Registered Charity No 208166

	Year Trained	Areas of Practice Finance	Children	All Issues
Jaqueline Klarfeld	1988	✓	✓	✓
Peter Martin	1992	✓	✓	✓
Suzy Power	1991	✓	✓	✓
Gloria Simmons	1991	✓	✓	✓
Jean Stogdon	1988	✓	✓	✓
Janet Tresman	1990	✓	✓	✓
Yvette Walczak	1988	✓	✓	✓
Ines Weyland	1991	✓	✓	✓
Cynthia Zneimer	1991	✓	✓	✓
Associates				
Anne Aitken	1995	✓	✓	✓
Sarah Anticoni	1995	✓	✓	✓
Jane Butler	1995	✓	✓	✓
Jayne Gilbert	1993	✓	✓	✓
Lea Harris	1996	✓	✓	✓
Kay Jones	1993	✓	✓	✓
Margaret Kelly	1995	✓	✓	✓
Susan Maidment	1995	✓	✓	✓
Jane Klauber	1996	✓	✓	✓

Facilities: 14 mediation rooms; separate waiting rooms; facilities for seeing children; disabled access on site; off site disabled access arrangements can be made; various central and widespread locations in North and Central London

Geographical area covered: North and Central London

Areas of practice: Finance Issues; Children Issues; All Issues

Areas of specialism: consultation with children; high income; wide variety of experience and skills

Courses provided: conflict resolution skills; impact of divorce on children; divorce experience course; parenting information; information for solicitors; service is willing to provide other courses subject to consultation

Additional training undertaken by members: consultation with children; domestic violence; mediator trainer training; Professional Practice Supervision/Consultancy; advanced mediation skills

Languages spoken: French; Polish; Spanish

Interpreters available ✓

Experience of working with different cultures: Black Carribean; Black African; Black Other; Jewish; Hindu; Sikh; Moslem; Arabian

▪ Penningtons Mediation Group

Manager / Co-ordinator of Regional Group / Service: Emma Harte

Bucklersbury House, 83 Cannon Street, London EC4N 8PE
Telephone 0171 457 3000, Facsimile 0171 457 3240, DX 98946
CHEAPSIDE 2, E-mail harteek@penningtons.co.uk

(cont'd)

Affiliation body: Family Mediators Association; Solicitors Family Law Association

		Areas of Practice		
	Year Trained	Finance	Children	All Issues
Members				
Henry Brown	1985	✓	✓	✓
Associates				
Susan Philips	1996	✓	✓	✓
Emma Harte	1997	✓	✓	✓

Facilities: 4 mediation rooms; fax; e-mail; extensive library; networking in the UK and abroad

Geographical area covered: UK and international

Areas of practice: All Issues

Areas of specialism: high income

Additional training undertaken by members: mediator trainer training; Professional Practice Supervision/Consultancy

PMG Information

The Penningtons Mediation Group (PMG) represents a commitment by the law firm Penningtons to offer mediation (sole or co-mediation) as a distinct alternative to the traditional legal process that it provides on separation and divorce.

The Group comprises:

Henry Brown: Experienced solicitor and family and commercial mediator. Trained with John Haynes in US (1985). Member of the All Issues pilot scheme 'Solicitors in Mediation' (1985-8) and co-founder of FMA (1988). Author of the Law Society's ADR Report (1991) and co-author of *ADR Principles and Practice*. Extensive training experience in the UK and abroad. Co-established the SFLA's mediation training and practice programme. Has Certificate in Fundamentals of Psychotherapy and Counselling.

Susan Philipps: Experienced family solicitor, heads Penningtons family law department. SFLA trained mediator and member of the SFLA's Education Committee and Mediation Committee.

Emma Harte: Senior solicitor in Penningtons family law department. SFLA trained mediator and member of its Mediation Committee. Has written articles on various aspects of family law.

Members of the PMG have extensive experience in dealing with issues that arise on separation and divorce, including children's issues, substantial and complex property, financial and trust aspects, and all other issues that people going through matrimonial breakdown may raise.

South East London Family Mediation Bureau

Manager / Co-ordinator of Regional Group / Service: Frederick Henry Gibbons

5 Upper Park Road, Bromley BR1 3HN
Telephone 0181 460 4606, Facsimile 0181 466 6572

Affiliation body: National Family Mediation

		Areas of Practice		
	Year Trained	Finance	Children	All Issues
Members				
Marian Roberts	1982	–	✓	–
Daphne Booker	1982	–	✓	✓
Francoise Grimshaw	1982	–	✓	–
Sonia Bufton	1979	–	✓	–
Mary Winner	1984	–	✓	✓
Vicky Leach	1984	–	✓	–
Fred Gibbons	1979	–	✓	–
Di Elliott	1984	–	✓	✓
Graham Jones	1993	–	✓	✓
Katherine Stylianou	1995	–	✓	✓
Colin Webb	1996	–	✓	✓
Arthur Charlton	1996	✓	✓	–
Associates				
Donna Harris	1993	–	✓	–
Peter Coupe	1993	–	✓	–
Geoffrey Claughton	1996	–	✓	✓

The Family Law Consortium

Manager / Co-ordinator of Regional Group / Service: Ruth Smallacombe

2 Henrietta Street, London WC2E 8PS
Telephone 0171 420 5000, Facsimile 0171 420 5005, DX 40012
COVENT GARDEN, E-mail flc@tflc.co.uk

Affiliation body: Family Mediators Association

		Areas of Practice		
	Year Trained	Finance	Children	All Issues
Members				
Gillian Bishop	1995	✓	✓	✓
David Hodson	1997	✓	✓	✓
Dominic Raeside	1990	✓	✓	✓
Sara Robinson	1990	✓	✓	✓
Ruth Smallacombe	1990	✓	✓	✓

Facilities: 2 mediation rooms; separate waiting rooms; facilities for seeing children; off site disabled access arrangements can be made

Geographical area covered: South East England, UK, worldwide

Areas of practice: All Issues

(cont'd)

Areas of specialism: consultation with children; high income; international

Courses provided: divorce experience course; information for solicitors; practice management consultancy; presentations

Additional training undertaken by members: consultation with children; domestic violence; initial information giving and/or assessment; mediator trainer training; Professional Practice Supervision/Consultancy; anti-discriminatory practice; welfare benefits

Experience of working with different cultures: Black Carribean; Black African; Black Other; Jewish; Hindu; Sikh; Moslem; Arabian

The Family Law Consortium

Established in 1995 by specialist family law solicitors, mediators and counsellors, committed to responding sensitively to the needs of separating and divorcing couples, The Family Law Consortium was the first multi-disciplinary service to offer access to mediation, counselling, legal advice and representation under one roof. Our comprehensive mediation service, run by accredited mediators from the legal and therapeutic professions, provides a constructive way for complex financial and children's issues to be resolved. Also on site we offer personal counselling for individuals or couples at any stage of separation or divorce and help for parents (and their children). An intake interview may be arranged to give information, explore options and assess eligibility for legal aid.

As mediators we work to high standards within FMA's Code of Practice We have many years' experience mediating a wide range of family issues. Several members of the team are mediation trainers and supervisors. Authors on mediation and family law and at the forefront of mediation practice, individuals participate in the UK College, FMA, SFLA, BALM and leading counselling organisations. Our service holds a Legal Aid Board Mediation Certificate. We offer consultancy to other professionals in developing innovative practices.

Clients of The Family Law Consortium will benefit from specialist mediation by highly experienced and qualified practitioners in addition to other professional services, tailored to their needs.

■ Bedford Family Mediators Association

Manager / Co-ordinator of Regional Group / Service: Stephen Holmes

Dixon House, 77-97 Harpur Street, Bedford, Bedfordshire MK40 2SY
Telephone 01234 353221, Facsimile 01234 353808, DX 5607 BEDFORI

Affiliation body: Family Mediators Association

■ Chiltern Family & Mediation Centre

Manager / Co-ordinator of Regional Group / Service: David Harris, Denise Bennett

1 King George V Road, Amersham, Buckinghamshire HP6 5TT
Telephone 01494 732782, Facsimile 01494 732783

(cont'c

Affiliation body: National Family Mediation

		Areas of Practice		
	Year Trained	Finance	Children	All Issues
Members				
Denise Bennett	1988	✓	✓	✓
Elizabeth Walsh	1995	✓	✓	✓
David Harris	1995	✓	✓	✓

■ Divorce Mediation Group

Manager / Co-ordinator of Regional Group / Service: Simon Pigott

16 Red Lion Square, London WC1R 4QT
Telephone 0171 404 2323, Facsimile 0171 831 0478, DX 35725
BLOOMSBURY

Affiliation body: Family Mediators Association

		Areas of Practice		
	Year Trained	Finance	Children	All Issues
Members				
John Cornwell	1988	–	–	✓
Irene Gee	1989	–	–	✓
Frances Hughes	1990	–	–	✓
Rhiannon Lewis	1992	–	–	✓
Brenda McHugh	1993	–	–	✓
Diana Parker	1988	–	–	✓
Simon Pigott	1989	–	–	✓
Dominic Raeside	1990	–	–	✓
Sara Robinson	1992	–	–	✓

Geographical area covered: London

Areas of practice: All Issues

Areas of specialism: consultation with children; high income;

Additional training undertaken by members: initial information giving and/or assessment

History of DMG
The Divorce Mediation Group was founded in 1993 to provide all issues mediation to couples with high service expectations who want to deal with professionals they respect.

All the members of the group are experienced mediators, trained by the Family Mediators Association to practise the co-mediation model. The Family Law specialists are practising solicitors who are recognised authorities on family law. The family systems specialists are members of the United Kingdom Council for Psychotherapy. All have impressive credentials.

They can be contacted on the Divorce Mediation Group telephone line or direct on the following numbers:

Family Law specialists: John Cornwell 0171 242 2556; Frances Hughes 0171 551 7777; Rhiannon Lewis 0171 242 2556; Diana Parker

(cont'd)

0171 936 1000; Simon Pigott 0171 242 7363; Sara Robinson 0171 420 5000

Family systems specialists: Irene Gee 0181 444 9832; Brenda McHugh 0171 704 6112; Dominic Raeside 0171 420 5000

A brochure is available on request.

■ Essex Family Mediators Association

Manager / Co-ordinator of Regional Group / Service: Margaret H Ridley

56 London Road, Southend-on-Sea SS1 1QQ
Telephone 01702 337315/466666, Facsimile 01702 431438, DX 2805 SOUTHEND

Affiliation body: Family Mediators Association

	Year Trained	Finance	Areas of Practice Children	All Issues
Members				
Margaret H Ridley	1992	✓	✓	✓
Gillian Roberts	1992	✓	✓	✓
Colin Smith	1995	✓	✓	✓
Associates				
Jenny Dutton	1993	✓	✓	✓
Priscilla Hall	1995	✓	✓	✓
Madeline Harmer	1995	✓	✓	✓
Howard E Kemp	1995	✓	✓	✓
Kate Taylor	1993	✓	✓	✓
Pat Taylor	1992	✓	✓	✓

■ Family Mediation in Sussex

Manager / Co-ordinator of Regional Group / Service: Penelope Dunne

6 West Drive, Queen's Park, Brighton, East Sussex BN2 2GD
Telephone 01273 621121, Facsimile 01273 621231, DX 2742 BRIGHTON 1

Affiliation body: Family Mediators Association

	Year Trained	Finance	Areas of Practice Children	All Issues
Members				
Jeremy Buckwell	1989	✓	✓	✓
Penelope Dunne	1990	✓	✓	✓
Mary Field	1989	✓	✓	✓
Ian Garner	1992	✓	✓	✓
Wendy Lidster	1989	✓	✓	✓
Sue Swift	1991	✓	✓	✓
Adam Taylor	1992	✓	✓	✓

TELEPHONE HELPLINE
to see you through the hard times

SEARCHING FOR A SOLUTION TO A PARTNERSHIP PROBLEM?

LOOKING FOR PRACTICAL INFORMATION OR PERSONAL ADVICE?

WANTING YOUR RELATIONSHIP TO CHANGE?

Volunteers are trained to listen sympathetically
whatever the problem is

RING
0345 573 921
LINES OPEN
MONDAYS AND THURSDAYS
3 P.M. - 9 P.M.

**For the price of a local call you can talk
to someone in confidence about
your relationship problems**

Marriage Care is a national charity serving the whole community
For more information contact: **Marriage Care**, Clitherow House, 1 Blythe Mews,
Blythe Road, London W14 0NW Registered Charity : 218159

Kent Family Mediation Service

Manager / Co-ordinator of Regional Group / Service: Lesley Gorlov

8 Park Road, Sittingbourne, Kent ME10 1DR
Telephone 01795 429689/476949, Facsimile 01795 429689

Affiliation body: National Family Mediation

		Areas of Practice		
	Year Trained	Finance	Children	All Issues
Members				
Ian Butlin	1984	–	✓	✓
Polly Read	1986	–	✓	–
Olive Hammock	1989	–	✓	–
Sharon Cavanagh	1993	–	✓	✓
Graham Jones	1994	–	✓	✓
Marshall Pearce	1994	–	✓	–
Carol O'Meara	1994	–	✓	–
Kathryn Lee	1994	–	✓	✓
Dawn Harrison	1996	–	✓	✓

Kent Family Mediators Association

Manager / Co-ordinator of Regional Group / Service: Sue Swift

Pimlico Cottage, Mark Cross, East Sussex TN6 3PF
Telephone 01892 783207, Facsimile 01892 783207

Affiliation body: Family Mediators Association

		Areas of Practice		
	Year Trained	Finance	Children	All Issues
Members				
Ian Garner	1992	–	–	✓
Graham Holleyman	1992	–	–	✓
Mark Leeson	1995	–	–	✓
Mary Stuart-Smith	1992	–	–	✓
Sue Swift	1991	–	–	✓
Susan Tilley	1993	–	–	✓
Barbara Wright	1992	–	–	✓
Karen Green	1994	–	–	✓
Associates				
Nicky Howe	1996	–	–	✓
Lorna Samuels	1996	–	–	✓
Derek Alexander	1997	–	–	✓
Nikki Chesterman	1997	–	–	✓
Sonja Jenkins	1995	–	–	✓
Indra Pucknell	1997	–	–	✓

Mediation for Families (Thames Valley and Central London)

Manager / Co-ordinator of Regional Group / Service: Valerie Anne
Kleanthous

(cont'd)

Thatchways, Bridle Lane, Loudwater, Rickmansworth, Hertfordshire
WD3 4JG
Telephone 01923 777739, Facsimile 01923 897618, E-mail
val_kleanthous@link.org

Affiliation body: Family Mediators Association

| | | Areas of Practice | | |
	Year Trained	Finance	Children	All Issues
Members				
Susan Andrews	1997	✓	✓	✓
Denise Bennett	1993	✓	✓	✓
Valerie Kleanthous	1989	✓	✓	✓
Marion Scourfield	1995	✓	✓	✓
Elizabeth Walsh	1994	✓	✓	✓

Facilities: 4 mediation rooms; separate waiting rooms; facilities for
seeing children; off site disabled access arrangements can be made

Geographical area covered: Herts; Bucks; Thames Valley; Central
London

Areas of practice: Finance Issues; Children Issues; All Issues

Areas of specialism: high income; mediation with Jewish and Greek
couples

Courses provided: information for solicitors; Introduction to Mediation

Additional training undertaken by members: consultation with
children; domestic violence; mediator trainer training; Professional
Practice Supervision/Consultancy

Languages spoken: Greek

Experience of working with different cultures: Black Carribean; Black
African; Black Other; Jewish; Hindu; Sikh; Moslem

▪ Mid-Essex Family Mediation Service

Manager / Co-ordinator of Regional Group / Service: Beryle Cornell

47 Broomfield Road, Chelmsford, Essex CM1 1SY
Telephone 01245 356256, Facsimile 01245 356241

Affiliation body: National Family Mediation

▪ Milton Keynes Family Mediation

Manager / Co-ordinator of Regional Group / Service: Dawn Ashby

City Counselling Centre, 320 Saxongate West, Central Milton Keynes
MK9 2ES
Telephone 01908 231293

Affiliation body: National Family Mediation

| | | Areas of Practice | | |
	Year Trained	Finance	Children	All Issues
Members				
Paul Clifford	1992	–	✓	–

(cont'd)

		Areas of Practice		
	Year Trained	Finance	Children	All Issues
Mary Lindsay	1992	–	✓	–
Alison Norton	1994	–	✓	–
Associates				
Dot Lucas	1993	–	✓	–
Sue George	1994	–	✓	–

▨ South Essex Family Mediation Service

Manager / Co-ordinator of Regional Group / Service: Audrey Stirling

29 Harcourt Avenue, Southend-on-Sea SS2 6HT
Telephone 01702 436466, Facsimile 01702 436466

Affiliation body: National Family Mediation

		Areas of Practice		
	Year Trained	Finance	Children	All Issues
Members				
Angela Allen	1994	–	✓	–
Sue Giffin	1994	–	✓	–

▨ Surrey Family Mediation Service

Manager / Co-ordinator of Regional Group / Service: Christopher Richards

316 High Street, Dorking, Surrey RH4 1QX
Telephone 01306 741777, Facsimile 01306 741383

Affiliation body: National Family Mediation

		Areas of Practice		
	Year Trained	Finance	Children	All Issues
Members				
Jenny Baldrey	1989	✓	✓	✓
Sally Gandon	1994	✓	✓	✓
Yvonne Payne	1993	✓	✓	✓
Christopher Richards	1988	✓	✓	✓
Laurence Singer	1995	✓	✓	✓
Virginia Thorpe	1994	–	✓	–
Margaret Vincent	1991	✓	✓	✓
Mary Winner	1986	✓	✓	✓

▨ Surrey & North Hampshire Family Mediators Association

Manager / Co-ordinator of Regional Group / Service: Sally Ann Gandon

10-12 Massetts Road, Horley, Surrey RH6 7DE
Telephone 01483 888370, Facsimile 01293 785642, DX 200402 HORLEY

Affiliation body: Family Mediators Association

(cont'd)

	Year Trained	Areas of Practice		
		Finance	Children	All Issues
Members				
Tricia Brinton	1989	✓	✓	✓
Eileen Whicker	1989	✓	✓	✓
Ruth Smallacombe	1990	✓	✓	✓
Julia Frimond	1990	✓	✓	✓
Elizabeth Perring	1992	✓	✓	✓
Anne Borghgraef	1991	✓	✓	✓
Sally Gandon	1991	✓	✓	✓
Francoise Grimshaw	1996	✓	✓	✓
Associates				
Ann Hellin	1995	✓	✓	✓
Jenny Schmit	1994	✓	✓	✓
Anne Bell	1996	✓	✓	✓
Neil Dawson	1994	✓	✓	✓
Indra Pucknell	1997	✓	✓	✓
Rama Sekhawat	1997	✓	✓	✓

■ Sussex Family Mediation Service

Manager / Co-ordinator of Regional Group / Service: Jean Mary Craggs

Garton House, 22 Stanford Avenue, Brighton BN1 6AA
Telephone 01273 550563, Facsimile 01273 555412

Affiliation body: National Family Mediation

	Year Trained	Areas of Practice		
		Finance	Children	All Issues
Members				
Richard Best	1993	✓	✓	✓
Jean Craggs	1986	–	✓	–
Mike Lloyd	1989	✓	✓	✓
Sue Knight	1991	✓	✓	✓
Ann Mehlig	1991	✓	✓	✓
Barbara Wilson	1991	✓	✓	✓
Jenny Baldrey	1989	✓	✓	✓
Ian Butlin	1986	✓	✓	✓
Associates				
Debbie Shannahan	1993	✓	✓	✓

■ Sussex Family Mediators Association

Manager / Co-ordinator of Regional Group / Service: Jeremy Buckwell

3 Pavilion Parade, Brighton BN2 1RY
Telephone 01273 621121, Facsimile 01273 621231, DX 2727
BRIGHTON 1

Affiliation body: Family Mediators Association

(cont'd)

| | Year Trained | Areas of Practice | | |
		Finance	Children	All Issues
Members				
Jeremy Buckwell	1989	✓	✓	✓
Penelope Dunne	1990	✓	✓	✓
Mary Field	1989	✓	✓	✓
Ian Garner	1992	✓	✓	✓
Wendy Lidster	1989	✓	✓	✓
Adam Taylor	1992	✓	✓	✓
Ruth Hindley	1992	✓	✓	✓
Associates				
Peter Bailey	1993	✓	✓	✓
Madeleine Richardson	1995	✓	✓	✓
Richard Thompson	1993	✓	✓	✓
Orla O'Hagan	1997	✓	✓	✓
Phillipa Cannan	1992	✓	✓	✓

Thames Valley Family Mediation

Manager / Co-ordinator of Regional Group / Service: David Harris

Windsor Magistrates Court, Alma Road, Windsor, Berkshire SL4 3HD
Telephone 01753 830770, Facsimile 01753 830770

Affiliation body: National Family Mediation

| | Year Trained | Areas of Practice | | |
		Finance	Children	All Issues
Members				
Auriol Ashley	1993	✓	✓	✓
Sioux Baker	1992	✓	✓	✓
Denise Bennett	1989	✓	✓	✓
Laurence Singer	1994	✓	✓	✓
Elizabeth Walsh	1995	✓	✓	✓
Christopher Richards	1989	✓	✓	✓
David Harris	1995	✓	✓	✓

Thames Valley Family Mediators Association

Manager / Co-ordinator of Regional Group / Service: Stephanie Mary
Alderwick

105 Oxford Road, Reading RG1 7UD
Telephone 01734 393999, Facsimile 01734 594072, DX 40114
READING

Affiliation body: Family Mediators Association

| | Year Trained | Areas of Practice | | |
		Finance	Children	All Issues
Members				
Auriol Ashley	1993	✓	✓	✓
Tricia Brinton	1980	✓	✓	✓
Andrew Don	1990	✓	✓	✓

(cont'd)

	Year Trained	Areas of Practice		
		Finance	Children	All Issues
Julie Weedon	1993	✓	✓	✓
Alan Williams	1995	✓	✓	✓
Associates				
Stephanie Alderwick	1993	✓	✓	✓
Christine Craddock	1993	✓	✓	✓
Martin Kelly	1993	✓	✓	✓
Theresa Lee	1993	✓	✓	✓
Seona Myerscough		✓	✓	✓
Wendy Klein	1996	✓	✓	✓
Judi Lyons	1996	✓	✓	✓

The Hertfordshire Comprehensive Mediation Service

Manager / Co-ordinator of Regional Group / Service: Steven Jacob

90 Stroud Green Road, London N4 3EN
Telephone 0181 292 2525, Facsimile 0181 292 3378, DX 57478
FINSBURY PARK

Affiliation body: Family Mediators Association

	Year Trained	Areas of Practice		
		Finance	Children	All Issues
Members				
Robin Blandford	1986	–	✓	✓
Rosemary Savage		–	–	✓
Valerie Kleanthous		–	–	✓
Denise Bennett		–	✓	✓
Associates				
Marion Scourfield		–	✓	✓
Dennis Sheridan	1994	–	–	✓
John Payne		–	–	✓
Louise Amswych		–	–	✓
Lin Cronin		–	–	✓
Deborah Levy		–	–	✓
Barbara Cohen		–	–	✓
Suzanne Stephenson		–	–	✓

West Essex Family Mediation Service

Manager / Co-ordinator of Regional Group / Service: Sarah Fahy

Sewell House, 349 The Hides, Harlow, Essex CM20 3QY
Telephone 01279 426749

Affiliation body: National Family Mediation

	Year Trained	Areas of Practice		
		Finance	Children	All Issues
Members				
Faith Davis	1986	–	✓	–

(cont'd)

	Year Trained	Areas of Practice		
		Finance	Children	All Issues
Roy Fitch	1994	–	✓	–
Maureen Yarnold	1986	–	✓	–
Cynthia Brill	1994	–	✓	–
Martin Ross	1995	–	✓	–
Associates				
Andrea Sorrell	1995	–	✓	–
Jackie Brown	1996	–	✓	–

▪ Bath District Family Mediators Association

Manager / Co-ordinator of Regional Group / Service: Lynden Lever

13 Queen Square, Bath BA1 2HJ
Telephone 01225 337599, Facsimile 01225 335437, DX 8001 BATH

Affiliation body: Family Mediators Association

	Year Trained	Areas of Practice		
		Finance	Children	All Issues
Members				
Lynden Lever	1991	–	–	✓
John Brownrigg	1991	–	–	✓
Brian Jones	1994	–	–	✓
Sarah Angell	1993	–	–	✓
Derek Indoe	1993	–	✓	–
Nicholas von Benzon	1988	–	–	✓
Jane Sellars	1991	–	✓	–
Associates				
David Wheeler	1996	–	–	✓
Richard Fountaine	1995	–	–	✓
Jonathan Palmer		–	–	–

▪ Bristol Family Mediation Service

Manager / Co-ordinator of Regional Group / Service: Trevor J Morkham

25 Hobbs Lane, Bristol BS1 5ED
Telephone 0117 929 2002, Facsimile 0117 929 2002

Affiliation body: National Family Mediation

	Year Trained	Areas of Practice		
		Finance	Children	All Issues
Members				
Kay Begg	1988	✓	✓	✓
Janet Forbes	1991	✓	✓	✓
Paul Foster	1991	✓	✓	✓
Tony Lewis	1993	✓	✓	✓
Trevor Morkham	1988	✓	✓	✓
Hilary Woodward	1992	✓	✓	✓

(cont'd)

Facilities: 3 mediation rooms; separate waiting rooms; facilities for seeing children; disabled access on site

Geographical area covered: Bristol conurbation

Areas of practice: All Issues

Areas of specialism: consultation with children

Courses provided: information for solicitors

Additional training undertaken by members: consultation with children; domestic violence; Professional Practice Supervision/ Consultancy; All Issues Mediation

The 'Pioneer' Service

BFMS is the oldest out-of-court family mediation service in the country. The service has mediated in over 5,000 cases since it was first established in 1979, and regularly mediates on average between 150 and 200 cases each year. BFMS was one of the original five NFM services to take part in the All Issues Mediation pilot scheme. Since 1991 all BFMS mediators have been trained to provide AIM and the service has acquired a considerable amount of experience in mediation on finance and property matters with approximately 120 such cases mediated to date. The service was selected to take part in Phase 1 of the Legal Aid Board Mediation Pilot Project and has also been participating (along with Northampton) in the initial pilot scheme for implementing Section 29 of the Family Law Act.

The Bristol service is fortunate in enjoying the support of a number of distinguished patrons, among them Dr George Carey, Archbishop of Canterbury and Dame Margaret Booth (UK College Chair). We are also proud of the fact that Kay Begg, who has been a mediator with the Bristol service since it was founded, is currently a Governor of the UK College of Family Mediators as well as being a past Vice-Chairman of National Family Mediation.

Bristol Family Mediators Association

Manager / Co-ordinator of Regional Group / Service: Sian Gwyneth Hopkin

52 Broad Street, Bristol BS1 2EP
Telephone 0117 962 6300, Facsimile 0117 925 0690, DX 7824 BRISTOL 1

Affiliation body: Family Mediators Association

		Areas of Practice		
	Year Trained	Finance	Children	All Issues
Members				
Monica Cockett		–	–	✓
Jane Elias		–	–	✓
Paul Foster		–	–	✓
Jim Gridley		–	–	✓
Sian Hopkin		–	–	✓
Derek Indoe		–	–	✓
Lisa Parkinson		–	–	✓

(cont'd)

		Areas of Practice		
	Year Trained	Finance	Children	All Issues
Helen Ramm		–	–	✓
Robert Clerke		–	–	✓
David Woodward		–	–	✓
Associates				
Maeve Egan		–	–	✓
Julie Cook		–	–	✓

◼ Dorset Family Mediation Service

Manager / Co-ordinator of Regional Group / Service: Tina Hunter

43 Oxford Road, Bournemouth BH8 8EY
Telephone 01202 314600

Affiliation body: National Family Mediation

		Areas of Practice		
	Year Trained	Finance	Children	All Issues
Members				
Tony Elliott	1993	–	✓	–
Jennifer Parkhouse	1995	–	✓	–
Anthony Shaw	1992	–	✓	–
Associates				
Victoria Hewitt	1996	–	✓	–

◼ Exeter & District Family Mediation Service

Manager / Co-ordinator of Regional Group / Service: Jean M Halliday

49 Polsloe Road, Exeter EX1 2DT
Telephone 01392 410529

Affiliation body: National Family Mediation

		Areas of Practice		
	Year Trained	Finance	Children	All Issues
Members				
Gerald Conyngham	1989	–	✓	–
David Patterson	1995	–	✓	–
Vivienne Rowe	1995	–	✓	–
Associates				
Jane Robey	1997	–	✓	–

◼ Gloucestershire Family Mediation

Manager / Co-ordinator of Regional Group / Service: Jenny Vowles

Breedon Suite, Spread Eagle Court, 106-114 Northgate Street,
Gloucester GL1 1SL

(cont'd)

Telephone 01452 411843, Facsimile 01452 411843, E-mail gfm@cableint.co.uk

Affiliation body: National Family Mediation

| | Year Trained | Areas of Practice | | |
		Finance	Children	All Issues
Associates				
Jeanie Boldero	1986	–	✓	–
Margaret Simpson	1985	–	–	–

■ North Devon Family Mediation Service

Manager / Co-ordinator of Regional Group / Service: Bill Whittaker

6 Bridge Chambers, Barnstaple, North Devon EX31 1HB
Telephone 01271 815475

Affiliation body: National Family Mediation

| | Year Trained | Areas of Practice | | |
		Finance	Children	All Issues
Members				
Sue Williamson	1995	–	✓	–
Christine Evans	1995	–	✓	–
Bill Whittaker	1987	–	–	–

■ Plymouth Mediation

Manager / Co-ordinator of Regional Group / Service: Sheila Kennard

St Peter's Centre, 18 Hastings Street, Plymouth PL21 9DA
Telephone 01752 671078, Facsimile 01752 255854, E-mail plymed@dial.pipex-com

Affiliation body: National Family Mediation

| | Year Trained | Areas of Practice | | |
		Finance	Children	All Issues
Members				
Sheila Kennard	1996	–	✓	–
Vivienne Rowe	1995	–	✓	–

■ Salisbury & District Family Mediation Service

Manager / Co-ordinator of Regional Group / Service: Ruth Morag Blacklock

24B St Edmunds Church Street, Salisbury SP1 1EF
Telephone 01722 332936

Affiliation body: National Family Mediation

| | Year Trained | Areas of Practice | | |
		Finance	Children	All Issues
Members				
Ruth Blacklock	1986	–	–	✓
Clare Druett	1996	–	–	✓

(cont'd)

Groups/Services by Region B

Robert Clerke & Co.

Solicitors   Mediators

6, Picton Street,
Montpelier,
Bristol BS6 5QA

Robert Clerke & Co. offer a range of specialist services to assist with Matrimonial and Family issues. As well as offering advice from experienced solicitors, specialist Family Mediation services are available from experienced mediators to who offer both sole and co-mediation on all or any issues. Legal Aid is available.

Robert Clerke is an experienced Solicitor who originally trained as a Mediator with the Family Mediators Association in 1991. He is now a full Member of the U.K. College of Family Mediators and accredited with The Family Mediators Association, The Solicitors Mediators. He also acts as a Trainer for the Solicitors Family Law Association and LawGroup UK.

Robert Clerke & Co. are proud to have **Lisa Parkinson** who acts as a Consultant and Co-Mediator with the practice. Lisa is the Director of Training for LawGroup UK and for CALM in Scotland. She was the first Director of the Family Mediators Association and is well known both in this country and internationally for her many writings on the subject of Mediation. She is the author of 'Family Mediation' recently published by Sweet and Maxwell which is regarded very highly by her colleagues. Lisa is accredited with the Family Mediators Association and a full member of the U.K. College of Family Mediators. Lisa has co-mediated with Robert Clerke for many years and he now co-trains with her for LawGroup UK.

Robert Clerke and Co. are also pleased to have **Monica Cockett** acting as External Consultant and Supervisor to the Practice. Monica is a Research Fellow in the Department of Child Health at Exeter University and is a Family Mediator of many year's experience. She is the co-author of 'The Exeter Family Study' regarded as one of the leading research works in this country about the effects of family breakdown on parents and children. Monica is accredited with and is a board member of the Family Mediators Association and a full member of the U.K. College of Family Mediators.

For further information about the Legal and Mediation Services available or to arrange an appointment or Mediation please call and let us know that you saw this advertisement.

Tel: 0117 9244346
Fax: 0117 9446776

		Areas of Practice		
	Year Trained	Finance	Children	All Issues
Paul Kidd	1995	–	–	✓
Katherine Rennie	1997	–	–	✓

■ Somerset Family Mediation Service

Manager / Co-ordinator of Regional Group / Service: Mary Adamson

The Myrtle Tree, 34 Bridge Street, Taunton, Somerset TA1 1UD
Telephone 01823 352013, Facsimile 01823 352013, DX 96113
TAUNTON

Affiliation body: National Family Mediation

		Areas of Practice		
	Year Trained	Finance	Children	All Issues
Members				
Lorna Chynoweth	1991	–	✓	–
Pauli Joyce	1992	–	✓	–
Tony Lewis	1987	–	✓	–

■ South West Region Family Mediators Association

Manager / Co-ordinator of Regional Group / Service: Joseph William Stanton

18 Roseland Avenue, Exeter EX1 2TW
Telephone 01392 420888

Affiliation body: Family Mediators Association

		Areas of Practice		
	Year Trained	Finance	Children	All Issues
Members				
Lindsey Bryning	1993	✓	✓	✓
Monica Cockett	1989	✓	✓	✓
Christopher Conbeer	1989	✓	✓	✓
Kay Firth-Butterfield	1989	✓	✓	✓
Norman Hartnell	1989	✓	✓	✓
Catherine Lockyear	1991	✓	✓	✓
Michael Pitt	1991	✓	✓	✓
Ian Scofield	1988	✓	✓	✓
Joe Stanton	1991	✓	✓	✓
Ann Truscott	1992	✓	✓	✓
Shirley May Yard	1991	✓	✓	✓
Associates				
Roderick Ball	1996	✓	✓	✓
Teresa Cambell	1997	✓	✓	✓
Maggie Cartridge	1995	✓	✓	✓
Monica Case	1992	✓	✓	✓
Helen Goodall	1997	✓	✓	✓
Christine Nicholl	1995	–	–	–
Christopher Thomas	1991	✓	✓	✓

▪ Swindon Family Mediation Service

Manager / Co-ordinator of Regional Group / Service: Wendy Hall

37a Regent Street, Swindon SN1 1JL
Telephone 01793 527285

Affiliation body: National Family Mediation

		Areas of Practice		
	Year Trained	Finance	Children	All Issues
Members				
Lorraine Bramwell	1996	–	✓	–
Kate Gardner	1989	✓	✓	✓
Stephen Moss	1995	✓	✓	✓
Chris Oswald	1996	✓	✓	✓
Ros Oswald	1995	✓	✓	✓
Karen Taylor	1989	✓	✓	✓

▪ Wiltshire Family Mediators Association

Manager / Co-ordinator of Regional Group / Service: Jennifer King

42 Cricklade Street, Old Town, Swindon, Wiltshire SN1 3HD
Telephone 01793 410800, Facsimile 01793 616294, DX 6204
SWINDON, E-mail forum@townsols.demon.co.uk

Affiliation body: Family Mediators Association

		Areas of Practice		
	Year Trained	Finance	Children	All Issues
Members				
Jenny King	1991	✓	✓	✓
Alan Sealey	1991	✓	✓	✓
Nicholas von Benzon	1988	–	–	✓
Associates				
Fred Tucker	1994	✓	✓	✓
Robin Littlewood	1996	✓	✓	✓
Richard Sharp	1996	✓	✓	✓
Stuart McNeil	1994	✓	✓	✓

▪ Berkshire Family Mediation

Manager / Co-ordinator of Regional Group / Service: Jessica Markwell

3rd Floor, 160-163 Friar Street, Reading RG1 1HE
Telephone 0118 957 1159, DX 98010 READING 6

Affiliation body: National Family Mediation

		Areas of Practice		
	Year Trained	Finance	Children	All Issues
Members				
John Banks	1997	✓	✓	✓
Colin Ferguson	1995	✓	✓	✓
Jessica Markwell	1992	✓	✓	✓

(cont'd)

		Areas of Practice		
	Year Trained	Finance	Children	All Issues
Wendy Moore	1991	✓	✓	✓
Linda Uncles	1991	✓	✓	✓

■ Hampshire and Isle of Wight Family Mediators Association

Manager / Co-ordinator of Regional Group / Service: William Anthony Meads

17 Hampshire Terrace, Portsmouth PO1 2PU
Telephone 01705 812511, Facsimile 01705 291847, DX 2207 PORTSMOUTH

Affiliation body: Family Mediators Association

		Areas of Practice		
	Year Trained	Finance	Children	All Issues
Associates				
Pat Bradley	1995	–	–	✓
Bill Meads	1995	–	–	✓

■ Hampshire Family Mediation

Manager / Co-ordinator of Regional Group / Service: John Foster

Hilsea House (Hilsea Lodge), Gatcombe Drive, Hilsea, Portsmouth PO2 0TX
Telephone 01705 660919, Facsimile 01705 660919

Affiliation body: National Family Mediation

		Areas of Practice		
	Year Trained	Finance	Children	All Issues
Members				
John Foster	1990	–	✓	–
John Ambrose	1988	–	✓	–
Peter Ford	1988	–	✓	–
Susan Smith	1990	–	✓	✓
Barbara Wilson	1991	–	✓	✓
Karen Postle	1993	–	✓	–
Anne Borghgraef	1993	–	✓	–
Frieda Davie	1992	–	✓	–
Renella Squires	1995	–	✓	–
Associates				
Sheila Parkes	1996	–	✓	✓

■ Birmingham and District Family Mediation

Manager / Co-ordinator of Regional Group / Service: John Bernard Akers

3 Kingston Row, Birmingham B1 2NU
Telephone 0121 233 1999, Facsimile 0121 233 1999, E-mail jbakers@netcomuk.co.uk

(cont'd)

Affiliation body: National Family Mediation

		Areas of Practice		
	Year Trained	Finance	Children	All Issues
Members				
J B Akers	1985	✓	✓	✓
L A Allport	1988	✓	✓	✓
Ralph James	1985	✓	✓	✓
Katherine Warner	1997	✓	✓	✓
Sarah Hobbs	1997	✓	✓	✓

Facilities: 3 mediation rooms; separate waiting rooms; facilities for seeing children; off site disabled access arrangements can be made

Geographical area covered: Birmingham/West Midlands

Areas of practice: All Issues

Areas of specialism: consultation with children; high income

Additional training undertaken by members: consultation with children; domestic violence; initial information giving and/or assessment; Professional Practice Supervision/Consultancy; counselling; heritage awareness

Interpreters available ✓

Experience of working with different cultures: Black Carribean; Black African; Jewish; Hindu; Sikh; Moslem; Arabian

The service has a 14-year history of professional mediation with trained, supervised and accredited mediators. The service has a consistent workload of 160 cases per annum, of which 25 per cent include finance issues. Additionally we counsel families, for example when there are step-family problems. The service manager is the Midlands regional representative to National Family Mediation's management committee and a trained supervisor. The service also provides mediation in Walsall and will shortly provide mediation in Solihull.

◼ Birmingham Family Mediators Association

Manager / Co-ordinator of Regional Group / Service: Susan Marie Vogel

41 Church Street, Birmingham B3 3RT
Telephone 0121 786 1158, Facsimile 0121 233 4546

Affiliation body: Family Mediators Association

		Areas of Practice		
	Year Trained	Finance	Children	All Issues
Members				
Ian Dippie	1994	✓	✓	✓
Judith Pugsley	1994	✓	✓	✓
Judith Green	1994	✓	✓	✓
Mari Meisel	1994	✓	✓	✓
Associates				
Susan Vogel	1994	✓	✓	✓
Andrew Guymer	1994	✓	✓	✓

(cont'd)

	Year Trained	Areas of Practice		
		Finance	Children	All Issues
Eric Healey	1994	✓	✓	✓
Marc Nye	1994	✓	✓	✓
Julia Bunting	1996	✓	✓	✓
Jackie Newport	1996	✓	✓	✓
Neil Robinson	1990	✓	✓	✓
Toni Brisby	1993	–	–	–
Rachel Beulah	1996	✓	✓	✓

Coventry & South Warwickshire Family Mediators Association

Manager / Co-ordinator of Regional Group / Service: Susan Pearce

c/o Varley Hibbs & Co Solicitors, Kirby House, Little Park Street, Coventry CV1 2JZ
Telephone 01203 631000, Facsimile 01203 630808, DX 712341 COVENTRY 13, E-mail vhibbs@demon.co.uk

Affiliation body: Family Mediators Association

	Year Trained	Areas of Practice		
		Finance	Children	All Issues
Associates				
Trish Holmes	1991	✓	✓	✓

Coventry & Warwickshire Family Mediation Service

Manager / Co-ordinator of Regional Group / Service: Jenny Lewington

Suite 21 & 22, Koco Building, The Arches, Spon End, Coventry CV1 3JQ
Telephone 01203 717109, Facsimile 01203 717119

Affiliation body: National Family Mediation

	Year Trained	Areas of Practice		
		Finance	Children	All Issues
Members				
Janet Ward	1985	✓	✓	✓
Virginia MacLellan	1990	✓	✓	✓
Denise Tracey	1992	✓	✓	✓
Associates				
Kath Neilson	1990	–	✓	–
Ann Walker	1998	–	✓	–
Julie Dick	1998	–	✓	–

Other mediation address: Outreach centres in Warwickshire

Facilities: 2 mediation rooms; disabled access on site

Geographical area covered: Coventry, Warwickshire and environs

Areas of practice: All Issues

Areas of specialism: welfare rights

(cont'd)

Additional training undertaken by members: consultation with children; domestic violence; mediator trainer training; Professional Practice Supervision/Consultancy

Interpreters available ✓

Coventry & Warwickshire Family Mediation Service (CWFMS) was founded in 1981 and is one of the longest established family mediation services in the voluntary sector. CWFMS was one of the five NFM affiliated services in the 1991-92 Rowntree Project to pilot a comprehensive mediation service, now known as All Issues Mediation (AIM). An added feature to the Coventry service is the inclusion of a welfare rights consultant. Additionally, a legal consultant is available to provide legal information to mediators and the service on issues and principles of AIM.

Typically, mediation takes place with a sole mediator, but co-working is available where appropriate. CWFMS has consistently been at the forefront in mediation development and has contributed to the NFM 'Separated Parenting Pack' and it has piloted Separated Parenting Courses in several local areas.

The service is in Phase 1 of the Legal Aid Board Franchise pilot scheme. A number of changes have taken place over the last year, a full time co-ordinator has been appointed and to meet the expected increase in workload two further mediators have been recruited. We have also moved to larger and more accessible premises.

Derbyshire Family Mediators Association

Manager / Co-ordinator of Regional Group / Service: Harry Shingleton

The Triangle, 131 Bridge Street, Belper, Derbyshire DE56 1BJ
Telephone 01773 825765, Facsimile 01773 826518, DX 15301 BELPER

Affiliation body: Family Mediators Association

| | | | Areas of Practice | |
	Year Trained	Finance	Children	All Issues
Members				
Harry Shingleton	1993	–	–	✓

Herefordshire Family Mediation Service

Manager / Co-ordinator of Regional Group / Service: Eileen Hyde

1st Floor, 25 Castle Street, Hereford HR1 2NW
Telephone 01432 264087, Facsimile 01432 351993

Affiliation body: National Family Mediation

| | | | Areas of Practice | |
	Year Trained	Finance	Children	All Issues
Members				
Claire Armstrong	1992	–	✓	✓
Cynthia Morrison	1994	–	✓	✓
Barbara Shore	1991	–	✓	✓

(cont'd)

| | | Areas of Practice | | |
	Year Trained	Finance	Children	All Issues
Michael Jacobs	1994	–	✓	✓
Barbara Ferris	1989	–	✓	✓
Philippa Frost	1994	–	✓	✓

■ Hereford & Worcestershire Family Mediators Association

Manager / Co-ordinator of Regional Group / Service: Jonathan Brew

c/o Harrison & Clark, 5 College Yard, Worcester WR1 2LD
Telephone 01905 619688

Affiliation body: Family Mediators Association

■ Lincolnshire Family Mediation Service

Manager / Co-ordinator of Regional Group / Service: Jacqui Blanchard

7 Lindum Terrace, Lincoln LN2 5RP
Telephone 01522 523308, Facsimile 01522 527685

Affiliation body: National Family Mediation

| | | Areas of Practice | | |
	Year Trained	Finance	Children	All Issues
Members				
Kathy Urwin		–	–	–
Associates				
Jacqui Blanchard	1997	–	✓	–

■ Mediation Advisory Services for Stafford & North Staffs

Manager / Co-ordinator of Regional Group / Service: Claire George

SDVS Centre, 131-141 North Walls, Stafford ST16 3AD
Telephone 0845 600 0084

Affiliation body: National Family Mediation

| | | Areas of Practice | | |
	Year Trained	Finance	Children	All Issues
Members				
Gwenyth Benson	1986	–	✓	–
Bernard Moss	1994	–	✓	–
Gill Woolridge	1991	–	✓	–

■ Mediation for Families (Oxfordshire)

Manager / Co-ordinator of Regional Group / Service: Peter Devlin

c/o 15 Ock Street, Abingdon, Oxfordshire OX14 5AN
Telephone 01235 553222, E-mail info@franklins-solicitors.co.uk

Affiliation body: Family Mediators Association

(cont'd)

	Year Trained	Areas of Practice		
		Finance	Children	All Issues
Members				
Roger Cullen	1989	✓	✓	✓
Julie Weedon	1993	✓	✓	✓
Felicity White	1986	✓	✓	✓
Alan Williams	1995	✓	✓	✓
Associates				
Peter Devlin	1995	✓	✓	✓
Catherine Eddy	1993	✓	✓	✓
Catherine Goode	1995	✓	✓	✓
Gill Wright	1997	✓	✓	✓

■ Milton Keynes & North Buckinghamshire FMA Group

Manager / Co-ordinator of Regional Group / Service: Susan Jane Hale

c/o 28 Huntingdon Crescent, Bletchley, Milton Keynes,
Buckinghamshire MK3 5NT
Telephone 01908 366960, Facsimile 01908 366960 (phone first)

Affiliation body: Family Mediators Association

	Year Trained	Areas of Practice		
		Finance	Children	All Issues
Associates				
Susan Jane Hale	1995	✓	✓	✓
Paul Montgomery	1990	✓	✓	✓
Beverly Parker	1995	✓	✓	✓
Patrick Perusko	1995	✓	✓	✓

■ Northamptonshire Family Mediation Service

Manager / Co-ordinator of Regional Group / Service: Rosemary
Bromwich

49 York Road, Northampton NN1 5QJ
Telephone 01604 636651, Facsimile 01604 637313

Affiliation body: National Family Mediation

	Year Trained	Areas of Practice		
		Finance	Children	All Issues
Members				
Rosemary Bromwich	1995	✓	✓	✓
Maeve Horton	1995	✓	✓	✓
Janet Bateman	1995	✓	✓	✓
Christine Bragg	1996	✓	✓	✓
Rita Bilson	1996	✓	✓	✓
Margo Ray	1996	✓	✓	✓

Facilities: 2 mediation rooms; separate waiting rooms; facilities for
seeing children; off site disabled access arrangements can be made;
facilities to mediate in Corby, Kettering, Wellingborough, Towcester
and Daventry

(cont'd)

Geographical area covered: Northamptonshire

Areas of practice: Children Issues; All Issues

Areas of specialism: consultation with children

Additional training undertaken by members: consultation with children; domestic violence

Experience of working with different cultures: European; Black Caribbean; Black Other; Hindu; Black African

Nottinghamshire Children & Families Mediation Service (FAME)

Manager / Co-ordinator of Regional Group / Service: Patricia Paris

Warren House, 2 Pelham Court, Pelham Road, Nottingham NG5 1AP
Telephone 0115 985 8855, Facsimile 0115 960 8374

Affiliation body: National Family Mediation

		Areas of Practice		
	Year Trained	Finance	Children	All Issues
Members				
Patricia Paris	1995	–	✓	–
Associates				
Deirdre Offord	1995	–	✓	–
Elizabeth Holloway	1996	–	✓	–

Facilities: 2 mediation rooms; separate waiting rooms; facilities for seeing children; disabled access on site

Geographical area covered: Nottinghamshire

Areas of practice: Children Issues

Areas of specialism: consultation with children; domestic violence

Additional training undertaken by members: consultation with children; domestic violence; initial information giving and/or assessment; Professional Practice Supervision/Consultancy; working with cultural difference

Interpreters available ✓

Experience of working with different cultures: Black Carribean; Hindu; Sikh

Nottinghamshire Family Mediators Association

Manager / Co-ordinator of Regional Group / Service: Bernadette Healy

46 Carrington Street, Nottingham NG1 7FG
Telephone 0115 958 3472, Facsimile 0115 948 4913, DX 702150
NOTTINGHAM 6

Affiliation body: Family Mediators Association

(cont'd)

	Year Trained	Areas of Practice Finance	Children	All Issues
Members				
Ann Clifford	1993	–	–	✓
Marion Griew	1993	–	–	✓
Associates				
Judith Speed	1994	–	–	✓
Bernadette Healy	1994	–	–	✓
Karon Flowerdew	1994	–	–	✓
Donella Nicholle	1997	–	–	✓

Oxford Family Mediators Association

Manager / Co-ordinator of Regional Group / Service: Linda Glees

42 Westgate, Oxford OX1 1PD
Telephone 01865 724977, Facsimile 01865 791300, DX 4317 OXFORD 1

Affiliation body: Family Mediators Association

	Year Trained	Areas of Practice Finance	Children	All Issues
Members				
Linda Glees	1993	–	–	✓
M L Payne	1992	–	–	✓
Marion Stevenson	1992	–	–	✓
Felicity White	1986	–	–	✓
Alan Williams	1995	–	–	✓
Associates				
Linda Barlow	1995	–	–	✓
Catherine Eddy	1993	–	–	✓
Peter Devlin	1995	–	–	✓
Catherine Goode	1995	–	–	✓
Wendy Klein	1996	–	–	✓
Judi Lyons	1996	–	–	✓
Gill Wright	1997	–	–	✓

Oxfordshire Family Mediation Service

Manager / Co-ordinator of Regional Group / Service: Elizabeth Whitwick

123 London Road, Headington, Oxford OX3 9HZ
Telephone 01865 741781, Facsimile 01865 744393

Affiliation body: National Family Mediation

	Year Trained	Areas of Practice Finance	Children	All Issues
Members				
Roger Cullen	1989	–	✓	✓
Isobel Filkin	1992	–	✓	✓
Jenny Harris	1992	–	✓	✓

(cont'd)

	Year Trained	Finance	Areas of Practice Children	All Issues
Marion Stevenson	1990	–	✓	✓
Karen Taylor	1987	–	✓	✓

▣ Resolve (Family and Commercial Mediation) Limited

Manager / Co-ordinator of Regional Group / Service: Paul John Turner

28 Church Street, Rushden, Northamptonshire NN10 9SA
Telephone 01933 356131, Facsimile 01933 356859, DX 18953

Affiliation body: Family Mediators Association

	Year Trained	Finance	Areas of Practice Children	All Issues
Members				
Adrian Wright	1993	–	–	✓
Associates				
Paul Turner	1995	–	–	✓
Elaine Clarke	1995	–	–	✓
Elaine Nunn	1995	–	–	✓

Other mediation address: 1 Lurke Street, Bedford, Bedfordshire MK40 3TN

Telephone 01234 400000, Facsimile 01234 401111, DX 5603 BEDFORD 1

Facilities: 2+ mediation rooms; separate waiting rooms; facilities for seeing children; disabled access on site

Geographical area covered: Northampton, Bedford, Milton Keynes

Areas of practice: All Issues

Areas of specialism: consultation with children; high income; child care

Additional training undertaken by members: consultation with children; domestic violence; Professional Practice Supervision/ Consultancy; welfare rights

Interpreters available ✓

Experience of working with different cultures: Black Other; Hindu; Moslem; Jewish; Sikh

Background

Personnel

Paul Turner – Paul is an experienced solicitor and a member of the Law Society's Children Panel. Paul trained as a mediator with the FMA in 1995. Paul is also a member of BALM, an associate of the UK College and a Legal Aid Board approved mediator.

Elaine Clarke – Elaine is a partner and an experienced family solicitor. Elaine qualified as a mediator with LawGroup UK.

(cont'd)

Adrian Wright – Adrian is the company's supervisor, has trained as a mediator since 1993 and is a recognised supervisor by the FMA and the College. Adrian is a Legal Aid Board approved mediator.

Elaine Nunn – Elaine is a family mediator who trained with the FMA in 1995 and is also the co-ordinator for the South Midlands FMA.

Shirley Danning – Shirley is one of the most experienced court welfare officers in the country and a LAB approved mediator. Shirley can directly consult with children if appropriate.

General

Resolve, created by Park Woodfine Solicitors, are one of the few mediation services in the country that have a franchise in mediation from the Legal Aid Board <u>and</u> have 'approved' mediators. We offer all types of mediation with male and female mediators. Legal Aid is available and the first appointment is free.

Shropshire Family Mediation Service

Manager / Co-ordinator of Regional Group / Service: Marilyn Webster

PO Box 571, 65 Withywood Drive, Telford TF3 2WD
Telephone 01952 502447, Facsimile 01952 502811

Affiliation body: National Family Mediation

		Areas of Practice		
	Year Trained	Finance	Children	All Issues
Members				
Marilyn Webster	1991	–	✓	–
Julia Winter	1991	–	✓	–
Peter Little	1992	–	✓	–
Clare Beeton	1992	–	✓	–
Associates				
Jeanie Boldero	1996	–	–	–

Shropshire Family Mediators Association

Manager / Co-ordinator of Regional Group / Service: Robin Mostyn ap Cynan

The Store Barn, Church Street, Madeley, Telford TF7 5BU
Telephone 01952 680284, E-mail rmapc@aol.com

Affiliation body: Family Mediators Association

		Areas of Practice		
	Year Trained	Finance	Children	All Issues
Members				
Robin M ap Cynan	1990	✓	✓	✓
Associates				
Peter Flint	1990	✓	✓	✓

(cont'd)

	Year Trained	Areas of Practice		
		Finance	Children	All Issue
Marc Nye	1995	✓	✓	✓

Smith Chamberlain – The Mediation Service

Manager / Co-ordinator of Regional Group / Service: Beverly Parker

61 & 62 Oxford Street, Wellingborough, Northamptonshire NN8 4JL
Telephone 01933 224971 (daytime); 0930 756010 (mobile); 01604
719443 (evenings), Facsimile 01933 271299, DX 12858

Affiliation body: Family Mediators Association

	Year Trained	Areas of Practice		
		Finance	Children	All Issue
Members				
Adrian Wright	1993	✓	✓	✓
Associates				
Helen York	1996	✓	✓	✓
Beverly Parker	1995	✓	✓	✓

South Midlands Family Mediators Association

Manager / Co-ordinator of Regional Group / Service: Elaine Nunn

Watersview, Highslade, Brixworth, Northampton, Northants NN6
9UH
Telephone 01604 881716, Facsimile 01604 881052

Affiliation body: Family Mediators Association

	Year Trained	Areas of Practice		
		Finance	Children	All Issue
Associates				
Elaine Nunn	1995	–	–	✓
David Eastwood	1993	–	–	✓
Moya Janko	1995	–	–	✓
Tony Mitchell	1993	–	–	✓
Paul Montgomery	1992	–	–	✓
Fiona Moore	1993	–	–	✓
Nick Levinge	1996	–	–	✓
Beverly Parker	1995	–	–	✓
Danka Neuborn	1993	–	–	✓
Paul Turner	1995	–	–	✓
Georgina Bland	1994	–	–	✓
Sue Hale	1995	–	–	✓
Julia Mitchell	1995	–	–	✓
Adrian Wright	1993	–	–	✓

SOUTHERNHAY MEDIATION SERVICES

SOUTHERNHAY CHAMBERS
33, SOUTHERNHAY EAST,
EXETER, EX1 1NX

ROBERT ALFORD   CHRISTOPHER NAISH

JACQUELINE AHMED   EMMA CRAWFORTH

We are in practice as specialist family law Counsel. As mediators we aim to combine the expertise and experience of conducting family litigation with the desire to help people find their own solutions to family breakdown and to alleviate bitterness.

We can be consulted as joint or sole mediators directly by individuals or by solicitors who would be able to remain as legal advisers in the case as may be requested by their clients.

We are fully insured and approved by the Bar Council to act as mediators.

We have successfully completed extensive assessed all issues family mediation training by Lisa Parkinson and Liz Allen with LawGroup UK under the auspices of Devon & Exeter Law Society.

We are all associate members of the UK College of Family Mediators and full members on the register of LawGroup UK Mediators.

We can be contacted as outlined below for details such as financial terms which normally include no separate charge for preparation or for production of written material such as mediation and financial summaries.

Appointments are available from 7 a.m. to 10 p.m. Each session normally lasts up to two hours. The number of sessions in a course is flexible.

Separate waiting facilities are available.

Third parties such as children, partners and other family members may join in some of the mediation process by agreement of the clients and at the discretion of the mediator(s).

Telephone: (01392) 255777   Fax: (01392) 412021
DX: 8353 - EXETER
E-Mail: southernhay.chambers@lineone.net

South Staffordshire Family Mediation Service

Manager / Co-ordinator of Regional Group / Service: Kay Johnson

33 Park Road, Cannock, Staffordshire WS11 1JN
Telephone 01543 572600, Facsimile 01543 572600

Affiliation body: National Family Mediation

		Areas of Practice		
	Year Trained	Finance	Children	All Issues
Members				
James Howe	1991	✓	✓	✓
Jonathan Smith	1995	✓	✓	✓
Jane Read	1996	✓	✓	✓
Associates				
Sue Hollywood	1997	✓	✓	✓

Worcestershire Family Mediation

Manager / Co-ordinator of Regional Group / Service: Mary-Louise Thompson

3 Shaw Street, Worcester WR1 3QQ
Telephone 01905 610925, Facsimile 01905 610925

Affiliation body: National Family Mediation

		Areas of Practice		
	Year Trained	Finance	Children	All Issues
Members				
Sarah Rennie	1990	–	✓	✓
Elizabeth Keogh-Smith	1990	–	✓	✓
Associates				
Gill Miller	1996	–	✓	–
Don Wilson	1994	–	✓	–

Cambridge Family and Divorce Centre

Manager / Co-ordinator of Regional Group / Service: Celia Dickinson

1 Brooklands Avenue, Cambridge CB2 2BB
Telephone 01223 576308/9, Facsimile 01223 576309

Affiliation body: National Family Mediation

		Areas of Practice		
	Year Trained	Finance	Children	All Issues
Members				
Alison Evans	1987	✓	✓	✓
Helen Casey	1995	✓	✓	✓
Len Cripps	1995	✓	✓	✓
Sarah Laughton	1990	✓	✓	✓
Frances Murton	1987	✓	✓	✓
Carmela Pearson	1992	✓	✓	✓

(cont'd)

	Year Trained	Areas of Practice		
		Finance	Children	All Issues
Wendy Pritchard	1987	✓	✓	✓
Associates Katherine Perry	1998	✓	✓	✓

Facilities: 2 mediation rooms; separate waiting rooms; facilities for seeing children; disabled access on site; signers available

Geographical area covered: Appointments mainly in Cambridge, also Ely and Huntingdon

Areas of practice: All Issues

Areas of specialism: consultation with children; welfare rights; high income; child counselling

Courses provided: initial information giving; assessment of eligibility for legally aided mediation

Additional training undertaken by members: consultation with children; domestic violence; Professional Practice Supervision/ Consultancy; welfare rights

Languages spoken: Japanese

Interpreters available ✓

Aims

Cambridge Family and Divorce Centre was established in 1982 and acts as a specialist multi-service centre for those involved in separation and divorce. In addition to mediation, the centre offers information and counselling, and its children's service works with young people between the ages of 6 and 19 years to provide counselling and support, both in groups and on an individual basis. The centre has been at the forefront of development and innovation in the field and has established a reputation for high quality pioneering work. Early in 1997 it was selected to take part in two pilot schemes under the Family Law Act: the Legal Aid Board pilot scheme for mediation and the Information Meeting Pilot. Its experienced mediation team deals with the full range of family matters and it works closely with the local FMA group, so that a choice of models is available. This year it has launched a new scheme offering Professional Practice Supervision/Consultancy to other providers.

Cambridge Family Mediators Association

Manager / Co-ordinator of Regional Group / Service: Celia Dickinson

1 Brooklands Avenue, Cambridge CB2 2BB
Telephone 01223 576308/9, Facsimile 01223 576309

Affiliation body: Family Mediators Association

(cont'd)

		Areas of Practice		
	Year Trained	Finance	Children	All Issues
Members				
Sarah Attle	1996	✓	✓	✓
Roger Bamber	1990	✓	✓	✓
Alison Evans	1990	✓	✓	✓
Carmela Pearson	1990	✓	✓	✓
Wendy Pritchard	1990	✓	✓	✓
Janet Reibstein	1993	✓	✓	✓
Rosemary Sands	1990	✓	✓	✓
Helen Watkins	1990	✓	✓	✓
Associates				
Amanda Brown	1996	✓	✓	✓
Sally Bullock	1996	✓	✓	✓
Jeannette Josse	1993	✓	✓	✓

Family Mediation in Norfolk

Manager / Co-ordinator of Regional Group / Service: Marilyn Jean Barnett

35 Exchange Street, Norwich NR2 1EN
Telephone 01603 619371, Facsimile 01603 619434, DX 5212
NORWICH, E-mail mjb@clapham-collinge.co.uk

Affiliation body: Family Mediators Association

		Areas of Practice		
	Year Trained	Finance	Children	All Issues
Members				
Marilyn Barnett	1990	–	–	✓
Catherine Iliff	1990	–	–	✓
Beryl Matthews	1990	–	–	✓
Yvonne Poles	1990	–	–	✓

Mediation East Anglia

Manager / Co-ordinator of Regional Group / Service: Angela Lake-Carroll

16 Angel Hill, Bury St Edmunds, Suffolk IP33 1UZ
Telephone 01284 706149, Facsimile 01284 706149

Affiliation body: Family Mediators Association

		Areas of Practice		
	Year Trained	Finance	Children	All Issues
Members				
Yvonne Poles	1989	✓	✓	✓
Angela Lake-Carroll	1986	✓	✓	✓
Colin Smith	1995	✓	✓	✓
Associates				
Priscilla Hall	1996	✓	✓	✓
Pat Taylor	1992	✓	✓	✓

(cont'd)

	Year Trained	Areas of Practice		
		Finance	Children	All Issues
Stephen Drake	1996	✓	✓	✓
Amanda Brown	1996	✓	✓	✓
Jayne Gilbert	1992	✓	✓	✓
Kate Taylor	1993	✓	✓	✓
Elizabeth Cleverley	1997	✓	✓	✓

Norfolk Family Mediation Service

Manager / Co-ordinator of Regional Group / Service: Virginia Furness

Charing Cross Centre, 17-19 St John Maddermarket, Norwich NR2 1DN
Telephone 01603 620588

Affiliation body: National Family Mediation

	Year Trained	Areas of Practice		
		Finance	Children	All Issues
Members				
Wendy Bainham	1996	✓	✓	✓
Julia Blackburn	1989	✓	✓	✓
Anne Krish	1983	✓	✓	✓
Beryl Matthews	1994	✓	✓	✓
Brigit de Waal	1996	✓	✓	✓

Peterborough & District Family Mediation Service

Manager / Co-ordinator of Regional Group / Service: Margaret Lewis

67 Broadway, Peterborough PE1 1SY
Telephone 01733 347353, Facsimile 01733 344138

Affiliation body: National Family Mediation

	Year Trained	Areas of Practice		
		Finance	Children	All Issues
Members				
Margaret Lewis	1990	✓	✓	✓
Catherine Ievins	1993	✓	✓	✓
Lesley Piggott	1994	✓	✓	✓
Len Cripps	1995	✓	✓	✓
Tony Whatling	1987	✓	✓	✓

Suffolk Family Mediation Service

Manager / Co-ordinator of Regional Group / Service: Judy Wright

Lowestoft and Great Yarmouth Relate, 88 Alexandra Road, Lowestoft, Suffolk NR32 1PL
Telephone

Affiliation body: National Family Mediation

(cont'd)

	Year Trained	Areas of Practice Finance	Children	All Issues
Members				
Alan Blackshaw	1982	–	✓	–
Jeannie Weir	1991	–	✓	–
Angela Lake-Carroll	1997	–	✓	–
George Jeffrey	1989	–	✓	–
Joy Jeffrey	1989	–	✓	–
John O'Sullivan	1989	–	✓	–
Barbara Robb	1995	–	✓	–
Liz Miles	1995	–	✓	–
Hilary Wilson	1987	–	✓	–

▦ Bradford Metropolitan Family Mediation Service

Manager / Co-ordinator of Regional Group / Service: Barbara Sanford

The Law Courts, Exchange Square, Drake Street, Bradford BD1 1DJ
Telephone 01274 732768, Facsimile 01274 730115

Affiliation body: National Family Mediation

	Year Trained	Areas of Practice Finance	Children	All Issues
Members				
Patricia Haigh	1998	–	–	✓
Patrick O'Byrne	1998	–	–	✓
Damayanti Shah	1991	–	✓	–

▦ Cleveland Family Mediation Service

Manager / Co-ordinator of Regional Group / Service: Jean Earnshaw, Gillian Walker

St Mary's Centre, 1st Floor, 82/90 Corporation Road, Middlesbrough, Teeside TS1 2RW
Telephone 01642 222967, Facsimile 01642 219122

Affiliation body: National Family Mediation

	Year Trained	Areas of Practice Finance	Children	All Issues
Members				
Jean Earnshaw	1989	–	✓	✓
Gillian Walker	1989	–	✓	✓
Catherine Jackson	1989	–	✓	✓
Barbara Sydney	1989	–	✓	✓
Carole Sheldon	1989	–	✓	✓
Jane Affleck	1994	–	✓	✓
Ruby Marshall	1989	–	✓	✓
Diana Wardill	1994	–	✓	✓
Associates				
Tony Jackson	1996	–	✓	✓
Martin Brown	1996	–	✓	✓
Tracy Stephenson	1996	–	✓	✓

(cont'd

	Year Trained	Finance	Areas of Practice Children	All Issues
Jill Patrick	1996	–	✓	✓

Durham Family Mediation

Manager / Co-ordinator of Regional Group / Service: Eileen Dunn

Alington House, 4 North Bailey, Durham DH1 3ET
Telephone 0191 386 5418, Facsimile 0191 386 3057

Affiliation body: National Family Mediation

	Year Trained	Finance	Areas of Practice Children	All Issues
Members				
Pauline Campbell	1993	–	✓	✓
Kath Hill	1996	–	✓	✓
Alison Hoare	1989	–	✓	✓
Charles Hocking	1992	–	✓	✓
Susan Sale	1991	–	✓	✓
Jenni Turner	1995	–	✓	✓
Alan Rutherford	1990	–	✓	✓

Facilities: 2 mediation rooms; separate waiting rooms; facilities for seeing children; disabled access on site; off site disabled access arrangements can be made

Geographical area covered: County Durham, Darlington and North Yorkshire

Areas of practice: Children Issues; All Issues

Areas of specialism: consultation with children

Additional training undertaken by members: consultation with children; domestic violence; initial information giving and/or assessment; mediator trainer training; Professional Practice Supervision/Consultancy; welfare rights

Interpreters available ✓

Background and Aims of Service

Durham Family Mediation was set up in 1989 in partnership with Durham County Probation Service. The project is an integrated service dealing with conflict management. This service is available to all separating or divorcing parents and close family members across the whole of County Durham, Darlington and North Yorkshire. The project offers advice, information, mediation and contact centre services. The project currently offers mediation services at its office based in Durham City and also outposts in Peterlee, Seaham, Consett, Stanley, Bishop Auckland, Barnard Castle and Darlington. The project specialises in Child Centred Mediation and All Issues Mediation. The project also operates two contact centres, these being in Durham City and Darlington. These centres offer practical help where contact has broken down. Durham Family Mediation enables parents and close family members to work out their own solutions to the difficulties faced during

(cont'd)

separation or divorce. The service helps parents and close family members make arrangements which are in the best interests of the children. All referrals are to be made through the office based in Durham City.

Family Mediation Service (Northumberland & Tyneside)

Manager / Co-ordinator of Regional Group / Service: Carolyn Gillis, Valerie Vaughan

4th Floor, MEA House, Ellison Place, Newcastle upon Tyne NE1 8XS
Telephone 0191 261 9212, Facsimile 0191 233 0634

Affiliation body: National Family Mediation

		Areas of Practice		
	Year Trained	Finance	Children	All Issues
Members				
Carolyn Gillis	1993	–	✓	✓
Valerie Vaughan	1990	–	✓	✓
Margaret Lacy	1996	–	✓	–
Alan Rutherford	1990	–	✓	✓
Wendy Linsley	1990	–	✓	✓
Colin Anderson	1993	–	✓	✓
Marjorie Helm	1986	–	✓	✓
Heather Wilson	1993	–	✓	✓
Pat Hanley	1995	–	✓	–
Brian Cantwell	1996	–	✓	–
Judith Singleton	1995	–	✓	–
Michael Binks	1986	–	✓	✓
Gail Williams	1990	–	✓	✓

Facilities: 4 mediation rooms; separate waiting rooms; facilities for seeing children; disabled access on site

Geographical area covered: Newcastle, Gateshead, North Tyneside, Northumberland

Areas of practice: Children Issues; All Issues

Areas of specialism: consultation with children

Additional training undertaken by members: consultation with children; domestic violence; initial information giving and/or assessment; mediator trainer training; Professional Practice Supervision/Consultancy; welfare rights

Interpreters available ✓

Experience of working with different cultures: Black Other; Hindu; Sikh; Moslem

Newcastle's Leading Mediation Service

Family Mediation Service (Northumberland & Tyneside) was established as an independent service in 1986 and now works in partnership with NCH Action for Children and Northumbria Probation Service. We aim to provide a safe, confidential and neutral environment

(cont'd)

where parents in conflict can meet to discuss and resolve issues relating to their separation or divorce.

The geographical cover is from Gateshead in the south to the Scottish border in the north and from North Tyneside to the Cumbrian border in the west. The main office is based in central Newcastle and our mediators travel to a number of outposts throughout the region.

The service currently employs 14 mediators who have undertaken NFM training. The majority are accredited and the remainder will complete their accreditation this year. The service provides Child Focused Mediation and All Issues Mediation, being one of the first in the country to offer this service. We have five lawyer mediators and one legal consultant working with us. We provide information to parents in four local courts.

We are in Phase 1 of the Legal Aid Board's Mediation Pilot Franchise Scheme.

Family Mediation Service (North-West Yorkshire)

Manager / Co-ordinator of Regional Group / Service: Angela Coleman

13 Dragon Parade, Harrogate HG1 5BZ
Telephone 01423 525156

Affiliation body: National Family Mediation

		Areas of Practice		
	Year Trained	Finance	Children	All Issues
Members				
Joanna Heywood	1985	–	✓	✓
Lars Thompson	1985	–	✓	✓
Diana Wakefield	1991	–	✓	✓
Carol Walker	1985	–	✓	✓

Scarborough & District Family Mediation Service

Manager / Co-ordinator of Regional Group / Service: Ann Jones

St Mary's Parish House, Auborough Street, Scarborough, North Yorkshire YO11 1HT
Telephone 01723 507775

Affiliation body: National Family Mediation

South Yorkshire Family Mediation Service

Manager / Co-ordinator of Regional Group / Service: Jo Howe

Queen's Buildings, 55 Queen Street, Sheffield S1 2OX
Telephone 0114 275 2227, Facsimile 0114 275 3996

Affiliation body: National Family Mediation

(cont'd)

	Year Trained	Areas of Practice		
		Finance	Children	All Issues
Members				
James Howe	1984	–	–	–
Rhoda Swindells	1986	–	–	–

South Yorkshire Family Mediators Association

Manager / Co-ordinator of Regional Group / Service: Joella Bruckshaw

1 Moncrieffe Road, Sheffield, South Yorkshire S7 1HQ
Telephone 0114 258 8645, Facsimile 0114 258 8645, E-mail
j.bruckshaw@sheffield.ac.uk

Affiliation body: Family Mediators Association

	Year Trained	Areas of Practice		
		Finance	Children	All Issues
Members				
Joella Bruckshaw	1992	–	–	✓
Adam Pemberton	1989	–	–	✓
Rhoda Swindells	1989	–	–	✓
John Atherton	1996	–	–	✓
John Hoult	1996	–	–	✓

Sunderland & South Tyneside Family Mediation Service

Manager / Co-ordinator of Regional Group / Service: Peter Bolton

4th Floor, Crown House, Borough Road, Sunderland, Tyne & Wear SR1
1HW
Telephone 0191 568 0433, E-mail sastfms@aol.com

Affiliation body: National Family Mediation

	Year Trained	Areas of Practice		
		Finance	Children	All Issues
Members				
Valerie Smith	1986	✓	✓	✓
Sadie Barkess	1993	✓	✓	✓
Hedley Redhead	1992	✓	✓	✓
Agnes Duckas	1990	–	✓	–
D Minchella	1994	✓	✓	✓
Anne Bloor	1994	✓	✓	✓
Margaret Byrne	1995	–	✓	–
Frances Walker	1994	–	✓	–
Margaret Crisell	1994	✓	✓	✓

West Yorkshire Family Mediation Service

Manager / Co-ordinator of Regional Group / Service: Barbara Sanford

The Law Courts, Exchange Square, Drake Street, Bradford, West
Yorkshire BD1 1JA
Telephone 0345 419403, Facsimile 01274 730115

Affiliation body: National Family Mediation

(cont'd)

	Year Trained	Areas of Practice		
		Finance	Children	All Issue
Members				
Liz Bond	1998	–	–	✓
Rosemary Coursey	1998	–	–	✓
Maureen Emsley	1998	–	–	✓
Margaret Nunnerley	1998	–	–	✓
Bridget Robson	1998	–	–	✓
Alexis Walker	1998	–	–	✓

West Yorkshire Family Mediators Association

Manager / Co-ordinator of Regional Group / Service: Anne Braithwaite

c/o Lupton Sawcett Solicitors, Yorkshire House, Greek Street, Leeds
LS1 5SX
Telephone

Affiliation body: Family Mediators Association

York Family Mediation Service

Manager / Co-ordinator of Regional Group / Service: Catharine Morris

82 Bootham, York YO3 7DF
Telephone 01904 646068

Affiliation body: National Family Mediation

	Year Trained	Areas of Practice		
		Finance	Children	All Issues
Members				
Eileen Wragge	1986	✓	✓	✓
Rosie Schatzberger	1992	✓	✓	✓
Mary Staples	1992	–	✓	–
Isabel Wakeman	1995	✓	✓	✓
David Wheeler	1995	–	✓	–
John Reynard	1996	✓	✓	✓
Andrea Jones	1996	✓	✓	✓
Dorothy Nott	1997	✓	✓	✓
Associates				
Mike Moran	1997	–	✓	–
Anne Jones	1997	–	✓	–
Julia Terry	1997	–	✓	–

York Family Mediators Association

Manager / Co-ordinator of Regional Group / Service: Valerie Airton

18 Hillcrest Drive, Molescroft, Beverley, East Yorkshire HU17 7JL
Telephone 01482 882476

Affiliation body: Family Mediators Association

(cont'd

| | | Areas of Practice | | |
	Year Trained	Finance	Children	All Issues
Associates				
Valerie Airton	1995	–	✓	✓
John Hoult	1995	–	–	✓

Cheshire Mediation Service

Manager / Co-ordinator of Regional Group / Service: Ian Chambers

Goss Chambers, Goss Street, Chester CH1 2BG
Telephone 01244 400658, Facsimile 01244 343751

Affiliation body: National Family Mediation

| | | Areas of Practice | | |
	Year Trained	Finance	Children	All Issues
Members				
Ian Chambers	1995	–	✓	✓
Christine Cannon	1995	–	✓	✓
Eileen Howard	1995	–	✓	✓
Glen Hagan	1995	–	✓	✓

Facilities: 2 mediation rooms; separate waiting rooms; facilities for seeing children; off site disabled access arrangements can be made

Geographical area covered: Cheshire

Areas of practice: Children Issues; All Issues

Additional training undertaken by members: domestic violence; Professional Practice Supervision/Consultancy

Interpreters available ✓

Experience of working with different cultures: Black African; Moslem

Cumbria Family Mediation Service

Manager / Co-ordinator of Regional Group / Service: Hazel Bartle-Ross

92 Stricklandgate, Kendal, Cumbria LA4 9PU
Telephone 01539 733705, Facsimile 01539 733705

Affiliation body: National Family Mediation

| | | Areas of Practice | | |
	Year Trained	Finance	Children	All Issues
Members				
Veronica Swenson		–	–	✓
Marjorie Helm		–	✓	✓
Shirley Bates	1995	–	–	✓
Ann Elvish		–	✓	–
Nigel Longworth	1995	–	–	✓
Michael Binks		–	✓	–
Associates				
John Oldroyd	1996	–	✓	–

▣ Derbyshire Family Mediation Service

Manager / Co-ordinator of Regional Group / Service: Eddie Leggett

32a Newbold Road, Chesterfield, Derbyshire S41 7PH
Telephone 01246 277422, Facsimile 01246 277363

Affiliation body: National Family Mediation

		Areas of Practice		
	Year Trained	Finance	Children	All Issues
Members				
Eddie Leggett	1995	✓	✓	✓
Elizabeth Ralph	1996	✓	✓	✓
Gillian Brooks	1996	✓	✓	✓
Russell Simmons	1996	✓	✓	✓
Malcolm Heaver	1996	✓	✓	✓

Facilities: 4 mediation rooms; separate waiting rooms; facilities for seeing children; disabled access on site; induction loop facilities

Geographical area covered: Derbyshire and Derby City

Areas of practice: All Issues

Areas of specialism: consultation with children

Additional training undertaken by members: consultation with children; domestic violence; Professional Practice Supervision/Consultancy

Interpreters available ✓

Experience of working with different cultures: Black Carribean

Background
Derbyshire Family Mediation Service was established in 1995 as a partnership between NCH Action for Children, Derbyshire Probation Service and the Derbyshire County Council Social Services. We provide an All Issues Family Mediation Service for the families of Derbyshire County and Derby City. We use mediation venues in Chesterfield, Chapel-en-le-Frith and Derby.

Derbyshire Family Mediation Service recognises that every family is unique. Our service is committed to the interests of children and parents; to respecting their dignity, needs, privacy, and beliefs.

Derbyshire Family Mediation Service provides a safe, confidential and neutral place where parents and other family members in conflict can meet to discuss issues relating to children. We assist parents to work out their own solutions in the best interests of their children. We ensure equality of opportunity to all service users. Anti-discriminatory practice is an integral part of our work. We offer a consumer complaints and representation policy.

Derbyshire Family Mediation Service employs five experienced mediators who have completed NFM training and are all members of the UK College of Mediators. We offer All Issues Mediation and offer counselling to those children whose parents are involved in mediation.

NYAS

National Youth Advocacy Service

- for children and young people aged 0 - 25 suffering the negative effects of family breakdown.

NYAS has a team of highly trained Advocate/Caseworkers, as well as in-house legal advice. NYAS's practitioners are experienced Guardians ad Litem or Family Court Welfare Officers. Some also have family mediation experience. In addition, a Young Citizen's Project Officer provides information and training on children's rights and welfare to schools and colleges.

AMONG THE SERVICES THE NATIONAL YOUTH ADVOCACY SERVICE CAN PROVIDE ARE:

● an independent and confidential advocacy service for young people in and leaving care;

● legal advice and representation in both public and private law proceedings, available from NYAS's in-house Children's Panel Solicitor;

● accurate information on the law relating to children, the welfare benefit system and obtaining help from social services, provided by a Young Citizen's Project Officer;

● an independent assessment of a young person's situation;

● an outreach information and children's rights service to schools and colleges which includes a video and training pack on the UN Convention on the Rights of the Child for young people, parents and professionals;

● help in cases of school exclusion.

'Representing Children' is NYAS's quarterly journal for all those professionals concerned with the rights and welfare of children. The journal will keep you up to date in an increasingly complex and specialised field, by bringing you articles, news, reviews and legal notes of particular relevance to you. Subscription rates are £25.00 per annum for individuals and £40.00 per annum for institutions. Overseas rates are available upon request.

For information about any of the services available from NYAS ring 0151 342 7852 (fax 0151 342 3174) or write to Judith Timms, Chief Executive, NYAS, 1 Downham Road South, Heswall, Wirral, Merseyside, L60 5RG.

Family Mediation Service (Greater Manchester)

Manager / Co-ordinator of Regional Group / Service: Kathryn Brown

21 Knowsley Street, Bury BL9 0ST
Telephone 0161 797 9910, Facsimile 0161 763 9311

Affiliation body: National Family Mediation

		Areas of Practice		
	Year Trained	Finance	Children	All Issues
Members				
Mai Bentley	1991	–	✓	✓
Louise Horne	1992	–	✓	✓
Kathryn Brown	1993	–	✓	✓
Maggie Wilson	1992	–	✓	✓
Beryl Tweedale	1994	–	✓	✓
Mark Noall	1991	–	✓	–
Neil McDonald	1994	–	✓	✓
Ben Raikes	1996	–	✓	✓
June Mitchell	1991	–	✓	✓
Olive Lennards	1994	–	✓	✓
Glen Hagan	1995	–	✓	✓
Catherine Vickerman	1997	–	✓	✓
Mary Gracie	1997	–	✓	✓
Peter Gordon	1991	–	✓	✓
Associates				
Maxine Boodhoo	1993	–	✓	–

Greater Manchester Family Mediators Association

Manager / Co-ordinator of Regional Group / Service: Jennifer Cragg

131 Old Street, Ashton-under-Lyne, Greater Manchester OL6 7SA
Telephone 0161 285 3355, Facsimile 0161 339 4150

Affiliation body: Family Mediators Association

		Areas of Practice		
	Year Trained	Finance	Children	All Issues
Members				
Guy Otten	1992	✓	✓	✓
Andrew Ayres	1993	✓	✓	✓
Beverley Sayers	1994	✓	✓	✓
Associates				
Jenny Cragg	1993	✓	✓	✓
Gillian Price	1994	✓	✓	✓
Collette Burke	1994	✓	✓	✓
Helen Whitehouse	1997	✓	✓	✓

Lancashire Family Mediation Service

Manager / Co-ordinator of Regional Group / Service: Brian Gray

19 Ribblesdale Place, Preston PR1 3NA
Telephone 01772 204248, Facsimile 01772 204248

Affiliation body: National Family Mediation

		Areas of Practice		
	Year Trained	Finance	Children	All Issues
Members				
Carol Maher	1994	✓	✓	✓
Irene Chenery-Baker	1996	✓	✓	✓
Tracy Lowe	1996	✓	✓	✓
Brian Gray	1996	✓	✓	✓
Sara Holmes	1994	✓	✓	✓
Ann McCann	1994	✓	✓	✓
Penny Craig	1994	✓	✓	✓

Lancashire Family Mediators Association

Manager / Co-ordinator of Regional Group / Service: Marion MacBean

8 Quernmore Road, Caton, Lancaster LA2 9QA
Telephone 01524 770507, Facsimile 01524 770507

Affiliation body: Family Mediators Association

		Areas of Practice		
	Year Trained	Finance	Children	All Issues
Members				
Irene Chenery-Baker	1993	✓	✓	✓
Marion MacBean	1993	✓	✓	✓
Carol L Maher	1993	✓	✓	✓
Adrian Swenson	1994	✓	✓	✓
Annette Latham	1994	✓	✓	✓
Associates				
Richard Hirst	1994	✓	✓	✓
Greta Martens	1997	✓	✓	✓

Merseyside Family Mediation Service

Manager / Co-ordinator of Regional Group / Service: Barbara Robertson

5a Swiss Road, Liverpool L6 3AT
Telephone 0151 260 9155, Facsimile 0151 260 0548

Affiliation body: National Family Mediation

		Areas of Practice		
	Year Trained	Finance	Children	All Issues
Members				
Barbara Robertson	1993	✓	✓	✓
Liz Hotchkiss	1995	✓	✓	✓
Anne Swanson	1995	✓	✓	✓

(cont'd)

Groups/Services by Region B

		Areas of Practice		
	Year Trained	Finance	Children	All Issues
Sheila Haines	1995	✓	✓	✓
Andrea Findlay	1995	✓	✓	✓
Ian Chambers	1996	✓	✓	✓
Associates				
Chris Hill	1995	✓	✓	✓

Merseyside Family Mediators Association

Manager / Co-ordinator of Regional Group / Service: Helen Broughton

Queen Building, 8 Dale Street, Liverpool L2 4TQ
Telephone 0151 236 8871, Facsimile 0151 236 8109, DX 14142
LIVERPOOL

Affiliation body: Family Mediators Association

Family Mediation Borders

Manager / Co-ordinator of Regional Group / Service: Isobel Bilsland

PO Box 13753, Peebles EH45 8ZY
Telephone 01721 724170

Affiliation body: Family Mediators Scotland

		Areas of Practice		
	Year Trained	Finance	Children	All Issues
Members				
Linda Hawthorn	1995	–	✓	–
Hazel Robertson	1991	–	✓	–
Mary Symons	1992	–	✓	–
Associates				
Isobel Bilsland	1996	–	✓	–

Family Mediation Central Scotland

Manager / Co-ordinator of Regional Group / Service: Sandra Farquhar

16 Melville Terrace, Stirling FK8 2NE
Telephone 01786 472984, DX ST 18

Affiliation body: Family Mediators Scotland

		Areas of Practice		
	Year Trained	Finance	Children	All Issues
Members				
Sandra Farquhar	1984	–	✓	✓
Christine Adam	1993	–	✓	✓
Rosemary Allison	1989	–	✓	✓
Ed Ashton	1984	–	✓	✓
Ron Bowie	1987	–	✓	–
Margaret Burns	1993	–	✓	✓

(cont'd)

| | | Areas of Practice | | |
	Year Trained	Finance	Children	All Issues
Norma Forbes	1994	–	✓	✓
Crawford Logan	1993	–	✓	–
Murielle Paterson	1991	–	✓	–
Freda Townend	1991	–	✓	–
Jane Vale	1984	–	✓	–
Sarah Welsh	1991	–	✓	✓
Associates				
Phillipa Clegg	1996	–	✓	–
Lorraine Love	1996	–	✓	–

■ Family Mediation Grampian

Manager / Co-ordinator of Regional Group / Service: Elizabeth Wallace

2nd Floor, 27 Huntly Street, Aberdeen AB10 1TJ
Telephone 01224 630050

Affiliation body: Family Mediators Scotland

| | | Areas of Practice | | |
	Year Trained	Finance	Children	All Issues
Members				
Kay Bevans Brown	1995	–	✓	–
Margaret Black	1995	–	✓	–
Frances Bole	1995	–	✓	–
Margaret Comfort	1989	–	✓	–
Catherine Hamilton	1996	–	✓	–
Jennifer MacGregor	1992	–	✓	–
Helen Mollison	1994	–	✓	–
Anne Oswald	1989	–	✓	–
Ingrid Pringle	1992	–	✓	–
Elizabeth Wallace	1994	–	✓	–
Associates				
Angela Johnson	1996	–	✓	–
Claire Ross	1994	–	✓	–

■ Family Mediation Lothian

Manager / Co-ordinator of Regional Group / Service: Carol Barrett

2nd Floor, 37 George Street, Edinburgh EH2 2HN
Telephone 0131 226 4507, Facsimile 0131 220 4324

Affiliation body: Family Mediators Scotland

| | | Areas of Practice | | |
	Year Trained	Finance	Children	All Issues
Members				
Edward Cleland	1989	–	✓	✓
George C Davidson	1989	–	✓	✓
Hugh Donald	1992	–	✓	–

(cont'd)

Groups/Services by Region B

| | Year Trained | Areas of Practice | | |
		Finance	Children	All Issues
Fiona Anne Garwood	1989	–	✓	✓
Margaret Elizabeth Harvey	1994	–	✓	✓
Olive Jean Kinnear	1994	–	✓	✓
Jane McLaren	1989	–	✓	✓
George Leonard Mair	1996	–	✓	–
Associates				
Bill Gibson	1995	–	✓	–
Kate Shirres	1995	–	✓	–
Caroline Smith	1995	–	✓	–
Pauline Linn	1997	–	✓	–
Carol Barrett	1997	–	✓	–
Jenny Haslam	1997	–	✓	–

Family Mediation Orkney

Manager / Co-ordinator of Regional Group / Service: Margaret Spooner

43 Junction Road, Kirkwall, Orkney KW15 1AR
Telephone 01856 870571

Affiliation body: Family Mediators Scotland

| | Year Trained | Areas of Practice | | |
		Finance	Children	All Issues
Associates				
Margaret A Spooner	1995	–	✓	–
Manda Balfour	1995	–	✓	–
Diana Preston	1996	–	✓	–
Pauline Linn	1997	–	✓	–
Carol Barrett	1997	–	✓	–
Jenny Haslam	1997	–	✓	–

Family Mediation Service (Highland)

Manager / Co-ordinator of Regional Group / Service: Mary Cormack

Top Floor, 62 Academy Street, Inverness IV1 1LP
Telephone 01463 712100, Facsimile 01463 717994, DX IN 35

Affiliation body: Family Mediators Scotland

| | Year Trained | Areas of Practice | | |
		Finance	Children	All Issues
Members				
Mary Cormack	1989	✓	✓	✓
Mary Lothian	1990	–	✓	–
Linda Lowe	1989	–	✓	–
Rhonda McRorie	1990	✓	✓	✓
Jean Muir	1991	–	✓	

(cont'd)

	Year Trained	Areas of Practice		
		Finance	Children	All Issues
Ian Stevenson	1990	–	✓	–
Associates				
Sally Tattum	1996	–	✓	–

Family Mediation Service Western Isles

Manager / Co-ordinator of Regional Group / Service: Catherine Mary Paterson

The Bridge Community Centre, Bayhead, Stornoway, Isle of Lewis HS1 2DU
Telephone 01851 706868, Facsimile 01851 706868

Affiliation body: Family Mediators Scotland

	Year Trained	Areas of Practice		
		Finance	Children	All Issues
Members				
Donna Macleod	1991	–	✓	–
Catherine Paterson	1993	–	✓	–

Family Mediation Shetland

Manager / Co-ordinator of Regional Group / Service: Kathy Hubbard

91-93 St Olaf Street, Lerwick, Shetland ZE1 0ES
Telephone 01595 744400, Facsimile 01595 744436

Affiliation body: Family Mediators Scotland

	Year Trained	Areas of Practice		
		Finance	Children	All Issues
Associates				
Elaine Cunnah	1997	–	✓	–

Family Mediation Tayside

Manager / Co-ordinator of Regional Group / Service: William Muir

132a Nethergate, Dundee DD1 4ED
Telephone 01382 201343, Facsimile 01382 201343

Affiliation body: Family Mediators Scotland

	Year Trained	Areas of Practice		
		Finance	Children	All Issues
Members				
William Muir	1995	✓	✓	✓
Jan Binnie	1992	✓	✓	✓
Joyce Brunton	1987	✓	✓	✓
Betty Edwards	1987	–	✓	–
Kerrie Howe	1992	–	✓	–
Isabel Morrison	1987	✓	✓	✓
Averil Valentine	1987	–	✓	–

(cont'd)

		Areas of Practice		
	Year Trained	Finance	Children	All Issues
Michael Danaher	1994	✓	✓	✓
Sheila Ritchie	1994	✓	✓	✓
Claire Broadhurst	1994	–	✓	–
Alison McKay	1994	–	✓	–
Katrina Liddell	1996	✓	✓	✓
Associates				
Irene Mooney	1996	–	✓	–
Jane Reed	1997	–	✓	–
Brett Antonson	1997	–	✓	–

Family Mediation (West of Scotland)

Manager / Co-ordinator of Regional Group / Service: Walter Nicol

1 Melrose Street, Queens Crescent, Glasgow G4 9BJ
Telephone 0141 332 2731, Facsimile 0141 353 3816

Affiliation body: Family Mediators Scotland

		Areas of Practice		
	Year Trained	Finance	Children	All Issues
Members				
Marion Norris	1986	–	–	✓
Moira Munro	1986	–	–	✓
Lilian Thomson	1986	–	✓	–
Walter Nicol	1986	–	✓	–
Doreen Laird	1986	–	–	✓
Lynn Palmer	1989	–	✓	–
Annie Small	1989	–	✓	–
Annabel Abbott	1990	–	–	✓
Dori Jackson	1991	–	–	✓
Charlie Irvine	1993	–	–	✓
Associates				
Dougie Gass	1995	–	✓	–
Alexis Hunter	1996	–	✓	–
John McKenzie	1996	–	✓	–
Rhona Foy	1996	–	✓	–
Rosemary Docherty	1997	–	✓	–
Isobel Dumigan	1997	–	✓	–
Kate Lynch	1997	–	✓	–
Kate Devlin	1997	–	✓	–

NCH Action for Children, Dumfries & Galloway Family Mediation Service

Manager / Co-ordinator of Regional Group / Service: Marie McIntosh

The Family Centre, 4 Cresswell Gardens, Dumfries DG1 2HH
Telephone 01387 263185, Facsimile 01387 263185, DX 580634

Affiliation body: Family Mediators Scotland

(cont'd)

| | Year Trained | Areas of Practice | | |
		Finance	Children	All Issues
Members				
Maureen Biggar	1991	–	✓	✓
Marie McIntosh	1989	–	✓	–
Annie McKenzie	1993	–	✓	✓
Fiona Waite	1990	–	✓	–

■ NCH Action for Children Family Mediation Fife

Manager / Co-ordinator of Regional Group / Service: Morag White

30 North Street, Glenrothes, Fife KY11 5NA
Telephone 01592 751095, Facsimile 01592 751095, DX 560727

Affiliation body: Family Mediators Scotland

| | Year Trained | Areas of Practice | | |
		Finance	Children	All Issues
Members				
Robin Waterston	1989	–	✓	–
Catherine Stevenson	1991	–	✓	–
Jean Kinloch	1992	–	✓	–
Morag White	1990	–	✓	–
Carole Miller	1997	–	✓	–

Facilities: 3 mediation rooms; separate waiting rooms; facilities for seeing children; off site disabled access arrangements can be made

Geographical area covered: Fife – main office and outreach clinics

Areas of practice: Children Issues

Courses provided: divorce experience course

Additional training undertaken by members: consultation with children; domestic violence; initial information giving and/or assessment; Professional Practice Supervision/Consultancy; Children (Scotland) Act 1995

■ Family Mediation Cardiff

Manager / Co-ordinator of Regional Group / Service: Julia Dawson

4th Floor, St David's House, Wood Street, Cardiff CF1 1EY
Telephone 01222 229692, Facsimile 01222 399505

Affiliation body: National Family Mediation

| | Year Trained | Areas of Practice | | |
		Finance	Children	All Issues
Members				
Moira Atherton	1989	–	✓	–
Daphne Barry	1983	–	✓	–
Peter Barry	1983	–	✓	–
Peter Brice	1996	–	✓	–
Gerry David	1983	–	✓	–
Bryan James	1983	–	✓	–

(cont'd)

	Year Trained	Areas of Practice		
		Finance	Children	All Issues
Miranda Kitchener	1986	–	✓	–
Philip Nicholas	1983	–	✓	–
Associates				
Claire Collier	1997	–	✓	–
Philip Harrington	1996	–	✓	–
Gill Rees	1996	–	✓	–
Jill Waterman	1997	–	✓	–

■ Family Mediators South Wales Ltd

Manager / Co-ordinator of Regional Group / Service: Katie McColgan

Brackla House, Brackla Street, Bridgend, Mid Glamorgan CF31 1BZ
Telephone 01656 645525, Facsimile 01656 645174, DX 38004
BRIDGEND

Affiliation body: Family Mediators Association

	Year Trained	Areas of Practice		
		Finance	Children	All Issues
Members				
Catherine E McColgan	1992	✓	✓	✓
Hanno Koppel	1992	✓	✓	✓
Associates				
Nigel Packer	1995	✓	✓	✓
Robert Hammerton	1995	✓	✓	✓
Diane Watkins	1996	✓	✓	✓
Frank Fincham	1996	✓	✓	✓
R Kelvin Evans	1996	✓	✓	✓
Pamela Bateman	1997	✓	✓	✓
David Brill	1997	✓	✓	✓
Margaret Noon	1997	✓	✓	✓
Jacqueline Smith	1997	✓	✓	✓
Carol Morgan	1997	✓	✓	✓

■ Gwent Mediation Service

nch
action
for
children
CYMRU

Manager / Co-ordinator of Regional Group / Service: Jonathan Price

Ty Asha, 30 Stow Park Avenue, Newport NP9 4FN
Telephone 01633 263065, Facsimile 01633 258616

Affiliation body: National Family Mediation

	Year Trained	Areas of Practice		
		Finance	Children	All Issues
Members				
Peter Brice	1996	–	✓	–
Jonathan Price	1996	–	✓	–

(cont'd)

	Year Trained	Finance	Areas of Practice Children	All Issues
Sarah Lindfield	1997	–	✓	–
Associates				
Jane Butler	1997	–	✓	–

Facilities: 2 mediation rooms; separate waiting rooms; facilities for seeing children; off site disabled access arrangements can be made

Geographical area covered: Gwent – Southern region

Areas of practice: Children Issues

Areas of specialism: consultation with children

Additional training undertaken by members: consultation with children; domestic violence; anti-discriminatory practice; equal opportunities

Interpreters available ✓

Experience of working with different cultures: Black Caribbean; Jewish; Sikh; Black African; Moslem

Additional Information

Gwent Mediation Service was established as a partnership between NCH Action For Children and Gwent Probation Service in 1996 to offer family mediation with a child centred focus to assist parents, or others with responsibilities for arrangements for children, to negotiate agreements about future arrangements for those children. We particularly offer a 'privileged' mediation service to those involved in court proceedings in relation to their children. In 1998 we plan to extend still further by offering mediation at 'outposts' in addition to our main office.

We are committed to the interests of children and parents, in particular to respecting their beliefs, culture, needs and privacy, and aim to ensure equality of opportunity to all service users. We operate a consumer 'complaints and representation' policy.

The service provides a safe, neutral place where parents and other family members in conflict can meet with a mediator to discuss issues relating to their children and to work out their own solutions in the best interests of the children.

Gwent Mediation Service employs mediators drawn from a range of professional backgrounds all of whom have also completed NFM training. We are committed to development and anticipate being able to offer other services to children and parents in due course.

North Wales Family Mediators Association

Manager / Co-ordinator of Regional Group / Service: Sally Dowding

123 High Street, Bangor, Gwynedd LL57 1NT

(cont'd)

Telephone 01248 370224, Facsimile 01248 352313, DX 18721 BANGOR 1

Affiliation body: Family Mediators Association

North Wales Mediation Service

Manager / Co-ordinator of Regional Group / Service: Alex Jaundrill

8 Riviere's Avenue, Colwyn Bay, Clwyd LL29 7DP
Telephone 01492 533830

Affiliation body: National Family Mediation

Northern Ireland Family Mediation Service

Manager / Co-ordinator of Regional Group / Service: Linda Kerr

76 Dublin Road, Belfast BT2 7HP
Telephone 01232 322914, Facsimile 01232 315298

Affiliation body: National Family Mediation

		Areas of Practice		
	Year Trained	Finance	Children	All Issues
Associates				
Linda Kerr	1987	–	✓	–
Sheena Bell	1987	–	✓	–
Muriel Orr	1995	–	✓	–

DIRECTORY

A–Z College Members and Associates

This section provides an alphabetical listing of Members or Associates of the UK College of Family Mediators. The information in this section was supplied by the individual Members and Associates, some of whom have taken the option of providing additional information on their practice and career.

A–Z of College Members and Associates

Abbott, J Annabel (M)

> *Approved Body:* Family Mediation Scotland
>
> *Regional Group / Service:* Family Mediation (West of Scotland)
>
> *Mediation telephone number:* 0141 332 2731

Abraham, Jeremy (M)

> *Approved Body:* Family Mediators Association
>
> *Regional Group / Service:* London South & Central Family Mediators Association
>
> *Mediation telephone number:* 0171 264 2027

Ackroyd, Peter William (M)

> *Approved Body:* Family Mediators Association
>
> *Regional Group / Service:* London South & Central Family Mediators Association
>
> *Mediation telephone number:* 0171 737 0909
>
> *Mediation address:* Hornby Ackroyd & Levy, 2-6 Atlantic Road, London SW9 8HR
> Facsimile 0171 274 0886, DX 58755 BRIXTON
>
> *Professional qualifications and experience:* solicitor; accredited mediator and supervisor with FMA
>
> *Year qualified in mediation:* 1991
>
> *Membership of professional bodies and organisations:* FMA
>
> *Willing to travel outside the region:* ✓
>
> *Willing to travel to:* South East England
>
> *Practice offered:* Finance Issues Mediation; Children Issues Mediation; All Issues Mediation; Professional Practice Supervision/Consultancy
>
> *Additional mediation training:*
>
> Professional Practice Supervision FMA 1997
>
> *Other additional mediation training:* sole and anchor 1997

Adam, Christine Murray (M)

> *Approved Body:* Family Mediation Scotland
>
> *Regional Group / Service:* Family Mediation Central Scotland
>
> *Mediation telephone number:* 01786 472984

■ **Adcock**, Deborah Jane (A)

> *Approved Body:* Solicitors Family Law Association
>
> *Regional Group / Service:* Member of Solicitors Family Law Association, telephone 01689 850227 for details
>
> *Mediation telephone number:* 01482 223693

■ **Adcock**, Margaret (M)

> *Approved Body:* National Family Mediation
>
> *Regional Group / Service:* Family Mediation Service – Institute of Family Therapy
>
> *Mediation telephone number:* 0171 391 9169

■ **Affleck**, Jane (M)

> *Approved Body:* National Family Mediation
>
> *Regional Group / Service:* Cleveland Family Mediation Service
>
> *Mediation telephone number:* 01642 222967

■ **Ahmed**, Jacqueline (A)

> *Approved Body:* LawGroup UK
>
> *Regional Group / Service:* Member of LawGroup UK's Family Mediation Register, telephone 01883 370000 for details
>
> *Mediation telephone number:* 01392 255777

■ **Airton**, Valerie (A)

> *Approved Body:* Family Mediators Association
>
> *Regional Group / Service:* York Family Mediators Association
>
> *Mediation telephone number:* 01482 882476

■ **Aitken**, Anne (A)

> *Approved Body:* Family Mediators Association
>
> *Regional Group / Service:* London North & Central Family Mediators Association
>
> *Mediation telephone number:* 0171 700 6006

■ **Akers**, John Bernard (M)

> *Approved Body:* National Family Mediation
>
> *Regional Group / Service:* Birmingham District Family Mediation
>
> *Mediation telephone number:* 0121 233 1999

■ **Alderwick**, Stephanie Mary (A)

> *Approved Body:* Family Mediators Association
>
> *Regional Group / Service:* Thames Valley Family Mediators Association
> *(cont'd)*

Mediation telephone number: 01189 393999

Alexander, Derek (A)

Approved Body: Family Mediators Association

Regional Group / Service: Kent Family Mediators Association

Mediation telephone number: 01424 437142

Alford, Robert John (A)

Approved Body: LawGroup UK

Regional Group / Service: Member of LawGroup UK's Family Mediation Register, telephone 01883 370000 for details

Mediation telephone number: 01392 255777

Ali, Javed (M)

Approved Body: National Family Mediation

Regional Group / Service: NCH Action for Children Eye to Eye Mediation

Mediation telephone number: 0171 701 1114

Allan, June Rita (A)

Approved Body: Family Mediators Association

Mediation telephone number: 0956 646177

Allen, Angela Elaine (M)

Approved Body: National Family Mediation

Regional Group / Service: South Essex Family Mediation Service

Mediation telephone number: 01702 436466

Mediation address: South Essex Family Mediation Service, 29 Harcourt Avenue, Southend-on-Sea, Essex SS2 6HT

Willing to travel outside the region: ✓

Willing to travel to: Essex, London, Suffolk, Herts, Kent, Surrey

Practice offered: Children Issues Mediation; divorce counselling/divorce recovery workshops offered in private counselling practice

Additional mediation training:

consultation with children　　　　　　　　　　NFM　　　　　　　1995

Allen, Elizabeth Ann (A)

Approved Body: LawGroup UK

Regional Group / Service: Member of LawGroup UK's Family Mediation Register, telephone 01883 370000 for details

Mediation telephone number: 01392 210700

▣ **Allen**, Roderick Anthony (A)

Approved Body: Solicitors Family Law Association

Regional Group / Service: Member of Solicitors Family Law Association, telephone 01689 850227 for details

Mediation telephone number: 01922 452860/458066/743516

Mediation address: Partridge Allen Portland Buildings, Aldridge, Walsall W39 8PR
Facsimile 01922 457614, DX MDX 29196 ALDRIDGE

Professional qualifications and experience: solicitor 13 years; SFLA All Issues trained mediator

Year qualified in mediation: 1998

Membership of professional bodies and organisations: The Law Society (Birmingham Law Society); SFLA (Relate Partnership) Probate section

Willing to travel outside the region: ✓

Willing to travel to: Staffordshire, Warwickshire, Leicestershire

Practice offered: All Issues Mediation; commercial

▣ **Allison**, Rosemary (M)

Approved Body: Family Mediation Scotland

Regional Group / Service: Family Mediation Central Scotland

Mediation telephone number: 01786 472984

▣ **Allport**, Lesley (M)

Approved Body: National Family Mediation

Regional Group / Service: Birmingham District Family Mediation

Mediation telephone number: 0121 233 1999/01922 611966

Mediation address: Birmingham District Family Mediation, 3 Kingston Row, Birmingham, West Midlands B1 2NU
Facsimile 0121 233 1999

Other mediation address: Family Mediation in Walsall, 15 Lower Hall Lane, Walsall, West Midlands WS1

Professional qualifications and experience: BA Hons Degree in Theology; Diploma in Pastoral Studies (DPS); domestic violence worker, trainer; voluntary sector development worker; information presenter

Year qualified in mediation: 1989

Willing to travel outside the region: ✓

Willing to travel to: Wolverhampton, Walsall, Black Country

Practice offered: Finance Issues Mediation; Children Issues Mediation; All Issues Mediation; mediation training

(cont'd)

Additional mediation training:

consultation with children
domestic violence   1995

Other additional mediation training: All Issues Mediation; trainer for NFM domestic violence course 1996

Almond, Lesley Eleanor (A)

Approved Body: Family Mediators Association

Regional Group / Service: Herts & Bucks Family Mediators Association

Mediation telephone number: 0181 423 6666

Ambrose, John (M)

Approved Body: National Family Mediation

Regional Group / Service: Hampshire Family Mediation

Mediation telephone number: 01983 825697

Amswych, Louise (A)

Approved Body: Family Mediators Association

Regional Group / Service: The Hertfordshire Comprehensive Mediation Service

Mediation telephone number: 01923 853358

Anderson, Colin (M)

Approved Body: National Family Mediation

Regional Group / Service: Family Mediation Service (Northumberland & Tyneside)

Mediation telephone number: 0191 261 9212

Angel, Stan (A)

Approved Body: National Family Mediation

Regional Group / Service: South Yorkshire Family Mediation Service

Mediation telephone number: 0114 275 2227

Angell, Sarah Jane (M)

Approved Body: Family Mediators Association

Regional Group / Service: Bath District Family Mediators Association

Mediation telephone number: 01225 484244

Mediation address: 5 Pierrepont Street, Bath BA1 1LB
Facsimile 01225 461055

Professional qualifications and experience: solicitor; qualified teacher; accredited mediator; member of the UK College of Family Mediators

Year qualified in mediation: 1996

(cont'd)

A–Z College Members and Associates

C

Membership of professional bodies and organisations: The Law Society
Family Mediators Association; Solicitors Family Law Association

Practice offered: Finance Issues Mediation; Children Issues Mediation;
All Issues Mediation; sole mediation

Additional mediation training:

domestic violence
initial information giving and/or assessment

Other additional mediation training: sole and anchor mediation (FMA)
1995

Anker, Karen Lesley (A)

Approved Body: Family Mediators Association

Mediation telephone number: 01223 355933

Anticoni, Sarah (A)

Approved Body: National Family Mediation; Family Mediators
Association

Regional Group / Service: London North & Central Family Mediators
Association

Mediation telephone number: 0171 222 9070

Mediation address: c/o Campbell Hooper, 35 Old Queen Street, London
SW1H 9JD
Facsimile 0171 222 5591, DX 2365 VICTORIA, E-mail sta@campbell-
hooper.co.uk

Other mediation address: 9 Menelik Road, London NW2 3RR

Professional qualifications and experience: solicitor, admitted 1988

Year qualified in mediation: 1995

Membership of professional bodies and organisations: Family
Mediators Association; Solicitors Family Law Association; The Law
Society

Willing to travel outside the region: ✓

Willing to travel to: North and Central London

Practice offered: Finance Issues Mediation; Children Issues Mediation;
All Issues Mediation

Background

I have been a partner with Campbell Hooper since 1992 and head up
the Family Law Group which consists of three partners, an assistant
and a trainee.

I presently sit on the Solicitors Family Law Association London
Regional Council and am an active member of the London North &
Central Family Mediators Association. I am a mother of two children.

Antonson, Brett (A)

Approved Body: Family Mediation Scotland

Regional Group / Service: Family Mediation Tayside

Mediation telephone number: 01382 201343

ap Cynan, Robin Mostyn (M)

Approved Body: Family Mediators Association

Regional Group / Service: Shropshire Family Mediators Association

Mediation telephone number: 01952 680284

Mediation address: The Store Barn, Church Street, Madeley, Telford
TF7 5BU
Facsimile 01952 680284, E-mail rmapc@aol.com

Other mediation address: Stephen Thomas, 15 English Walls,
Oswestry, Shropshire SY11 2PA

Professional qualifications and experience: mediator-solicitor; The Law
Society Children Panel Member; accredited supervisor/PPSC; FMA
anchor trainer; accredited Divorce Information Presenter

Year qualified in mediation: 1990

Membership of professional bodies and organisations: FMA; SFLA;
BALM; SCL; BAAF; The Law Society

Willing to travel outside the region: ✓

Willing to travel to: West Midlands, Cheshire, Wales

Practice offered: Finance Issues Mediation; Children Issues Mediation;
All Issues Mediation; mediation training; Professional Practice
Supervision/Consultancy; solo, sole and anchor, and co-mediation

Additional mediation training:

initial information giving and/or assessment	NCFP	1997
mediation trainer training	FMA	1997
Professional Practice Supervision/Consultancy	FMA	1996

Other additional mediation training: welfare benefits (College of Law)
1997

Armstrong, Claire Elisabeth (M)

Approved Body: National Family Mediation

Regional Group / Service: Herefordshire Family Mediation Service

Mediation telephone number: 01432 264087

Arnold, Helen Jane (A)

Approved Body: Solicitors Family Law Association

Regional Group / Service: Member of Solicitors Family Law Association,
telephone 01689 850227 for details

Mediation telephone number: 0121 552 2382

Ashley, Auriol Mary (M)

Approved Body: National Family Mediation; Family Mediators Association

Regional Group / Service: Thames Valley Family Mediation

Mediation telephone number: 01628 667100

Ashton, Edwin Taylor (M)

Approved Body: Family Mediation Scotland

Regional Group / Service: Family Mediation Central Scotland

Mediation telephone number: 01786 472984

Atherton, Frederick John (M)

Approved Body: Family Mediators Association

Regional Group / Service: South Yorkshire Family Mediators Association

Mediation telephone number: 01302 320621

Atherton, Moira Christine (M)

Approved Body: National Family Mediation

Regional Group / Service: Family Mediation Cardiff

Mediation telephone number: 01222 229692

Attle, Sarah Jane (A)

Approved Body: Family Mediators Association

Regional Group / Service: Cambridge Family Mediators Association

Mediation telephone number: 01223 364422

Attwood, Caroline (A)

Approved Body: Solicitors Family Law Association

Regional Group / Service: Member of Solicitors Family Law Association telephone 01689 850227 for details

Mediation telephone number: 0181 678 5500

Austin, Linda Mary (A)

Approved Body: Solicitors Family Law Association

Regional Group / Service: Member of Solicitors Family Law Association telephone 01689 850227 for details

Mediation telephone number: 01440 762511/704821

A–Z College Members and Associates
C

Ayres, Andrew (M)

Approved Body: Family Mediators Association

Regional Group / Service: Greater Manchester Family Mediators Association

Mediation telephone number: 0161 480 5229

Mediation address: 5 St Petersgate, Stockport, Cheshire SK1 1EB Facsimile 0161 476 2549, DX 19665 STOCKPORT 1, E-mail info@ayreswaters.u-net.com

Professional qualifications and experience: a solicitor for 19 years

Year qualified in mediation: 1992

Membership of professional bodies and organisations: FMA; SFLA

Willing to travel outside the region: ✓

Willing to travel to: throughout Greater Manchester, as well as High Peak and Cheshire

Practice offered: All Issues Mediation; Professional Practice Supervision/Consultancy

Additional mediation training:

Professional Practice Supervision/Consultancy   FMA   1997

Baglee, Karen Therese (A)

Approved Body: LawWise

Regional Group / Service: Member of LawWise Family Mediators Register, telephone 01483 237300 for details

Mediation telephone number: 0191 416 4848

Bailey, Peter Edward Hughes (A)

Approved Body: Family Mediators Association

Regional Group / Service: Sussex Family Mediators Association

Mediation telephone number: 01273 551630

Bainham, Wendy Wolf (M)

Approved Body: National Family Mediation

Regional Group / Service: Norfolk Family Mediation Service

Mediation telephone number: 01603 620588

Baker, Deborah (A)

Approved Body: LawGroup UK

Regional Group / Service: Member of LawGroup UK's Family Mediation Register, telephone 01883 370000 for details

Mediation telephone number: 01271 374132

Baker, Sioux (M)

>*Approved Body:* National Family Mediation
>
>*Regional Group / Service:* Thames Valley Family Mediation
>
>*Mediation telephone number:* 01753 830770

Baldrey, Jenny (M)

>*Approved Body:* National Family Mediation
>
>*Regional Group / Service:* Surrey Family Mediation Service
>
>*Mediation telephone number:* 01306 741777

Balfour, Elaine Manda (A)

>*Approved Body:* Family Mediation Scotland
>
>*Regional Group / Service:* Family Mediation Orkney
>
>*Mediation telephone number:* 01856 870571

Ball, Lynn Hilary (A)

>*Approved Body:* Solicitors Family Law Association
>
>*Regional Group / Service:* Member of Solicitors Family Law Association, telephone 01689 850227 for details
>
>*Mediation telephone number:* 01865 244661

Ball, Roderick Kevan (A)

>*Approved Body:* Family Mediators Association
>
>*Regional Group / Service:* South West Region Family Mediators Association
>
>*Mediation telephone number:* 01271 43026

Ball, Sheridan Lesley (A)

>*Approved Body:* LawWise
>
>*Regional Group / Service:* Member of LawWise Family Mediators Register, telephone 01483 237300 for details
>
>*Mediation telephone number:* 01482 323239

Bankole Jones, Evangeline Indira (A)

>*Approved Body:* National Family Mediation
>
>*Regional Group / Service:* African Caribbean Family Mediation Service
>
>*Mediation telephone number:* 0171 738 2366

Banks, John (M)

>*Approved Body:* National Family Mediation
>
>*Regional Group / Service:* Berkshire Family Mediation
>
>*Mediation telephone number:* 0118 957 1159

(cont'd)

Bardell, Eric Edwin (A)

Approved Body: LawGroup UK

Regional Group / Service: Member of LawGroup UK's Family Mediation
Register, telephone 01883 370000 for details

Mediation telephone number: 01372 724961

Barkees, Sadie (A)

Approved Body: National Family Mediation

Regional Group / Service: Sunderland & South Tyneside Family
Mediation Service

Mediation telephone number: 0191 568 0433

Barlow, Linda (A)

Approved Body: Family Mediators Association

Regional Group / Service: Oxford Family Mediators Association

Mediation telephone number: 01865 880578

Barnett, Marilyn (M)

Approved Body: Family Mediators Association

Regional Group / Service: Family Mediation in Norfolk

Mediation telephone number: 01603 619371

Barnett, Sylvia Dina (A)

Approved Body: Family Mediators Association

Regional Group / Service: London North & Central Family Mediators
Association; Herts & Bucks Family Mediators Association

Mediation telephone number: 0181 953 9111

■ **Barrett**, Carol (A)

> *Approved Body:* Family Mediation Scotland
>
> *Regional Group / Service:* Family Mediation Lothian
>
> *Mediation telephone number:* 0131 226 4507

■ **Barry**, Daphne Joan (M)

> *Approved Body:* National Family Mediation
>
> *Regional Group / Service:* Family Mediation Cardiff
>
> *Mediation telephone number:* 01222 229692

■ **Barry**, Peter John (M)

> *Approved Body:* National Family Mediation
>
> *Regional Group / Service:* Family Mediation Cardiff
>
> *Mediation telephone number:* 01222 229692

■ **Bastyan**, Terry (A)

> *Approved Body:* LawGroup UK
>
> *Regional Group / Service:* Member of LawGroup UK's Family Mediation Register, telephone 01883 370000 for details
>
> *Mediation telephone number:* 01392 424242

■ **Bateman**, Janet (M)

> *Approved Body:* National Family Mediation
>
> *Regional Group / Service:* Northamptonshire Family Mediation Service
>
> *Mediation telephone number:* 01604 636651

■ **Bateman**, Pamela (A)

> *Approved Body:* Family Mediators Association
>
> *Regional Group / Service:* Family Mediators South Wales Ltd
>
> *Mediation telephone number:* 01656 645525

■ **Beashel**, Rosaleen Emily (A)

> *Approved Body:* Solicitors Family Law Association
>
> *Regional Group / Service:* Member of Solicitors Family Law Association telephone 01689 850227 for details
>
> *Mediation telephone number:* 01373 462017

■ **Beatson**, Kim (M)

> *Approved Body:* Family Mediators Association
>
> *Mediation telephone number:* 0181 678 5500

■ **Bedell-Pearce,** Sheron (A)

Approved Body: Family Mediators Association

Regional Group / Service: West Yorkshire Family Mediators Association

Mediation telephone number: 01943 817230

■ **Beeton,** Clare (M)

Approved Body: National Family Mediation

Regional Group / Service: Shropshire Family Mediation Service

Mediation telephone number: 01952 502447

■ **Begg,** Kay (M)

Approved Body: National Family Mediation

Regional Group / Service: Bristol Family Mediation Service

Mediation telephone number: 0117 929 2002

■ **Bell,** Jayne Anne (A)

Approved Body: Family Mediators Association

Regional Group / Service: Hampshire & Isle of Wight Family Mediators Association

Mediation telephone number: 01983 527308

■ **Bell,** Sheena Mary (M)

Approved Body: National Family Mediation

Regional Group / Service: Northern Ireland Family Mediation Service

Mediation telephone number: 01232 322914

Mediation address: Northern Ireland Family Mediation Service, 76 Dublin Road, Belfast, Antrim BT2 7HP
Facsimile 01232 315298

Other mediation address: 26 Osborne Gardens, Belfast, Antrim BT9 6LF

Professional qualifications and experience: MA (Sociology); nurse teacher (1977-83); couple counsellor

Year qualified in mediation: 1987

Membership of professional bodies and organisations: UK College of Family Mediators

Willing to travel outside the region: ✓

Willing to travel to: UK and Irish Republic

Practice offered: Children Issues Mediation; mediation training; Professional Practice Supervision/Consultancy

(cont'd)

Additional mediation training:

consultation with children	NFM	1996
domestic violence	NFM	1997
initial information giving and/or assessment	NFM & Relate	1989
mediation trainer training	Northern Ireland Council for Voluntary Action	1995
Professional Practice Supervision/Consultancy	NFM	1995

Other additional mediation training: have trained with and provided training for Mediation Network Northern Ireland

Benfield, Sarah Bridget (A)

Approved Body: Solicitors Family Law Association

Regional Group / Service: Member of Solicitors Family Law Association, telephone 01689 850227 for details

Mediation telephone number: 0118 957 4291

Bennett, Denise (M)

Approved Body: National Family Mediation; Family Mediators Association

Regional Group / Service: Thames Valley Family Mediation; Mediation for Families (South Bucks)

Mediation telephone number: 01494 875018

Benson, Gwenyth (M)

Approved Body: National Family Mediation

Regional Group / Service: Mediation Advisory Service for Stafford and North Staffordshire

Mediation telephone number: 01785 214933

Bentley, Mai (M)

Approved Body: National Family Mediation

Regional Group / Service: Family Mediation Service (Greater Manchester)

Mediation telephone number: 0161 797 4410

Bentley, Sally (M)

Approved Body: National Family Mediation

Regional Group / Service: Divorce Mediation & Counselling Service

Mediation telephone number: 0171 730 2422

■ **Bergin**, Timothy William (A)

Approved Body: LawWise

Regional Group / Service: Member of LawWise Family Mediators Register, telephone 01483 237300 for details

Mediation telephone number: 01273 607953

■ **Best**, Richard (M)

Approved Body: National Family Mediation

Regional Group / Service: Sussex Family Mediation Service

Mediation telephone number: 01273 550563

■ **Betteridge**, Mark Alan (A)

Approved Body: Solicitors Family Law Association

Regional Group / Service: Member of Solicitors Family Law Association, telephone 01689 850227 for details

Mediation telephone number: 01992 505406

Mediation address: 17 Bull Plain, Hertford, Hertfordshire SG14 1DX Facsimile 01992 501979, DX 57927 HERTFORD, E-mail markbetteridge@dial.pipex.com

Professional qualifications and experience: admitted as solicitor February 1989; member of SFLA since 1994; SFLA trained All Issues sole solicitor-mediator since June 1996

Year qualified in mediation: 1996

Membership of professional bodies and organisations: SFLA; UK College of Family Mediators; NFU

Willing to travel outside the region: ✓

Willing to travel to: London and Home Counties

Practice offered: All Issues Mediation

Career

Solicitor since 1989, specialising in family law. Joined SFLA in 1994 becoming All Issues solicitor-mediator in 1996.

Main area of specialisation is farming divorce cases. Acted for many farmers nationally. Member of the National Farmers Union Professional Group. Experience of dispute resolution in difficult farming cases.

Mediated both heterosexual and homosexual/lesbian couples with regard to property disputes.

■ **Bevans Brown**, Kay (M)

Approved Body: Family Mediation Scotland

Regional Group / Service: Family Mediation Grampian

Biggar, Maureen (M)

Approved Body: Family Mediation Scotland

Regional Group / Service: NCH Action for Children Dumfries & Galloway Family Mediation Service

Mediation telephone number: 01387 263185

Bilsland, Isobel M G (A)

Approved Body: Family Mediation Scotland

Regional Group / Service: Family Mediation Borders

Mediation telephone number: 01721 724170

Bilson, Rita Frances (M)

Approved Body: National Family Mediation

Regional Group / Service: Northamptonshire Family Mediation Service

Mediation telephone number: 01604 631651

Bilton, Elizabeth Jane (A)

Approved Body: Solicitors Family Law Association

Regional Group / Service: Member of Solicitors Family Law Association, telephone 01689 850227 for details

Mediation telephone number: 01623 624613

Mediation address: 27-28 St John Street, Mansfield, Nottinghamshire NG18 1QJ
Facsimile 01623 420101, DX 10348

Professional qualifications and experience: LLB (Hons); SFLA All Issues Mediation

Year qualified in mediation: 1997

Membership of professional bodies and organisations: The Law Society; SFLA

Willing to travel outside the region: ✓

Willing to travel to: Nottingham, Chesterfield and surrounding districts

Practice offered: All Issues Mediation

Binks, Michael (M)

Approved Body: National Family Mediation

Regional Group / Service: Cumbria Family Mediation Service; Family Mediation Service (Northumberland & Tyneside)

Mediation telephone number: 0191 261 9212

Binnie, Jan (M)

Approved Body: Family Mediation Scotland

Regional Group / Service: Family Mediation Tayside

(cont'd)

Mediation telephone number: 01382 201343

Bird, Donald John (A)

Approved Body: Solicitors Family Law Association

Regional Group / Service: Member of Solicitors Family Law Association, telephone 01689 850227 for details

Mediation telephone number: 01302 320621

Bird, Grant Harvey (A)

Approved Body: Solicitors Family Law Association

Regional Group / Service: Member of Solicitors Family Law Association, telephone 01689 850227 for details

Mediation telephone number: 0121 233 2904/200 3026

Mediation address: Fountain Court, Steelhouse Lane, Birmingham B4 6EE
Telephone 0121 200 3026/233 2904, Facsimile 0121 236 8913, DX 23534 BIRMINGHAM 3

Professional qualifications and experience: solicitor specialising in all areas of family law

Year qualified in mediation: 1998

Membership of professional bodies and organisations: The Law Society Children Panel; SFLA – West Midlands region committee member

Willing to travel outside the region: ✓

Willing to travel to: Coventry, Worcester, Warwickshire

Practice offered: All Issues Mediation

Bishop, Gillian (M)

Approved Body: Family Mediators Association

Regional Group / Service: London South & Central Family Mediators Association

Mediation telephone number: 0171 420 5000

Mediation address: The Family Law Consortium, 2 Henrietta Street, London WC2E 8PS
Facsimile 0170 420 5005, DX 40012 COVENT GARDEN, E-mail flc@tflc.co.uk

Professional qualifications and experience: solicitor – admitted to roll 1982

Year qualified in mediation: 1995

Membership of professional bodies and organisations: The Law Society; FMA; SFLA

Practice offered: All Issues Mediation

(cont'd)

Additional mediation training:

mediation trainer training	FMA	1997

I am a solicitor (qualified 1982) and specialising in family law. I am a founding partner of The Family Law Consortium, probably the first multi-disciplinary practice in the country combining solicitors, counsellors and mediators. I qualified as a mediator in 1995 with FMA and am qualified to conduct all issue mediations on both a co-working and a sole and anchor basis. I have trained as a mediation trainer. I am an active member of the Solicitors Family Law Association, chairing its Education Committee (which develops ways of educating the legal profession in the dynamics of family breakdown) and am a member of its National Committee. I am a trustee of the Oxford Institute of Legal Practice (OILP) and a trustee of the London Marriage Guidance Council. As a trustee of OILP I have been involved in the creation of the Postgraduate Certificate and Diploma in Family Mediation to be awarded by the University of Oxford. I am a co-author of *Divorce Reform: A Guide for Lawyers and Mediators* (FT Law & Tax).

■ **Black**, Margaret (M)

Approved Body: Family Mediation Scotland

Regional Group / Service: Family Mediation Grampian

Mediation telephone number: 01343 540801

■ **Blackburn**, A Julia (M)

Approved Body: National Family Mediation

Regional Group / Service: Norfolk Family Mediation Service

Mediation telephone number: 01603 620588

■ **Blacklock**, Ruth Morag (M)

Approved Body: National Family Mediation

Regional Group / Service: Salisbury & District Family Mediation Service

Mediation telephone number: 01722 332936

Mediation address: Salisbury & District Family Mediation Service, 24B St Edmunds Church Street, Salisbury, Wiltshire SP1 1EF

Other mediation address: Lambs House, East Stour, Gillingham, Dorset SP8 5JR

Professional qualifications and experience: NFM supervisor (Salisbury, Somerset and Plymouth services); NFM selector; accreditor, management consultant for AIM Development

Year qualified in mediation: 1986

Membership of professional bodies and organisations: NFM; UK College of Family Mediators

Willing to travel outside the region: ✓

Willing to travel to: Southern and Western England, London

(cont'd)

Practice offered: Children Issues Mediation; All Issues Mediation; Professional Practice Supervision/Consultancy

Additional mediation training:

domestic violence	NFM	1997
Professional Practice Supervision/Consultancy	NFM	1996

Other additional mediation training: advanced supervisors training (NFM) 1998

Blackshaw, Alan George (M)

Approved Body: National Family Mediation

Regional Group / Service: Suffolk Family Mediation Service

Blandford, Robin Andrew (M)

Approved Body: Family Mediators Association

Regional Group / Service: The Hertfordshire Comprehensive Mediation Service

Mediation telephone number: 01582 833757

Block, Marion Daniel (A)

Approved Body: LawWise

Regional Group / Service: Member of LawWise Family Mediators Register, telephone 01483 237300 for details

Mediation telephone number: 01253 302822

Bloor, Anne Miriam (M)

Approved Body: National Family Mediation

Regional Group / Service: Sunderland & South Tyneside Family Mediation Service

Boldero, Jeanie (A)

Approved Body: National Family Mediation

Regional Group / Service: Shropshire Family Mediation Service

Mediation telephone number: 01952 502447

Bole, Frances Elizabeth (M)

Approved Body: Family Mediation Scotland

Regional Group / Service: Family Mediation Grampian

Mediation telephone number: 01224 630050

Bond, Elizabeth Jennifer (A)

Approved Body: National Family Mediation

Regional Group / Service: West Yorkshire Family Mediation Service

■ **Boodhoo,** Maxine Ann (A)

> *Approved Body:* National Family Mediation
>
> *Regional Group / Service:* Family Mediation Service (Greater Manchester)
>
> *Mediation telephone number:* 0161 797 9910

■ **Booker,** Daphne Anne (M)

> *Approved Body:* National Family Mediation
>
> *Regional Group / Service:* South East London Family Mediation Service
>
> *Mediation telephone number:* 0181 460 4606

■ **Booth,** Joy (A)

> *Approved Body:* LawGroup UK
>
> *Regional Group / Service:* Member of LawGroup UK's Family Mediation Register, telephone 01883 370000 for details
>
> *Mediation telephone number:* 0161 278 1800 (chambers)

■ **Borghgraef,** Anne (M)

> *Approved Body:* Family Mediators Association
>
> *Regional Group / Service:* Surrey & North Hampshire Family Mediators Association
>
> *Mediation telephone number:* 01420 511440

■ **Borland,** Donald Fergus (M)

> *Approved Body:* National Family Mediation
>
> *Regional Group / Service:* Family Mediation Service (Greater Manchester)
>
> *Mediation telephone number:* 0161 797 9910

■ **Boutcher,** Andrea Frances (A)

> *Approved Body:* Solicitors Family Law Association
>
> *Regional Group / Service:* Member of Solicitors Family Law Association, telephone 01689 850227 for details
>
> *Mediation telephone number:* 01373 463311

■ **Bowie,** Ron (M)

> *Approved Body:* Family Mediation Scotland
>
> *Regional Group / Service:* Family Mediation Central Scotland
>
> *Mediation telephone number:* 01786 472984

Brabbs, Ian Richard (A)

>*Approved Body:* LawGroup UK
>
>*Regional Group / Service:* Member of LawGroup UK's Family Mediation Register, telephone 01883 370000 for details
>
>*Mediation telephone number:* 01723 364321

Bradbury, Charlotte Emma (A)

>*Approved Body:* Solicitors Family Law Association
>
>*Regional Group / Service:* Member of Solicitors Family Law Association, telephone 01689 850227 for details
>
>*Mediation telephone number:* 01709 892063

Bradley, Patricia (A)

>*Approved Body:* Family Mediators Association
>
>*Regional Group / Service:* Hampshire & Isle of Wight Family Mediators Association
>
>*Mediation telephone number:* 01705 828131

Bragg, Christine Margaret (M)

>*Approved Body:* National Family Mediation
>
>*Regional Group / Service:* Northamptonshire Family Mediation Service
>
>*Mediation telephone number:* 01604 636651

Bramwell, Lorraine Lisa (M)

>*Approved Body:* National Family Mediation
>
>*Regional Group / Service:* Swindon Family Mediation Service
>
>*Mediation telephone number:* 01793 527285

Brennan, Carole Ann (A)

>*Approved Body:* LawGroup UK
>
>*Regional Group / Service:* Member of LawGroup UK's Family Mediation Register, telephone 01883 370000 for details
>
>*Mediation telephone number:* 0151 924 9234

Brew, Jonathan (A)

>*Approved Body:* Family Mediators Association
>
>*Regional Group / Service:* Hereford & Worcester Family Mediators Association

Brice, Peter Michael (M)

>*Approved Body:* National Family Mediation
>
>*Regional Group / Service:* Gwent Mediation Service

(cont'd)

Mediation telephone number: 01633 263065

Briggs, Joanne M R (A)

Approved Body: LawWise

Regional Group / Service: Member of LawWise Family Mediators Register, telephone 01483 237300 for details

Mediation telephone number: 01273 607953

Brighton, Francesca (A)

Approved Body: Solicitors Family Law Association

Regional Group / Service: Member of Solicitors Family Law Association, telephone 01689 850227 for details

Mediation telephone number: 01225 426292

Brill, Cynthia Avril (M)

Approved Body: National Family Mediation

Regional Group / Service: West Essex Family Mediation Service

Mediation telephone number: 01279 426749

Brill, David (A)

Approved Body: Family Mediators Association

Regional Group / Service: Family Mediators South Wales Ltd

Mediation telephone number: 01685 723519

Brinton, Patricia (M)

Approved Body: Family Mediators Association

Regional Group / Service: Surrey & North Hampshire Family Mediators Association

Mediation telephone number: 01252 622488

Brisby, Toni (A)

Approved Body: Family Mediators Association

Regional Group / Service: Birmingham Family Mediators Association

Mediation telephone number: 01889 882559

Broadhurst, Claire (M)

Approved Body: Family Mediation Scotland

Regional Group / Service: Family Mediation Tayside

Mediation telephone number: 01382 201343

(M) = Member   (A) = Associate

Bromwich, Rosemary E M (M)

Approved Body: National Family Mediation

Regional Group / Service: Northamptonshire Family Mediation Service

Mediation telephone number: 01604 636551

Mediation address: 49 York Road, Northampton, Northants NN1 5QJ
Facsimile 01604 637313

Other mediation address: 52 Billing Road (Family Court Welfare
Service), Northampton, Northants NN1 5DB

Professional qualifications and experience: National Family Mediation
(CTP); Certificate in Qualification for Social Work (CQSW)

Year qualified in mediation: 1995

Willing to travel outside the region: ✓

Practice offered: Children Issues Mediation; All Issues Mediation;
recognised mediator by Legal Aid Board for Section 29 of Family Law
Act

Additional mediation training:

domestic violence   NFM   1998

Brooks, Gill (M)

Approved Body: National Family Mediation

Regional Group / Service: Derbyshire Family Mediation Service

Mediation telephone number: 01246 277422

Bross, Ruth Vivian (A)

Approved Body: Family Mediators Association

Regional Group / Service: London North & Central Family Mediators
Association

Mediation telephone number: 0171 431 9408

Brown, Amanda J (A)

Approved Body: Family Mediators Association

Regional Group / Service: Cambridge Family Mediators Association

Mediation telephone number: 01440 702485

Brown, Anne (A)

Mediation telephone number: 0191 383 1900

Brown, Henry (M)

Approved Body: Family Mediators Association; Solicitors Family Law
Association

(cont'd)

Regional Group / Service: London North & Central Family Mediators Association; Member of Solicitors Family Law Association, telephone 01689 850 227 for details

Mediation telephone number: 0171 457 3000

Brown, Jacqueline Mary (A)

Approved Body: National Family Mediation

Regional Group / Service: West Essex Family Mediation Service

Mediation telephone number: 01279 426749

Brown, Kathryn (M)

Approved Body: National Family Mediation

Regional Group / Service: Family Mediation Service (Greater Manchester)

Mediation telephone number: 0161 797 9910

Brown, Martin Leigh (A)

Approved Body: National Family Mediation

Regional Group / Service: Cleveland Family Mediation Service

Mediation telephone number: 01642 222967

Brownrigg, John (M)

Approved Body: Family Mediators Association

Regional Group / Service: Bath District Family Mediators Association

Mediation telephone number: 01225 337599

Mediation address: 13 Queen Square, Bath, Bath & N E Somerset BA1 2HJ
Facsimile 01225 335437, DX 8001 BATH, E-mail johnbrownrigg@stoneking.demon.co.uk

Professional qualifications and experience: solicitor

Year qualified in mediation: 1991

Membership of professional bodies and organisations: FMA; SFLA

Willing to travel outside the region: ✓

Willing to travel to: within 25 miles of Bath

Practice offered: Children Issues Mediation; All Issues Mediation; Professional Practice Supervision/Consultancy; mediation training – co-mediation, sole and anchor mediation and accredited supervisor; additional practice/experience/knowledge; solicitor specialising in family law

Additional mediation training:

Professional Practice Supervision/Consultancy   1996

Other additional mediation training: sole mediator – All Issues 1995

▦ **Bruckshaw,** Joella (M)

Approved Body: Family Mediators Association

Regional Group / Service: South Yorkshire Family Mediators Association

Mediation telephone number: 0114 258 8645

▦ **Brunton,** Joyce Duncan (M)

Approved Body: Family Mediation Scotland

Regional Group / Service: Family Mediation Tayside

Mediation telephone number: 01382 201343

▦ **Bryan,** Carol Ann (A)

Approved Body: Solicitors Family Law Association

Regional Group / Service: Member of Solicitors Family Law Association, telephone 01689 850227 for details

Mediation telephone number: 01341 280317

Mediation address: Glanaig, High Street, Barmouth, Gwynedd LL42 1DW
Facsimile 01341 281306

Other mediation address: Waterloo Chambers, Bridge Street, Dolgellau, Gwynedd LL40 1AT

Professional qualifications and experience: solicitor with 17 years' experience in family law practice

Year qualified in mediation: 1996

Membership of professional bodies and organisations: The Law Society; Solicitors Family Law Association

Willing to travel outside the region: ✓

Willing to travel to: mid Wales, North Wales (counties of Ceredigion, North Powys and Gwynedd, and Anglesey)

Practice offered: family mediation (divorce, financial ancillary matters and children)

▦ **Bryning,** Elizabeth Lindsey (M)

Approved Body: Family Mediators Association

Regional Group / Service: Devon Family Mediators Association

Mediation telephone number: 01326 573845

▦ **Buckland,** Phillippa Jane (A)

Approved Body: Solicitors Family Law Association

Regional Group / Service: Member of Solicitors Family Law Association, telephone 01689 850227 for details

Mediation telephone number: 01566 772375

■ **Buckwell,** Jeremy (M)

Approved Body: Family Mediators Association

Regional Group / Service: Sussex Family Mediators Association

Mediation telephone number: 01273 452692

Mediation address: Adur Lodge, The Street, Old Shoreham, Shoreham-by-Sea, West Sussex BN42 5NJ
Facsimile 01273 452866, DX 2727 BRIGHTON 1, E-mail fitzhughbrighton@fastnet.co.uk

Other mediation address: 3 Pavilion Parade, Brighton, East Sussex BN2 1RY

Professional qualifications and experience: solicitor

Year qualified in mediation: 1989

Membership of professional bodies and organisations: The Law Society; FMA

Willing to travel outside the region: ✓

Willing to travel to: Sussex

Practice offered: Finance Issues Mediation; Children Issues Mediation; All Issues Mediation; mediation training

Other additional mediation training: sole mediation (FMA) 1995

Experience

I obtained my degree at Cambridge University after National Service in the Royal Navy. I then became a solicitor and specialised in family and planning. I have dealt with national and international family matters and been on the council of the Royal Town Planning Institiution. I was trained as a mediator by the FMA in 1989 and have been the co-ordinator of the Sussex group since it was formed following that training. I have been through a divorce myself so know what that is like.

■ **Bufton,** Sonia W M (M)

Approved Body: National Family Mediation

Regional Group / Service: South East London Family Mediation Bureau

Mediation telephone number: 0181 460 4606

■ **Bullock,** Sally (A)

Approved Body: Family Mediators Association

Regional Group / Service: Cambridge Family Mediators Association

Mediation telephone number: 0171 430 1660

■ **Bunting,** Julia (A)

Approved Body: Family Mediators Association

Regional Group / Service: Birmingham Family Mediators Association

(cont'd)

Mediation telephone number: 0121 786 1158

Burke, Colette Lucia (A)

Approved Body: Family Mediators Association

Regional Group / Service: Greater Manchester Family Mediators Association

Mediation telephone number: 0161 790 1411

Burkett, Victoria (A)

Approved Body: Solicitors Family Law Association

Regional Group / Service: Member of Solicitors Family Law Association, telephone 01689 850227 for details

Mediation telephone number: 01953 453774

Burns, Mark Richard (A)

Approved Body: Solicitors Family Law Association

Regional Group / Service: Member of Solicitors Family Law Association, telephone 01689 850227 for details

Mediation telephone number: 0113 246 0622

Mediation address: c/o Mc Cormicks, Britannia Chambers, 4 Oxford Place, Leeds, West Yorkshire LS1 3AX
Facsimile 0113 246 7488, E-mail mccormicks@btinternet.com

Professional qualifications and experience: solicitor; family practitioner for eight years

Year qualified in mediation: 1997

Membership of professional bodies and organisations: SFLA; The Law Society's Children Panel

Willing to travel outside the region: ✓

Willing to travel to: North and South Yorkshire

Practice offered: All Issues Mediation

Burrough, Jon Charles Wilson (A)

Approved Body: LawWise

Regional Group / Service: Member of LawWise Family Mediators Register, telephone 01483 237300 for details

Mediation telephone number: 01865 248607

Mediation address: Greyfriars Court, Paradise Square, Oxford OX1 1BB
Facsimile 01865 728445, DX 82261 OXFORD 2, E-mail jcb@linnells.co.uk

Other mediation address: The Old House, High Street, Islip, Oxon OX5 2RX

(cont'd)

Professional qualifications and experience: solicitor; over 30 years' experience as practising family law solicitor

Year qualified in mediation: 1998

Membership of professional bodies and organisations: Member of British Association of Lawyer Mediators (BALM); OXMED

Willing to travel outside the region: ✓

Willing to travel to: 25 mile radius of Oxford

Practice offered: All Issues Mediation

Bushell, David Thomas (A)

Approved Body: Solicitors Family Law Association

Regional Group / Service: Member of Solicitors Family Law Association, telephone 01689 850227 for details

Mediation telephone number: 01704 536777/500361

Mediation address: 11 St Georges Palace, Southport, Sefton PR9 0AL Telephone 01704 542002, Facsimile 01704 543144, DX 20104 SPT, E-mail vf86@dial.pipex.com

Professional qualifications and experience: solicitor; family law specialist

Year qualified in mediation: 1997

Membership of professional bodies and organisations: The Law Society; The Law Society's Children Panel

Willing to travel outside the region: ✓

Willing to travel to: North England

Practice offered: All Issues Mediation

Butler, Jane Elisabeth (A)

Approved Body: Family Mediators Association

Regional Group / Service: London North & Central Family Mediators Association

Mediation telephone number: 0171 435 1444

Butlin, Ian Thomas (M)

Approved Body: National Family Mediation

Regional Group / Service: Kent Family Mediation Service

Mediation telephone number: 01273 507821

Mediation address: 145 Osborne Road, Brighton, East Sussex BN1 6LW

Other mediation address: Kent Family Mediation Service, 8 Park Road, Sittingbourne, Kent ME10 1DR

Professional qualifications and experience: BA (Hons); CQSW; Dip Counselling; 20 years' experience as a social worker, 14 years as a mediator; 9 years as a counsellor

(cont'd)

Year qualified in mediation: 1984

Membership of professional bodies and organisations: MCFM

Willing to travel outside the region: ✓

Willing to travel to: Southern England

Practice offered: Finance Issues Mediation; Children Issues Mediation; All Issues Mediation; mediation training; Professional Practice Supervision/Consultancy; mediation in family disputes (non-divorce); pre-mediation counselling; family meetings

Additional mediation training:

consultation with children	NFM	1994
domestic violence	NFM	1997
Professional Practice Supervision/Consultancy	NFM	1997

Other additional mediation training: welfare rights (CPAG) 1996; All Issues mediation (J Haynes) 1990

General Background and Career

Background: Ian began his career as a social worker in 1973, specialising in child and family guidance. This experience led him to train in mediation with Sussex Family Mediation Service in 1984. Since 1991 he has been working as a mediator, counsellor and family therapist with Barnardos in Tunbridge Wells and since 1996 as a supervisor with three other mediation services.

Practice: Ian has mediated over 400 cases (30 All Issues Mediation). He gained his own accreditation in 1994 and is an accreditor for practice competence with NFM. Practice remains his primary interest.

Supervision: Ian is a practice supervisor with a number of family mediation services and specialises in the supervision and development of All Issues Mediation. He is also a supervisor for Diploma in Counselling students.

Training: As part of NFM's training team in All Issues Mediation, Ian has a keen interest in the development of best practice standards for mediators. He is particularly interested in the development and application of mediation principles to other areas of family dispute and relationship breakdown. In family mediation he is interested in the provision of pre-mediation counselling and post-divorce family meetings as an adjunct to the mediation process and has developed considerable experience in this field.

■ **Butner**, Paul L M (A)

Approved Body: Family Mediators Association

Regional Group / Service: London South & Central Family Mediators Association

Mediation telephone number: 01171 242 5473

▓ **Caldwell**, Jennifer (A)

> *Approved Body:* LawGroup UK
>
> *Regional Group / Service:* Member of LawGroup UK's Family Mediation Register, telephone 01883 370000 for details
>
> *Mediation telephone number:* 0161 278 1800

▓ **Calthrop-Owen**, Stephanie (A)

> *Approved Body:* Solicitors Family Law Association
>
> *Regional Group / Service:* Member of Solicitors Family Law Association, telephone 01689 850227 for details
>
> *Mediation telephone number:* 01737 763405/0374 690560

▓ **Campbell**, Helen Marian (A)

> *Approved Body:* LawWise
>
> *Regional Group / Service:* Member of LawWise Family Mediators Register, telephone 01483 237300 for details
>
> *Mediation telephone number:* 01189 331641

▓ **Campbell**, Pauline (M)

> *Approved Body:* National Family Mediation
>
> *Regional Group / Service:* Durham Family Mediation
>
> *Mediation telephone number:* 0191 386 5418

▓ **Campbell**, Teresa (A)

> *Approved Body:* Family Mediators Association
>
> *Regional Group / Service:* Devon Family Mediators Association
>
> *Mediation telephone number:* 01363 82489

▓ **Cannan**, Philippa (A)

> *Approved Body:* Family Mediators Association
>
> *Regional Group / Service:* Sussex Family Mediators Association
>
> *Mediation telephone number:* 01273 476063

▓ **Canning**, Martin Paul (A)

> *Approved Body:* Solicitors Family Law Association
>
> *Regional Group / Service:* Member of Solicitors Family Law Association, telephone 01689 850227 for details
>
> *Mediation telephone number:* 0121 749 5577
>
> *Mediation address:* 301/3 Chester Road, Castle Bromwich, Birmingham, West Midlands B36 0JG
> Facsimile 0121 749 2765, DX 23251 CASTLE BROMWICH

(cont'd)

Professional qualifications and experience: LLB (Hons); admitted to Roll of Solicitors in 1975

Year qualified in mediation: 1998

Membership of professional bodies and organisations: The Law Society; Solicitors Family Law Association; British Association of Lawyer Mediators

Willing to travel outside the region: ✓

Willing to travel to: West Midlands

Practice offered: All Issues Mediation

Cantwell, Brian Jack (M)

Approved Body: National Family Mediation

Regional Group / Service: Family Mediation Service (Northumberland & Tyneside)

Mediation telephone number: 0191 261 9212

Carlisle, Kenneth Alan (A)

Approved Body: LawGroup UK

Regional Group / Service: Member of LawGroup UK's Family Mediation Register, telephone 01883 370000 for details

Mediation telephone number: 0191 2842818

Carlton, James Mark (A)

Approved Body: LawGroup UK

Regional Group / Service: Member of LawGroup UK's Family Mediation Register, telephone 01883 370000 for details

Mediation telephone number: 01507 606161

Carr, Shani Sarah (A)

Approved Body: Solicitors Family Law Association

Regional Group / Service: Member of Solicitors Family Law Association, telephone 01689 850227 for details

Mediation telephone number: 01889 583871

Cartridge, John (A)

Approved Body: LawGroup UK

Regional Group / Service: Member of LawGroup UK's Family Mediation Register, telephone 01883 370000 for details

Mediation telephone number: 01392 256854

■ **Cartridge**, Margaret Carol (A)

> *Approved Body:* Family Mediators Association
>
> *Regional Group / Service:* South West Region Family Mediators Association
>
> *Mediation telephone number:* 01392 258031

■ **Cartwright-Harwood**, Susan Katrina (A)

> *Approved Body:* LawGroup UK
>
> *Regional Group / Service:* Member of LawGroup UK's Family Mediation Register, telephone 01883 370000 for details
>
> *Mediation telephone number:* 01554 746295/01792 646864

■ **Case**, Monica (A)

> *Approved Body:* Family Mediators Association
>
> *Regional Group / Service:* South West Region Family Mediators Association
>
> *Mediation telephone number:* 01271 373364

■ **Casey**, Helen (M)

> *Approved Body:* National Family Mediation
>
> *Regional Group / Service:* Cambridge Family & Divorce Centre
>
> *Mediation telephone number:* 01223 576308

■ **Cashdon**, Gill (M)

> *Approved Body:* National Family Mediation
>
> *Regional Group / Service:* Mediation in Divorce
>
> *Mediation telephone number:* 0181 891 6860

■ **Caswell**, Carol (A)

> *Approved Body:* LawWise
>
> *Regional Group / Service:* Member of LawWise Family Mediators Register, telephone 01483 237300 for details
>
> *Mediation telephone number:* 01222 864888

■ **Cavanagh**, Sharon (M)

> *Approved Body:* National Family Mediation
>
> *Regional Group / Service:* Kent Family Mediation Service
>
> *Mediation telephone number:* 01795 429689

■ **Chanter**, Mark Henwood (A)

> *Approved Body:* LawGroup UK
>
> *Regional Group / Service:* Member of LawGroup UK's Family Mediation Register, telephone 01883 370000 for details
>
> *Mediation telephone number:* 01872 273077

■ **Chappell**, Nigel Robert (A)

> *Approved Body:* Solicitors Family Law Association
>
> *Regional Group / Service:* Member of Solicitors Family Law Association, telephone 01689 850227 for details
>
> *Mediation telephone number:* 01773 530000

■ **Charlton**, Arthur (A)

> *Approved Body:* National Family Mediation
>
> *Regional Group / Service:* NCH Action for Children Eye to Eye Mediation
>
> *Mediation telephone number:* 0181 766 6153

■ **Checkley**, Amanda Ellen (M)

> *Approved Body:* National Family Mediation
>
> *Regional Group / Service:* Divorce Mediation & Counselling Service
>
> *Mediation telephone number:* 0171 730 2422

■ **Chenery-Baker**, Irene Lillian Anne (M)

> *Approved Body:* National Family Mediation; Family Mediators Association
>
> *Regional Group / Service:* Lancashire Family Mediators Association; Lancashire Family Mediation Service
>
> *Mediation telephone number:* 01200 422264
>
> *Mediation address:* 21 Church Street, Clitheroe, Lancashire BB7 2DF Facsimile 01200 428986
>
> *Professional qualifications and experience:* LLB (Hons); LSF; FMA accredited
>
> *Year qualified in mediation:* 1996
>
> *Membership of professional bodies and organisations:* The Law Society; Solicitors Family Law Association; Family Mediators Association; Lancashire Family Mediation Service
>
> *Willing to travel outside the region:* ✓
>
> *Willing to travel to:* anywhere within reason in the North West
>
> *Practice offered:* Children Issues Mediation; All Issues Mediation
>
> *Additional mediation training:*
>
> | consultation with children | NFM | 1997 |
> |---|---|---|

(cont'd)

domestic violence

■ **Chesterman**, Nicola (A)

> *Approved Body:* Family Mediators Association

■ **Chynoweth**, Lorna (M)

> *Approved Body:* National Family Mediation
>
> *Regional Group / Service:* Somerset Family Mediation Service
>
> *Mediation telephone number:* 01823 352013

■ **Clarke**, Elaine Joy (A)

> *Approved Body:* LawGroup UK
>
> *Regional Group / Service:* Member of LawGroup UK's Family Mediation Register, telephone 01883 370000 for details
>
> *Mediation telephone number:* 01234 400000

■ **Clarke**, Nigel Adrian (A)

> *Approved Body:* LawGroup UK
>
> *Regional Group / Service:* Member of LawGroup UK's Family Mediation Register, telephone 01883 370000 for details
>
> *Mediation telephone number:* 01227 762888

■ **Clarke**, Susan Myra (A)

> *Approved Body:* Family Mediators Association
>
> *Regional Group / Service:* Somerset Family Mediators Association
>
> *Mediation telephone number:* 01935 424581

■ **Claughton**, Geoffrey Brian (A)

> *Approved Body:* National Family Mediation
>
> *Regional Group / Service:* South East London Family Mediation Bureau
>
> *Mediation telephone number:* 0181 460 4606

■ **Clegg**, Philippa Anne (M)

> *Approved Body:* Family Mediation Scotland
>
> *Regional Group / Service:* Family Mediation Central Scotland
>
> *Mediation telephone number:* 01786 472984

■ **Cleland**, Edward (M)

> *Approved Body:* Family Mediation Scotland
>
> *Regional Group / Service:* Family Mediation Lothian
>
> *Mediation telephone number:* 0131 226 4507

Clennel-White, Johanna (A)

Approved Body: LawGroup UK

Regional Group / Service: Member of LawGroup UK's Family Mediation Register, telephone 01883 370000 for details

Mediation telephone number: freephone 0500 328886

Clerke, Robert William (M)

Approved Body: Family Mediators Association; Solicitors Family Law Association/LawGroup UK

Regional Group / Service: Member of LawGroup UK's Family Mediation Register, telephone 01883 370000 for details; Bristol Family Mediators Association; Member of Solicitors Family Law Association, telephone 01689 850227 for details

Mediation telephone number: 0117 924 4346

Mediation address: 6 Picton Street, Montpelier, Bristol BS6 5QA Facsimile 0117 9446 776

Professional qualifications and experience: BA Hons; admitted solicitor 1982; lecturer, University of the West of England

Year qualified in mediation: 1991

Membership of professional bodies and organisations: The Law Society; FMA; SFLA; LawGroup UK Register of Family Mediators; UK College of Family Mediators

Willing to travel outside the region: ✓

Willing to travel to: by agreement

Practice offered: All Issues Mediation; mediation training; Professional Practice Supervision/Consultancy; both sole and co-mediation available

Additional mediation training:

mediation trainer training	SFLA	1996
Professional Practice Supervision/Consultancy	SFLA	1996

Additional Information

Robert Clerke is an experienced family practitioner. He qualified as a solicitor in 1982 as a 'mature entrant'. He formed his own firm Robert Clerke and Co in 1989. He trained as a mediator with the Family Mediators Association in 1991. Since that time he has been an enthusiastic mediator practising 'all issues mediation' initially in co-mediation and more recently as a sole mediator.

Because of his experience as a mediator and as a lecturer he was subsequently invited to become a trainer for the Solicitors Family Law Association in 1996. He continues to act as a trainer and consultant for the Solicitors Family Law Association and also now trains for LawGroup UK. As well as being a full member of the UK College he is also a member of the Family Mediators Association, the LawGroup Register of Family Mediators and of the Solicitors Family Law Association.

Cliff, Elisabeth Ann (M)

>   *Approved Body:* Family Mediators Association
>
>   *Regional Group / Service:* London South & Central Family Mediators Association; London South & West Family Mediators Association
>
>   *Mediation telephone number:* 0181 780 0289

Clifford, Ann M (M)

>   *Approved Body:* Family Mediators Association
>
>   *Regional Group / Service:* Nottinghamshire Family Mediators Association
>
>   *Mediation telephone number:* 0115 981 2496

Clifford, Paul (M)

>   *Approved Body:* National Family Mediation
>
>   *Regional Group / Service:* Milton Keynes Family Mediation
>
>   *Mediation telephone number:* 01908 606376

Cockett, Monica (M)

>   *Approved Body:* Family Mediators Association
>
>   *Regional Group / Service:* Devon Family Mediators Association
>
>   *Mediation telephone number:* 01392 420888

Cohen, Barbara (A)

>   *Approved Body:* Family Mediators Association
>
>   *Regional Group / Service:* The Hertfordshire Comprehensive Mediation Service
>
>   *Mediation telephone number:* 01923 773984

Coleman, Brenda Margaret (A)

>   *Approved Body:* LawWise
>
>   *Regional Group / Service:* Member of LawWise Family Mediators Register, telephone 01483 237300 for details
>
>   *Mediation telephone number:* 01245 283872

Colley, Graham David (A)

>   *Approved Body:* LawWise
>
>   *Regional Group / Service:* Member of LawWise Family Mediators Register, telephone 01483 237300 for details
>
>   *Mediation telephone number:* 0171 287 8296
>
>   *Mediation address:* 2 Westminster Palace Gardens, Artillery Row, Westminster, London SW1P 1RL
>   Telephone 0171 976 7555 ext 111, Facsimile 0171 976 7184, DX 99926 VICTORIA, E-mail graham.colley@colleysolicitors.btinternet.com

(cont'd

Other mediation address: 284 High Street, Chatham, Kent ME4 4BP

Professional qualifications and experience: solicitor (qualified 1978); senior partner, Graham & Rose Colley, solicitors; trained by Dr John Haynes and IDR Group; secretary Southwark Mediation Project

Year qualified in mediation: 1994

Membership of professional bodies and organisations: The Law Society; BALM

Willing to travel outside the region: ✓

Practice offered: All Issues Mediation

Additional mediation training:

consultation with children
domestic violence
initial information giving and/or assessment

About Graham Colley

Genuine warmth, excellent negotiating skills and a sparkling imagination are descriptions which make Graham Colley a very special mediator. He brings to mediation much experience. He has a career as a senior partner of a large family law practice in London and Kent. He has been a parliamentary candidate and a co-chair of a county council committee. He has studied cultural diversity and business and has an MBA from City University. He has given presentations on mediation in Brussels and Jersey as well as in England. He is the secretary of Southwark Mediation Centre. He is a father of three and understands the problems of parents and families. Whilst he has mediated neighbour, commercial and public issues problems, helping couples mediate their future lives is a special interest.

Collier, Claire Flavia (A)

Approved Body: National Family Mediation

Regional Group / Service: Family Mediation Cardiff

Mediation telephone number: 01222 229692

Collinson, Joan MacDonald (M)

Approved Body: National Family Mediation

Regional Group / Service: Cleveland Family Mediation Service

Mediation telephone number: 01661 832011

Mediation address: Mediation & Brief Therapy Practice, Forge House, Main Road, Ovingham, Northumberland NE42 6AG

Professional qualifications and experience: BL 1959; Lecturer in Law for many years, including at Glasgow University, Nottingham University, University of Newcastle upon Tyne, Auckland University; Tutor at St. Anne's, Oxford; Accredited Mediator; NFM trainer

Year qualified in mediation: 1983

Membership of professional bodies and organisations: NFM Accreditor
(cont'd)

Willing to travel outside the region: ✓

Willing to travel to: for training, supervision and consultancy as far as York

Practice offered: All Issues Mediation; mediation training; Professional Practice Supervision/Consultancy

Additional mediation training:

consultation with children	trainer NFM	
domestic violence	NCMC	1993
initial information giving and/or assessment	NCMC	1993
mediation trainer training	NFM	
Professional Practice Supervision/Consultancy	NFM	

Other additional mediation training: developed Stage 2 Advanced Supervision training for NFM and trained pilot 1997

Career

After completing my law degree I practised as a solicitor and then lectured at the Universities of Glasgow, Nottingham, Newcastle upon Tyne and Auckland, also tutoring at St Anne's College, Oxford. I still run courses for solicitors for Continuing Education. I subsequently trained with Relate, then trained as a mediator and became Project Leader of Northumberland & Tyneside FMS for ten years. I later trained with John Haynes and with the Northern California Mediation Center. I have been a trainer for NFM for many years, having trained in Core Training, AIMS, Conciliation for Health Services and currently train Consultation with Children. I recently developed the Stage 2 Advanced Supervision Training for NFM with Margaret Nunnerley and we piloted it last year.

I run brief therapy courses for the University of Newcastle, having qualified as a brief therapist, supervisor and trainer with the Brief Therapy Practice, Milwaukee and NIK Bremen. I am also a clinical affiliate in brief therapy for PPC, and have a private brief therapy practice, specialising in working with individuals, couples or families, where they choose that route rather than mediation.

■ **Comfort,** Margaret Joy (M)

Approved Body: Family Mediation Scotland

Regional Group / Service: Family Mediation Grampian

Mediation telephone number: 01343 540801

■ **Conbeer,** Christopher (M)

Approved Body: Family Mediators Association

Regional Group / Service: South West Region Family Mediators Association

Mediation telephone number: 01404 871213

Conrath, Philip Bernard (A)

>*Approved Body:* LawWise

>*Regional Group / Service:* Member of LawWise Family Mediators Register, telephone 01483 237300 for details

>*Mediation telephone number:* 0171 353 9942

Conyngham, Gerald Peter (M)

>*Approved Body:* National Family Mediation

>*Regional Group / Service:* Exeter & District Family Mediation Service

>*Mediation telephone number:* 01392 410529

Cooke, Julie Maureen (A)

>*Approved Body:* Family Mediators Association

>*Regional Group / Service:* Bristol Family Mediators Association

>*Mediation telephone number:* 0117 962 6300

Cooper, Paul Stanford (A)

>*Approved Body:* Family Mediators Association

>*Regional Group / Service:* Northants, Bucks and Leics Family Mediators Association

>*Mediation telephone number:* 01205 311511

Cormack, Mary (M)

>*Approved Body:* Family Mediation Scotland

>*Regional Group / Service:* Family Mediation Service (Highland)

>*Mediation telephone number:* 01463 712100

Cornwell, John Rainsford (M)

>*Approved Body:* Family Mediators Association

>*Regional Group / Service:* Member of Solicitors Family Law Association, telephone 01689 850227 for details; Divorce Mediation Group

>*Mediation telephone number:* 0171 242 2556

>*Mediation address:* Dawson Cornwell & Co, 16 Red Lion Square, London WC1R 4QT
>Facsimile 0171 831 0478, DX 35725 BLOOMSBURY

>*Professional qualifications and experience:* Solicitor

>*Membership of professional bodies and organisations:* SFLA

>*Year qualified in mediation:* 1984

>*Practice offered:* All Issues Mediation; Professional Practice Supervision/Consultancy

(cont'd)

A–Z College Members and Associates C

Additional mediation training:

mediation trainer training	SFLA	1996
Professional Practice Supervision/Consultancy	SFLA	1996

Cottingham, Una (M)

Approved Body: National Family Mediation

Regional Group / Service: Divorce Mediation & Counselling Service

Mediation telephone number: 0181 730 2422

Coulson, John David (A)

Approved Body: LawGroup UK

Regional Group / Service: Member of LawGroup UK's Family Mediation Register, telephone 01883 370000 for details

Mediation telephone number: 01626 863456

Coupe, Peter George (M)

Approved Body: National Family Mediation

Regional Group / Service: South East London Family Mediation Bureau

Mediation telephone number: 0181 460 4606

Coursey, Rosemary Elizabeth (M)

Approved Body: National Family Mediation

Regional Group / Service: West Yorkshire Family Mediation Service

Mediation telephone number: 0345 419403

Cox, Jane (A)

Approved Body: Family Mediators Association

Regional Group / Service: Family Mediation in Norfolk

Mediation telephone number: 01502 533014

Mediation address: 148 London Road North, Lowestoft, Suffolk NR32 1HF
Facsimile 01502 533014, DX 41200 LOWESTOFT

Professional qualifications and experience: solicitor specialising in family law and child care work

Year qualified in mediation: 1996

Membership of professional bodies and organisations: FMA; SFLA

Willing to travel outside the region: ✓

Willing to travel to: Norfolk, Suffolk, North-East Essex

Practice offered: All Issues Mediation

Crabtree, Margaret (M)

>*Approved Body:* National Family Mediation
>
>*Regional Group / Service:* Mediation in Divorce
>
>*Mediation telephone number:* 0181 891 6860

Craddock, Christine Mary (A)

>*Approved Body:* Family Mediators Association
>
>*Regional Group / Service:* Thames Valley Family Mediators Association
>
>*Mediation telephone number:* 01189 639751

Cragg, Jennifer Mary Claire (A)

>*Approved Body:* Family Mediators Association
>
>*Regional Group / Service:* Greater Manchester Family Mediators Association
>
>*Mediation telephone number:* 0161 224 4541

Craggs, Jean Mary (M)

>*Approved Body:* National Family Mediation
>
>*Regional Group / Service:* Sussex Family Mediation Service
>
>*Mediation telephone number:* 01273 550563

Crawford, Barry Miles (A)

>*Approved Body:* Solicitors Family Law Association
>
>*Regional Group / Service:* Member of Solicitors Family Law Association, telephone 01689 850227 for details
>
>*Mediation telephone number:* 01245 258892
>
>*Mediation address:* Threadneedle House, 9/10 Market Road, Chelmsford, Essex CM1 1XH
>Facsimile 01245 490480, DX 3301 CHELMSFORD, E-mail hill.abbott@easynet.co.uk
>
>*Professional qualifications and experience:* solicitor
>
>*Year qualified in mediation:* 1997
>
>*Membership of professional bodies and organisations:* SFLA
>
>*Willing to travel outside the region:* ✓
>
>*Willing to travel to:* London and East Anglia
>
>*Practice offered:* All Issues Mediation
>
>*Additional mediation training:*

| domestic violence | CLT | 1998 |

Crawforth, Emma (A)

Approved Body: LawGroup UK

Regional Group / Service: Member of LawGroup UK's Family Mediation Register, telephone 01883 370000 for details

Mediation telephone number: 01392 255777

Cripps, Len (M)

Approved Body: National Family Mediation

Regional Group / Service: Peterborough & District Family Mediation Service

Mediation telephone number: 01733 347353

Crisell, Margaret (M)

Approved Body: National Family Mediation

Regional Group / Service: Sunderland & South Tyneside Family Mediation Service

Mediation telephone number: 0191 568 0433

Crisp, Henry (A)

Approved Body: Family Mediators Association

Regional Group / Service: Surrey & North Hants Family Mediators Association

Mediation telephone number: 01483 570810

Crisp, Wendy (M)

Approved Body: Family Mediators Association

Regional Group / Service: London North & Central Family Mediators Association

Mediation telephone number: 0171 722 5100

Crowther, Felicity (M)

Approved Body: Family Mediators Association

Regional Group / Service: London North & Central Family Mediators Association

Mediation telephone number: 0171 833 4433

Cullen, Roger (M)

Approved Body: National Family Mediation; Family Mediators Association

Regional Group / Service: Oxfordshire Family Mediation Service; Mediation in Divorce; Milton Keynes Family Mediation; Mediation for Families (Oxfordshire)

Mediation telephone number: 01993 891596

■ **Cullen**, Teresa Elizabeth (A)

> *Approved Body:* Solicitors Family Law Association
>
> *Regional Group / Service:* Member of Solicitors Family Law Association, telephone 01689 850227 for details
>
> *Mediation telephone number:* 0171 544 2424

■ **Cummings**, David Michael (A)

> *Approved Body:* Solicitors Family Law Association
>
> *Regional Group / Service:* Member of Solicitors Family Law Association, telephone 01689 850227 for details
>
> *Mediation telephone number:* 01902 427561

■ **Cunnah**, Elaine (A)

> *Approved Body:* Family Mediation Scotland
>
> *Regional Group / Service:* Family Mediation Shetland
>
> *Mediation telephone number:* 01595 744443

■ **Cunnington**, Judy (M)

> *Approved Body:* Family Mediators Association
>
> *Regional Group / Service:* London South & Central Family Mediators Association
>
> *Mediation telephone number:* 0171 586 2681

■ **Curtis**, Angela (A)

> *Approved Body:* Family Mediators Association
>
> *Regional Group / Service:* London North & Central Family Mediators Association
>
> *Mediation telephone number:* 0181 731 8763

■ **Daldorph**, Martyn John (A)

> *Approved Body:* LawWise; LawGroup UK
>
> *Regional Group / Service:* Member of LawWise Family Mediators Register, telephone 01483 237300 for details; Member of LawGroup UK's Family Mediation Register, telephone 01883 370000 for details
>
> *Mediation telephone number:* 0171 353 6221
>
> *Mediation address:* Alexanders, 203 Temple Chambers, Temple Avenus, London EC4Y 0DB
> Facsimile 0171 583 0662, DX LDE 264 CHANCERY LANE, E-mail mjd@alexanders-solicitors.co.uk
>
> *Professional qualifications and experience:* solicitor (qualified 1971)
>
> *Year qualified in mediation:* 1996

(cont'd)

Membership of professional bodies and organisations: The Law Society; Solicitors Family Law Association; British Association of Lawyer Mediators

Willing to travel outside the region: ✓

Willing to travel to: South East England

Practice offered: Finance Issues Mediation; Children Issues Mediation; All Issues Mediation

Additional mediation training:

consultation with children
domestic violence
initial information giving and/or assessment

Other additional mediation training: advanced family mediation training course (LawWise) 1998; continuing family mediation training (LawGroup) 1997/8; (general) mediation accreditation course (ADR Group) 1996

Danaher, Michael Joseph (M)

Approved Body: Family Mediation Scotland

Regional Group / Service: Family Mediation Tayside

Mediation telephone number: 01382 201343

Daniell, Victoria (A)

Approved Body: Solicitors Family Law Association

Regional Group / Service: Member of Solicitors Family Law Association, telephone 01689 850227 for details

Mediation telephone number: 0117 926 8981

Mediation address: Wansbroughs Willey Hargrave, 103 Temple Street, Bristol BS99 7UD
Facsimile 0117 929 1582, DX 7846 BRISTOL, E-mail vdaniell@wwh.co.uk

Professional qualifications and experience: qualified as a solicitor in 1979; head of family law department at Wansbroughs Willey Hargrave dealing primarily with financial settlements in larger asset cases

Year qualified in mediation: 1996

Membership of professional bodies and organisations: SFLA; The Law Society

Willing to travel outside the region: ✓

Willing to travel to: anywhere within the South West

Practice offered: All Issues Mediation

David, Geraldine (M)

Approved Body: National Family Mediation

Regional Group / Service: Family Mediation Cardiff

■ **Davidson**, George Cook (M)

> *Approved Body:* Family Mediation Scotland
>
> *Regional Group / Service:* Family Mediation Lothian
>
> *Mediation telephone number:* 0131 226 4507

■ **Davie**, Freida Margaret (M)

> *Approved Body:* National Family Mediation
>
> *Regional Group / Service:* Hampshire Family Mediation
>
> *Mediation telephone number:* 01705 660919

■ **Davies**, Ceri (A)

> *Approved Body:* LawGroup UK
>
> *Regional Group / Service:* Member of LawGroup UK's Family Mediation Register, telephone 01883 370000 for details
>
> *Mediation telephone number:* 01639 630844

■ **Davies**, Neil Llewellyn (A)

> *Approved Body:* LawWise
>
> *Regional Group / Service:* Member of LawWise Family Mediators Register, telephone 01483 237300 for details
>
> *Mediation telephone number:* 01703 482482

■ **Davis**, Faith Elizabeth (M)

> *Approved Body:* National Family Mediation
>
> *Regional Group / Service:* West Essex Family Mediation Service
>
> *Mediation telephone number:* 01279 426749

■ **Davis**, Sally Janine (A)

> *Approved Body:* Family Mediators Association
>
> *Regional Group / Service:* London South & Central Family Mediators Association; London South & West Family Mediators Association
>
> *Mediation telephone number:* 0181 748 7670
>
> *Mediation address:* 141 Castelnau, Barnes, London SW13 9EW Facsimile 0181 748 7670
>
> *Professional qualifications and experience:* barrister; lawyer/mediator; lawyer for Official Solicitor; government policy maker for family law
>
> *Year qualified in mediation:* 1996
>
> *Membership of professional bodies and organisations:* Member of Family Law Bar Association and Family Mediators Association (FMA); Associate of UK College of Family Mediators and Local Authority Medical Research Ethics Committee (LREC)
>
> *Willing to travel outside the region:* ✓

(cont'd)

Willing to travel to: London and Home Counties

Practice offered: All Issues Mediation

Other additional mediation training: sole and anchor 1998

Dawson, George (M)

Approved Body: National Family Mediation

Regional Group / Service: Family Mediation Service: Barnet, Haringey & Hertsmere

Mediation telephone number: 0181 202 9887

Daymond-King, Lisa Elizabeth (A)

Approved Body: Solicitors Family Law Association

Regional Group / Service: Member of Solicitors Family Law Association, telephone 01689 850227 for details

Mediation telephone number: 0121 212 9393

Delaney, Susan Mary (A)

Approved Body: Solicitors Family Law Association

Regional Group / Service: Member of Solicitors Family Law Association, telephone 01689 850227 for details

Mediation telephone number: 0151 647 9821

Delve, Stuart (M)

Approved Body: Family Mediators Association

Regional Group / Service: London South & Central Family Mediators Association

Mediation telephone number: 0181 471 7498

Devlin, Kathleen (A)

Approved Body: Family Mediation Scotland

Regional Group / Service: Family Mediation (West of Scotland)

Mediation telephone number: 0141 332 2731

Devlin, Peter John Hugh (A)

Approved Body: Family Mediators Association

Regional Group / Service: Mediation for Families (Oxfordshire)

Mediation telephone number: 01235 553222

De Waal, Brigit Elizabeth Townsend (M)

Approved Body: National Family Mediation

Regional Group / Service: Norfolk Family Mediation Service

Mediation telephone number: 01603 620588

(M) = Member (A) = Associate

Dippie, Ian Robert Thomas (M)

Approved Body: Family Mediators Association

Regional Group / Service: Birmingham Family Mediators Association

Mediation telephone number: 0121 355 4537

Dixon, John (A)

Approved Body: Family Mediators Association

Regional Group / Service: Bedford Family Mediators Association

Mediation telephone number: 01234 273282

Docherty, Rosemary (A)

Approved Body: Family Mediation Scotland

Regional Group / Service: Family Mediation (West of Scotland)

Mediation telephone number: 0141 332 2731

Dodds, Simon (A)

Approved Body: LawGroup UK

Regional Group / Service: Member of LawGroup UK's Family Mediation Register, telephone 01883 370000 for details

Mediation telephone number: 01323 730543

Dolan, Philippa (A)

Approved Body: Solicitors Family Law Association

Regional Group / Service: Member of Solicitors Family Law Association, telephone 01689 850227 for details

Mediation telephone number: 0171 544 2424

Don, Andrew Montagu Wyatt (M)

Approved Body: Family Mediators Association

Regional Group / Service: Thames Valley Family Mediators Association

Mediation address: 1 Friar Street, Reading, Berkshire RG1 1DA Facsimile 0118 958 3032, DX 4008 READING, E-mail law@blandy.co.uk

Professional qualifications and experience: solicitor; head of family dept; mediation trainer with FMA and LawGroup; delivered a paper on mediation at the Milan Conference August 1997; made a training video in 1998 to demonstrate sole mediation produced by LawGroup UK and Legal Network Television

Year qualified in mediation: 1990

Membership of professional bodies and organisations: SFLA; FMA

Willing to travel outside the region: ✓

Willing to travel to: within Europe if expenses are paid

(cont'd)

A–Z College Members and Associates

C

Practice offered: Children Issues Mediation; All Issues Mediation; mediation training; Professional Practice Supervision/Consultancy; presentations; lectures; conferences etc

Other additional mediation training: sole mediation training 1995

■ **Donald**, Hugh (M)

Approved Body: Family Mediation Scotland

Regional Group / Service: Family Mediation Lothian

■ **Dove**, Colin Nigel (A)

Approved Body: LawWise

Regional Group / Service: Member of LawWise Family Mediators Register, telephone 01483 237300 for details

Mediation telephone number: 01206 576151

Mediation address: John Fowler Oldman, 63 High Street, Colchester, Essex CO1 1DS
Facsimile 01206 761916, DX 3605 COLCHESTER

Professional qualifications and experience: solicitor admitted in 1967

Year qualified in mediation: 1996

Membership of professional bodies and organisations: BALM; The Law Society

Practice offered: All Issues Mediation

■ **Dowding**, Sally (A)

Approved Body: Family Mediators Association

Regional Group / Service: North Wales Family Mediators Association

Mediation telephone number: 01248 370224

■ **Drake**, Stephen (A)

Approved Body: Family Mediators Association

Regional Group / Service: Mediation East Anglia

Mediation telephone number: 01379 652141

■ **Druett**, Clare (M)

Approved Body: National Family Mediation

Regional Group / Service: Salisbury & District Family Mediation Service

Mediation telephone number: 01722 332936

■ **Duckas**, Agnes (M)

Approved Body: National Family Mediation

Regional Group / Service: Sunderland & South Tyneside Family Mediation Service

(cont'd)

Mediation telephone number: 0191 5680433

■ **Dumigan,** Isabella C R (A)

Approved Body: Family Mediation Scotland

Regional Group / Service: Family Mediation (West of Scotland)

Mediation telephone number: 01563 572429

■ **Dunkerley,** Angeli (A)

Approved Body: Solicitors Family Law Association

Regional Group / Service: Member of Solicitors Family Law Association, telephone 01689 850227 for details

Mediation telephone number: 01793 615011

■ **Dunne,** Penelope Anne Phyllis (M)

Approved Body: Family Mediators Association

Regional Group / Service: Sussex Family Mediators Association; Family Mediation in Sussex

Mediation telephone number: 01273 621121

■ **Du Pre,** David Roger Kirkham (M)

Approved Body: Family Mediators Association

Regional Group / Service: London North & Central Family Mediators Association

Mediation telephone number: 0171 284 3040

Mediation address: 90-92 Parkway, Regent's Park, London NW1 7AN Facsimile 0171 485 1145, DX 57070 CAMDEN

Professional qualifications and experience: solicitor

Year qualified in mediation: 1992

Membership of professional bodies and organisations: Family Mediators Association; The Law Society; Solicitors Family Law Association; International Society of Family Law

Willing to travel outside the region: ✓

Practice offered: All Issues Mediation

Background

Long experience specialising in family law including the handling of complex disputes where substantial assets or an international element may be involved. Completed a degree in law in 1972. Practised as a barrister 1974 to 1978. Worked in specialist matrimonial law departments of city firms Stephenson Harwood and Theodore Goddard between 1979 and 1991. Set up own solicitors practice in 1991 specialising in family law. Trained as family mediator in 1992 and joined North London Group of Family Mediators Association. All mediations are conducted with another professional FMA mediator and

(cont'd)

generally take place during evenings at premises in Camden, close to the Underground station (Northern Line) and Regent's Park, but may be arranged at other such central/north London venues as may be mutually convenient.

Durkin, Timothy Francis (A)

Approved Body: LawGroup UK

Regional Group / Service: Member of LawGroup UK's Family Mediation Register, telephone 01883 370000 for details

Mediation telephone number: 01482 223693

Durman, Matt Richard (A)

Approved Body: Solicitors Family Law Association

Regional Group / Service: Member of Solicitors Family Law Association, telephone 01689 850227 for details

Mediation telephone number: 01483 887766

Dutton, Jennifer Carol (A)

Approved Body: Family Mediators Association

Regional Group / Service: Essex Family Mediators Association

Mediation telephone number: 01702 437600

Dyer, Christine Ann (A)

Approved Body: Solicitors Family Law Association

Regional Group / Service: Member of Solicitors Family Law Association, telephone 01689 850227 for details

Mediation telephone number: 01239 612262

Mediation address: Glyncoed Chambers, Priory Street, Cardigan, Ceredigion SA43 1BX
Facsimile 01239 615319, DX 92652 CARDIGAN

Professional qualifications and experience: LLB (Hons); solicitor for 20 years; member of The Law Society Children Panel; specialised in family law last 10 years

Year qualified in mediation: 1998

Membership of professional bodies and organisations: Solicitors Family Law Association; The Law Society, British Agency Fostering Adoption; Education Law Association

Willing to travel outside the region: ✓

Willing to travel to: Carmarthen, HaverfordWest, Narberth, Aberaeron

Practice offered: Finance Issues Mediation; Children Issues Mediation; All Issues Mediation

■ **Dyer,** Michael William **(A)**

Approved Body: Solicitors Family Law Association

Regional Group / Service: Member of Solicitors Family Law Association, telephone 01689 850227 for details

Mediation telephone number: 01489 788922

Mediation address: Eric Robinson & Co, 5A St Johns Road, Hedge End, Southampton SO30 4AA
Facsimile 01489 786348, DX 95100 HEDGE END

Professional qualifications and experience: 14 years' experience in matrimonial and family work as solicitor (LLB)

Year qualified in mediation: 1997

Membership of professional bodies and organisations: The Law Society; Hampshire Law Society; SFLA member

Willing to travel outside the region: ✓

Willing to travel to: within 20 miles of Southampton

Practice offered: All Issues Mediation

Other additional mediation training: SFLA mediation course 1997

■ **Earnshaw,** Jean **(M)**

Approved Body: National Family Mediation

Regional Group / Service: Cleveland Family Mediation Service

Mediation telephone number: 01642 222967

■ **Eastwood,** David Dean **(M)**

Approved Body: Family Mediators Association; LawWise

Regional Group / Service: Northants, Bucks and Leics Family Mediators Association; Member of LawWise Family Mediators Register, telephone 01483 237300 for details

Mediation telephone number: 01604 258524

Mediation address: The Family Mediation Centre, Toller, Hales & Collcutt, 2 Castilian Street, Northampton, Northamptonshire NN1 1JX
Facsimile 01604 258500, DX 12422

Other mediation address: Croft House, 45 Headlands, Kettering, Northants NN15 7ET

Professional qualifications and experience: LLB; specialist family lawyer with 20 years' experience; head of Family Law Department in Legal Practice; head of the Family Mediation Centre

Year qualified in mediation: 1993

Membership of professional bodies and organisations: The Law Society; FMA; BALM

Willing to travel outside the region: ✓

(cont'd)

Willing to travel to: Bedfordshire, Buckinghamshire, Cambridgeshire, Leicestershire

Practice offered: All Issues Mediation

Other additional mediation training: Relate Quality Partnership Training in Mediation 1997

Eaves, John David (A)

Approved Body: Family Mediators Association

Regional Group / Service: Northants, Bucks and Leics Family Mediators Association

Mediation telephone number: 01455 634851

Eddy, Catherine (A)

Approved Body: Family Mediators Association

Regional Group / Service: Oxford Family Mediators Association

Mediation telephone number: 01865 247294

Edwards, Elizabeth Ann (M)

Approved Body: Family Mediators Association

Regional Group / Service: London South & Central Family Mediators Association

Mediation telephone number: 0181 681 5544

Edwards, Elizabeth Strout (M)

Approved Body: Family Mediation Scotland

Regional Group / Service: Family Mediation Tayside

Mediation telephone number: 01382 201343

Egan, Diana Mary (M)

Approved Body: National Family Mediation

Regional Group / Service: Family Mediation (Central Middlesex)

Mediation telephone number: 0181 427 2076

Egan, Maeve Mary (A)

Approved Body: Family Mediators Association

Regional Group / Service: Bristol Family Mediators Association

Mediation telephone number: 0117 973 1561

Elias, Jane (M)

Approved Body: Family Mediators Association

Regional Group / Service: Bristol Family Mediators Association

Mediation telephone number: 0117 962 6300

(M) = Member   (A) = Associate

Elliott, Anthony (M)

Approved Body: National Family Mediation

Regional Group / Service: Dorset Family Mediation Service

Mediation telephone number: 01202 314600

Elliott, Diana (M)

Approved Body: National Family Mediation

Regional Group / Service: Family Mediation Service – Institute of Family Therapy

Mediation telephone number: 01273 564275

Mediation address: Family Mediation Service – Institute of Family Therapy, 24-32 Stephenson Way, London NW1 2HX
Telephone 0171 391 9150, Facsimile 0171 391 9169

Other mediation address: 41 Preston Drove, Brighton, Sussex BN1 6LA

Professional qualifications and experience: Social Work (CQSW); Accredited Family Mediator; NFM Accreditor, Supervisor and Trainer

Year qualified in mediation: 1986

Willing to travel outside the region: ✓

Practice offered: Finance Issues Mediation; Children Issues Mediation; All Issues Mediation; mediation training; Professional Practice Supervision/Consultancy; trainer All Issues Mediation and other mediation contexts; Governor UK College of Family Mediators

Additional mediation training:

consultation with children
initial information giving and/or assessment
Professional Practice Supervision/Consultancy   NFM Part II   1997

Elmer, Alison Elizabeth (A)

Approved Body: LawGroup UK

Regional Group / Service: Member of LawGroup UK's Family Mediation Register, telephone 01883 370000 for details

Mediation telephone number: 01522 523215

Elvish, Anne (M)

Approved Body: National Family Mediation

Regional Group / Service: Cumbria Family Mediation Service

Mediation telephone number: 01539 733705

Emsley, Maureen (M)

Approved Body: National Family Mediation

Regional Group / Service: West Yorkshire Family Mediation Service

Mediation telephone number: 0345 419403

■ **Ephraim**, Nona Wyn (A)

> *Approved Body:* Family Mediators Association
>
> *Regional Group / Service:* North Wales Family Mediators Association
>
> *Mediation telephone number:* 01407 840706

■ **Evans**, Alison (M)

> *Approved Body:* National Family Mediation; Family Mediators Association
>
> *Regional Group / Service:* Cambridge Family Mediators Association; Cambridge Family & Divorce Centre
>
> *Mediation telephone number:* 01223 843442

■ **Evans**, Christine (M)

> *Approved Body:* National Family Mediation
>
> *Regional Group / Service:* North Devon Family Mediation Service
>
> *Mediation telephone number:* 01271 32188

■ **Evans**, Diana Christine (A)

> *Approved Body:* Solicitors Family Law Association
>
> *Regional Group / Service:* Member of Solicitors Family Law Association, telephone 01689 850227 for details
>
> *Mediation telephone number:* 01732 770867
>
> *Mediation address:* Max Barford & Co, 134 High Street, Tonbridge, Kent TN9 1BB
> Facsimile 01732 367905, DX 5525 TONBRIDGE
>
> *Professional qualifications and experience:* LLB (Hons); qualified as a solicitor in 1984 and have specialised in all areas of family law since that date; member of Children Panel since 1988
>
> *Year qualified in mediation:* 1997
>
> *Membership of professional bodies and organisations:* SFLA; The Law Society
>
> *Willing to travel outside the region:* ✓
>
> *Willing to travel to:* Tonbridge, Tunbridge Wells, Maidstone, Sevenoaks
>
> *Practice offered:* All Issues Mediation

■ **Evans**, Robert Kelvin (A)

> *Approved Body:* Family Mediators Association
>
> *Regional Group / Service:* Family Mediators South Wales Ltd
>
> *Mediation telephone number:* 01792 652007

(M) = Member   (A) = Associate

▪ **Evans**, Timothy (A)

Approved Body: Solicitors Family Law Association

Regional Group / Service: Member of Solicitors Family Law Association, telephone 01689 850227 for details

Mediation telephone number: 01246 211006

Mediation address: Bradley & Clarke, 36 Clarence Road, Chesterfield, Derbyshire S40 1XB
Facsimile 01246 209786, E-mail timevans2@compuserve.com

Professional qualifications and experience: BA (Hons); 18 years' qualified as solicitor; family law specialist

Year qualified in mediation: 1997

Membership of professional bodies and organisations: The Law Society

Willing to travel outside the region: ✓

Willing to travel to: 30 mile radius of Sheffield

Practice offered: All Issues Mediation

Other additional mediation training: All Issues (NFM) 1998

▪ **Falkus**, Caroline (M)

Approved Body: National Family Mediation

Regional Group / Service: Mediation for Families (East London & City)

Mediation telephone number: 0171 613 1666

▪ **Farquhar**, Sandra (M)

Approved Body: Family Mediation Scotland

Regional Group / Service: Family Mediation Central Scotland

Mediation telephone number: 01786 472984

▪ **Fazan**, Gillian Patricia (A)

Approved Body: Solicitors Family Law Association

Regional Group / Service: Member of Solicitors Family Law Association, telephone 01689 850227 for details

Mediation telephone number: 01548 856663

Mediation address: 3 South Place, The Promenade, Kingsbridge, Devon TQ7 1JE
Facsimile 01548 857071, DX 81404 KINGSBRIDGE

Professional qualifications and experience: solicitor, 20 years qualified; family law practitioner; trained by FMA and SFLA

Year qualified in mediation: 1990

Membership of professional bodies and organisations: SFLA

Willing to travel outside the region: ✓

Willing to travel to: whole of Devon and Cornwall

(cont'd)

Practice offered: Children Issues Mediation; All Issues Mediation

■ **Fearnley**, Thomas (A)

Approved Body: Solicitors Family Law Association

Regional Group / Service: Member of Solicitors Family Law Association, telephone 01689 850227 for details

Mediation telephone number: 01625 427303

■ **Fedorski**, Nina (A)

Approved Body: Solicitors Family Law Association

Regional Group / Service: Member of Solicitors Family Law Association, telephone 01689 850227 for details

Mediation telephone number: 0161 225 6718

■ **Ferguson**, Colin Drummond (M)

Approved Body: National Family Mediation

Regional Group / Service: Berkshire Family Mediation

Mediation telephone number: 0118 957 1159

■ **Ferguson**, Jeremy John (A)

Approved Body: LawGroup UK

Regional Group / Service: Member of LawGroup UK's Family Mediation Register, telephone 01883 370000 for details

Mediation telephone number: 01237 478751

■ **Ferguson**, Joan Margaret (A)

Approved Body: Solicitors Family Law Association

Regional Group / Service: Member of Solicitors Family Law Association, telephone 01689 850227 for details

Mediation telephone number: 0161 795 2869

■ **Ferris**, Barbara Elaine (M)

Approved Body: National Family Mediation

Regional Group / Service: Herefordshire Family Mediation Service

■ **Field**, Howard Stephen (A)

Approved Body: Solicitors Family Law Association

Regional Group / Service: Member of Solicitors Family Law Association, telephone 01689 850227 for details

Mediation telephone number: 01472 358686

■ **Field**, Mary Margaret (M)

> *Approved Body:* Family Mediators Association
>
> *Regional Group / Service:* Sussex Family Mediators Association
>
> *Mediation telephone number:* 01444 400989
>
> *Mediation address:* Family Mediation in Sussex, The Lodge, Brantridge Forest, Balcombe, West Sussex RH17 6JY
> Facsimile 01444 401801
>
> *Other mediation address:* c/o David Laing & Co, 22 Ship Street, Brighton, East Sussex BN1 1AD
>
> *Professional qualifications and experience:* BA (Hons) Law; long experience as a solicitor specialising in family law; Post Graduate Diploma in Counselling
>
> *Year qualified in mediation:* 1989
>
> *Membership of professional bodies and organisations:* The Law Society; FMA; SFLA; British Association for Counselling
>
> *Practice offered:* Finance Issues Mediation; All Issues Mediation

■ **Fielding**, J Matthew (A)

> *Approved Body:* Solicitors Family Law Association
>
> *Regional Group / Service:* Member of Solicitors Family Law Association, telephone 01689 850227 for details
>
> *Mediation telephone number:* 01689 824075
>
> *Mediation address:* Waldron & Co, 146a High Street, Orpington BR6 0JR
> Facsimile 01689 830537, DX 31602 ORPINGTON, E-mail jmfielding@compuserve.com
>
> *Professional qualifications and experience:* solicitor
>
> *Year qualified in mediation:* 1996
>
> *Membership of professional bodies and organisations:* The Law Society; Solicitors Family Law Association
>
> *Willing to travel outside the region:* ✓
>
> *Willing to travel to:* South East London; North Kent
>
> *Practice offered:* All Issues Mediation

■ **Filkin**, Isobel Margaret (M)

> *Approved Body:* National Family Mediation
>
> *Regional Group / Service:* Oxfordshire Family Mediation Service
>
> *Mediation telephone number:* 01865 741781

■ **Fincham**, Frank (M)

> *Approved Body:* Family Mediators Association
>
> *Regional Group / Service:* Family Mediators South Wales Ltd

(cont'd)

Mediation telephone number: 01222 874567

Findlay, Andrea May (M)

Approved Body: National Family Mediation

Regional Group / Service: Merseyside Family Mediation Service

Mediation telephone number: 0151 625 2403

Fine, Ruth (M)

Approved Body: National Family Mediation

Regional Group / Service: Family Mediation (Central Middlesex)

Mediation telephone number: 0181 427 2076

Finnis, Kim Hazel (A)

Approved Body: Solicitors Family Law Association

Regional Group / Service: Member of Solicitors Family Law Association, telephone 01689 850227 for details

Mediation telephone number: 01276 20021

Fitch, Roy (M)

Approved Body: National Family Mediation

Regional Group / Service: West Essex Family Mediation Service

Mediation telephone number: 01279 426749

Flint, Peter John (A)

Approved Body: Family Mediators Association

Regional Group / Service: Shropshire Family Mediators Association

Mediation telephone number: 01743 236400

Flowerdew, Karon (A)

Approved Body: Family Mediators Association

Regional Group / Service: Nottinghamshire Family Mediators Association

Mediation telephone number: 0115 941 7275

Foley, Charlotte Louise (A)

Approved Body: Solicitors Family Law Association

Regional Group / Service: Member of Solicitors Family Law Association, telephone 01689 850227 for details

Mediation telephone number: 01263 712835

■ **Follis**, Michael Ian (A)

> *Approved Body:* Solicitors Family Law Association
>
> *Regional Group / Service:* Member of Solicitors Family Law Association, telephone 01689 850227 for details
>
> *Mediation telephone number:* 0121 212 9393

■ **Forbes**, Janet Louise Agnes (M)

> *Approved Body:* National Family Mediation
>
> *Regional Group / Service:* Bristol Family Mediation Service
>
> *Mediation telephone number:* 0117 9292002

■ **Forbes**, Norma (M)

> *Approved Body:* Family Mediation Scotland
>
> *Regional Group / Service:* Family Mediation Central Scotland
>
> *Mediation telephone number:* 01786 472984

■ **Ford**, Peter Kenneth (M)

> *Approved Body:* National Family Mediation
>
> *Regional Group / Service:* Hampshire Family Mediation
>
> *Mediation telephone number:* 01705 660919

■ **Foster**, Paul (M)

> *Approved Body:* National Family Mediation; Family Mediators Association
>
> *Regional Group / Service:* Bristol Family Mediation Service; Bristol Family Mediators Association
>
> *Mediation telephone number:* 0117 942 1069

■ **Fountaine**, Richard Maurice (A)

> *Approved Body:* Family Mediators Association
>
> *Regional Group / Service:* Bath District Family Mediators Association
>
> *Mediation telephone number:* 01225 465833

■ **Fowler**, Pauline Juliet (M)

> *Approved Body:* Family Mediators Association
>
> *Regional Group / Service:* London South & Central Family Mediators Association
>
> *Mediation telephone number:* 0171 551 7855

■ **Foy**, Rhona T (A)

> *Approved Body:* Family Mediation Scotland
>
> *Regional Group / Service:* Family Mediation (West of Scotland)

(cont'd)

(M) = Member   (A) = Associate

Mediation telephone number: 0141 332 2731

▦ **Francis**, Richard (M)

Approved Body: LawWise

Regional Group / Service: Member of LawWise Family Mediators
Register, telephone 01483 237300 for details

Mediation telephone number: 01222 700131

Mediation address: The Mediation Practice, 9 Park Place, Cardiff CF1
3DP
Facsimile 01222 222542, DX 50751 CARDIFF 2

Other mediation address: The Administrator, The Mediation Practice, 4
Tower Hill, Penarth, Vale of Glamorgan CF64 3BH

Professional qualifications and experience: trained a a family mediator
with John Haynes and LawWise, April 1996; subsequently in advanced
family mediation with LawWise March 1998; in private practice with
The Mediation Practice since July 1996; providing Legal Aid in
Mediation Pilot Project since September 1997

Year qualified in mediation: 1996

Membership of professional bodies and organisations: practising
barrister (Gray's Inn 1974) specialising in family and civil law; Family
Law Bar Association; BALM; UK College of Family Mediators

Willing to travel outside the region: ✓

Willing to travel to: throughout Wales and South West England

Practice offered: All Issues Mediation

Additional mediation training:

initial information giving and/or assessment   LawWise   1996

Other additional mediation training: advanced family mediation
(LawWise) 1998

Career/Experience

Richard Francis is one of the few practising members of the Family Law
Bar in South Wales to have trained as a mediator and the only one to
date to have established his own mediation firm. His initial training
was with John Haynes in 1996, which has been supplemented by
advanced training with LawWise. He now combines his long experience
specialising in family law with The Mediation Practice, which was
established in July 1996. Since September 1997 The Mediation Practice
has offered Legal Aid under the Mediation Pilot Project. A sole
mediation service is offered in Cardiff at 9 Park Place, which is well
located in the city centre, and at Barry for the Vale of Glamorgan. He is
also prepared to travel within the regions of Wales and the south west
of England, if a suitable venue is available.

Freeman, Hilary (A)

> *Approved Body:* Solicitors Family Law Association
>
> *Regional Group / Service:* Member of Solicitors Family Law Association, telephone 01689 850227 for details
>
> *Mediation telephone number:* 0115 958 6262

French, Denise (A)

> *Approved Body:* Solicitors Family Law Association
>
> *Regional Group / Service:* Member of Solicitors Family Law Association, telephone 01689 850227 for details
>
> *Mediation telephone number:* 0121 355 4571

Frimond, Julia Mary (M)

> *Approved Body:* Family Mediators Association
>
> *Regional Group / Service:* Surrey & North Hampshire Family Mediators Association
>
> *Mediation telephone number:* 01483 452224

Frost, Philippa Louise (M)

> *Approved Body:* National Family Mediation
>
> *Regional Group / Service:* Herefordshire Family Mediation Service
>
> *Mediation telephone number:* 01432 264087

Fulcher, David Stedwell (A)

> *Approved Body:* LawWise
>
> *Regional Group / Service:* Member of LawWise Family Mediators Register, telephone 01483 237300 for details
>
> *Mediation telephone number:* 01483 750300

Gandon, Sally Ann (M)

> *Approved Body:* National Family Mediation; Family Mediators Association
>
> *Regional Group / Service:* Surrey & North Hampshire Family Mediators Association; Surrey Family Mediation Service
>
> *Mediation telephone number:* 01293 432132/772424

Gardener, Howard (M)

> *Approved Body:* Family Mediators Association
>
> *Regional Group / Service:* Hampshire & Isle of Wight Family Mediators Association
>
> *Mediation telephone number:* 01256 460830
>
> *Mediation address:* Wolverton Court, 15-16 London Street, Basingstoke, Hampshire RG21 7NT

(cont'd)

Facsimile 01256 364333, DX 3019 BASINGSTOKE

Professional qualifications and experience: solicitor; Deputy District Judge

Year qualified in mediation: 1993

Membership of professional bodies and organisations: FMA; SFLA; RQP

Practice offered: All Issues Mediation

Gardner, Kate (M)

Approved Body: National Family Mediation

Regional Group / Service: Swindon Family Mediation Service

Mediation telephone number: 01793 527285

Garner, Ronald Ian (M)

Approved Body: Family Mediators Association

Regional Group / Service: Kent Family Mediators Association; Sussex Family Mediators Association

Mediation telephone number: 01424 721234

Mediation address: Robertson Chambers, The Memorial, Hastings, East Sussex TN34 1JB
Facsimile 01424 721376, DX 7030 HASTINGS

Other mediation address: 3 Coach House, Great Sanders, Hurst Lane, Sedlescombe, Battle, East Sussex TN33 0PE

Professional qualifications and experience: solicitor 24 years qualified specialising in family law; mediator with five years' experience

Year qualified in mediation: 1992

Membership of professional bodies and organisations: The Law Society; Family Mediators Association; UK College of Family Mediators; Solicitors Family Law Association

Practice offered: Finance Issues Mediation; Children Issues Mediation; All Issues Mediation; Professional Practice Supervision/Consultancy

Additional mediation training:

Professional Practice Supervision/Consultancy   FMA   1996

Garwood, Fiona (M)

Approved Body: Family Mediation Scotland

Regional Group / Service: Family Mediation Lothian

Mediation telephone number: 0131 226 4507

Gass, Douglas McMillan (A)

Approved Body: Family Mediation Scotland

Regional Group / Service: Family Mediation (West of Scotland)

Mediation telephone number: 01563 572429

■ **Gee**, Irene (M)

> *Approved Body:* National Family Mediation; Family Mediators Association
>
> *Regional Group / Service:* Family Mediation Service – Institute of Family Therapy; London South & Central Family Mediators Association
>
> *Mediation telephone number:* 0181 444 9832

■ **Genders**, Diane (A)

> *Approved Body:* LawGroup UK
>
> *Regional Group / Service:* Member of LawGroup UK's Family Mediation Register, telephone 01883 370000 for details
>
> *Mediation telephone number:* 01522 512123

■ **George**, Peter Michael (M)

> *Approved Body:* Family Mediators Association
>
> *Regional Group / Service:* London South & Central Family Mediators Association
>
> *Mediation telephone number:* 0171 203 5098

■ **George**, Sue (M)

> *Approved Body:* National Family Mediation
>
> *Regional Group / Service:* Milton Keynes Family Mediation
>
> *Mediation telephone number:* 01908 231293

■ **Gerard**, Antonia (Non-Practising Member)

> *Approved Body:* National Family Mediation

■ **Gibbons**, Frederick Henry (M)

> *Approved Body:* National Family Mediation
>
> *Regional Group / Service:* South East London Family Mediation Bureau
>
> *Mediation telephone number:* 0181 460 4606

■ **Gibson**, William (A)

> *Approved Body:* Family Mediation Scotland
>
> *Regional Group / Service:* Family Mediation Lothian

■ **Giffin**, Susan Elizabeth (M)

> *Approved Body:* National Family Mediation
>
> *Regional Group / Service:* South Essex Family Mediation Service
>
> *Mediation telephone number:* 01702 436466

(M) = Member   (A) = Associate

Gifford, Richard David (A)

Approved Body: Solicitors Family Law Association

Regional Group / Service: Member of Solicitors Family Law Association, telephone 01689 850227 for details

Mediation telephone number: 0171 404 0444

Gilbert, Jayne (A)

Approved Body: Family Mediators Association

Regional Group / Service: London North & Central Family Mediators Association; Mediation East Anglia

Mediation telephone number: 01284 789335/0171 609 0041

Mediation address: Meadowsweet Cottage, Stansfield, Suffolk CO10 8LN
Facsimile 01284 789335, DX LDE 485

Other mediation address: 3 Temple Gardens, Temple, London EC4Y 9AU

Professional qualifications and experience: Member of the Bar, called 1976; appointed Deputy District Judge 1987

Year qualified in mediation: 1993

Membership of professional bodies and organisations: Middle Temple; Family Mediators Association

Willing to travel outside the region: ✓

Willing to travel to: Herts, Cambridge, Essex, North of Thames within M25

Practice offered: Finance Issues Mediation; All Issues Mediation

Gillard, Josephine Richmond (M)

Approved Body: National Family Mediation

Regional Group / Service: Family Mediation (Central Middlesex)

Mediation telephone number: 0181 427 2076

Gillis, Carolyn (M)

Approved Body: National Family Mediation

Regional Group / Service: Family Mediation Service (Northumberland & Tyneside)

Mediation telephone number: 0191 261 9212

Gillman, Michael John (A)

Approved Body: LawWise

Regional Group / Service: Member of LawWise Family Mediators Register, telephone 01483 237300 for details

Mediation telephone number: 0171 631 4141

Glanville, Susan (A)

Approved Body: LawGroup UK

Regional Group / Service: Member of LawGroup UK's Family Mediation Register, telephone 01883 370000 for details

Mediation telephone number: 0171 583 8233

Glass, Amanda Louise (A)

Approved Body: Solicitors Family Law Association

Regional Group / Service: Member of Solicitors Family Law Association, telephone 01689 850227 for details

Mediation telephone number: 01243 786111

Glass, David Anthony (A)

Approved Body: LawWise

Regional Group / Service: Member of LawWise Family Mediators Register, telephone 01483 237300 for details

Mediation telephone number: 01242 514707

Glees, Linda Ann (M)

Approved Body: Family Mediators Association

Regional Group / Service: Oxford Family Mediators Association

Mediation telephone number: 01865 724977

Mediation address: Faulkners Solicitors, 42 Westgate, Oxford OX1 1PD Facsimile 01865 791300, DX 4317 OXFORD 1

Professional qualifications and experience: solicitor; qualified mediator for five years; additional training and experience in sole mediation

Year qualified in mediation: 1993

Membership of professional bodies and organisations: Family Mediators Association; Solicitors Family Law Association

Willing to travel outside the region: ✓

Willing to travel to: London

Practice offered: All Issues Mediation; Professional Practice Supervision/Consultancy; sole mediation

Additional mediation training:

Professional Practice Supervision/Consultancy   FMA   1997

Glentworth, Margaret Marie (A)

Approved Body: Solicitors Family Law Association

Regional Group / Service: Member of Solicitors Family Law Association, telephone 01689 850227 for details

Mediation telephone number: 0113 243 0391

A–Z College Members and Associates

▣ **Godfrey**, Jacqueline N (A)

Approved Body: Solicitors Family Law Association

Regional Group / Service: Member of Solicitors Family Law Association, telephone 01689 850227 for details

Mediation telephone number: 01254 390915

Mediation address: Barlow Rowland, 18-24 St James Street, Accrington, Lancashire BB5 1NY
Facsimile 01254 871253, DX 23751 ACCRINGTON

Professional qualifications and experience: solicitor, family law, admitted 1987

Year qualified in mediation: 1997

Membership of professional bodies and organisations: Solicitors Family Law Association

Willing to travel outside the region: ✓

Willing to travel to: North West region

Practice offered: All Issues Mediation

▣ **Goldman**, Jill (A)

Approved Body: Solicitors Family Law Association

Regional Group / Service: Member of Solicitors Family Law Association, telephone 01689 850227 for details

Mediation telephone number: 01403 214500

▣ **Goldup**, Ian Frank (A)

Approved Body: LawGroup UK

Regional Group / Service: Member of LawGroup UK's Family Mediation Register, telephone 01883 370000 for details

Mediation telephone number: 01843 863479

▣ **Goodall**, Helen (A)

Approved Body: Family Mediators Association

Regional Group / Service: South West Region Family Mediators Association

Mediation telephone number: 01752 770820

▣ **Goode**, Catherine Anne (A)

Approved Body: Family Mediators Association

Regional Group / Service: Oxford Family Mediators Association; Mediation for Families (Oxfordshire)

Goodstone, Jennifer Ann (A)

Approved Body: Family Mediators Association

Regional Group / Service: London North & Central Family Mediators Association

Mediation telephone number: 0171 485 8741

Goorney, Caroline (A)

Approved Body: Solicitors Family Law Association

Regional Group / Service: Member of Solicitors Family Law Association, telephone 01689 850227 for details

Mediation telephone number: 0191 565 6056

Mediation address: 36 W Sunniside, Sunderland, Tyne & Wear SR1 1BU
Facsimile 0191 510 0348, DX 60741 SUNDERLAND

Other mediation address: 36 Osbaldeston Gardens, Gosforth, Newcastle upon Tyne NE3 4JE

Professional qualifications and experience: LLB (Hons); solicitor, qualified 1984; ten years' experience in family law

Year qualified in mediation: 1997

Membership of professional bodies and organisations: The Law Society; Solicitors Family Law Association

Willing to travel outside the region: ✓

Willing to travel to: North West, Yorkshire

Practice offered: Children Issues Mediation; All Issues Mediation

Gordon, Peter W (M)

Approved Body: National Family Mediation

Regional Group / Service: Family Mediation Service (Greater Manchester)

Mediation telephone number: 0161 797 9910

Gracie, Mary P (M)

Approved Body: National Family Mediation; Family Mediation Scotland

Regional Group / Service: Family Mediation Service (Greater Manchester)

Mediation telephone number: 0161 797 9910

Gray, Brian Lawrence (M)

Approved Body: National Family Mediation

Regional Group / Service: Lancashire Family Mediation Service

Mediation telephone number: 01772 204248

(M) = Member (A) = Associate

■ **Greaves**, Margaret Ellen (M)

> *Approved Body:* Family Mediators Association
>
> *Mediation telephone number:* 01703 263604

■ **Green**, Carolyn Anne (A)

> *Approved Body:* LawWise
>
> *Regional Group / Service:* Member of LawWise Family Mediators Register, telephone 01483 237300 for details
>
> *Mediation telephone number:* 01242 224422

■ **Green**, Judith (A)

> *Approved Body:* Family Mediators Association
>
> *Regional Group / Service:* Birmingham Family Mediators Association
>
> *Mediation telephone number:* 0121 200 3026

■ **Green**, Karen Elizabeth (A)

> *Approved Body:* Family Mediators Association
>
> *Regional Group / Service:* Kent Family Mediators Association
>
> *Mediation telephone number:* 0181 658 3922

■ **Greenall**, Liz (M)

> *Approved Body:* National Family Mediation
>
> *Regional Group / Service:* Family Mediation Service (Greater Manchester)
>
> *Mediation telephone number:* 0161 797 9910

■ **Greenleaves**, Michael John (A)

> *Approved Body:* LawGroup UK
>
> *Regional Group / Service:* Member of LawGroup UK's Family Mediation Register, telephone 01883 370000 for details
>
> *Mediation telephone number:* 01929 423301

■ **Gregory**, Kathryn (A)

> *Approved Body:* Solicitors Family Law Association
>
> *Regional Group / Service:* Member of Solicitors Family Law Association, telephone 01689 850227 for details
>
> *Mediation telephone number:* 01204 387710

■ **Gregory-Jones**, Rosemary Jane (A)

> *Approved Body:* LawWise
>
> *Regional Group / Service:* Member of LawWise Family Mediators Register, telephone 01483 237300 for details

(cont'd)

A–Z College Members and Associates

C

Mediation telephone number: 01222 385600

Gridley, James (M)

> *Approved Body:* Family Mediators Association
>
> *Regional Group / Service:* Bristol Family Mediators Association
>
> *Mediation telephone number:* 0117 961 1451

Grierson, Nigel Jonathan (M)

> *Approved Body:* Family Mediators Association
>
> *Regional Group / Service:* Greater Manchester Family Mediators Association
>
> *Mediation telephone number:* 0161 480 1000 and 01625 872748/878020
>
> *Mediation address:* 49 Middle Hillgate, Stockport, Cheshire SK1 3DL Facsimile 0161 429 0211, DX 22631 STOCKPORT 2
>
> *Other mediation address:* 39 Park Lane, Poynton, Cheshire SK12 1RD
>
> *Professional qualifications and experience:* solicitor; mediator for four years
>
> *Year qualified in mediation:* 1994
>
> *Membership of professional bodies and organisations:* SFLA
>
> *Willing to travel outside the region:* ✓
>
> *Willing to travel to:* Greater Manchester and Cheshire
>
> *Practice offered:* All Issues Mediation
>
> *Other additional mediation training:* sole and anchor mediation 1997

Griew, Marian Esther (M)

> *Approved Body:* Family Mediators Association
>
> *Regional Group / Service:* Nottinghamshire Family Mediators Association
>
> *Mediation telephone number:* 0115 923 4552

Griffin, John Philip (A)

> *Approved Body:* Family Mediators Association
>
> *Regional Group / Service:* Hampshire & Isle of Wight Family Mediators Association
>
> *Mediation telephone number:* 01705 828661

Griffiths, Stephanie (A)

> *Approved Body:* Solicitors Family Law Association
>
> *Regional Group / Service:* Member of Solicitors Family Law Association, telephone 01689 850227 for details
>
> *Mediation telephone number:* 0181 546 5986

(M) = Member   (A) = Associate

Grimshaw, Francoise (M)

Approved Body: National Family Mediation; Family Mediators Association

Regional Group / Service: South East London Family Mediation Bureau

Mediation telephone number: 0181 288 2796

Guest, Rosemary Eva (M)

Approved Body: Family Mediators Association

Regional Group / Service: London South & Central Family Mediators Association

Mediation telephone number: 0181 309 0558

Gunn, Joyce M M (M)

Approved Body: Family Mediation Scotland

Regional Group / Service: Family Mediation Lothian

Mediation telephone number: 0131 226 4507

Gunningham, Patricia (M)

Approved Body: National Family Mediation

Regional Group / Service: Mediation in Divorce

Mediation telephone number: 0181 891 6860

Guymer, Andrew Geoffrey (A)

Approved Body: Family Mediators Association

Regional Group / Service: Birmingham Family Mediators Association

Mediation telephone number: 0121 236 8931

Gwyther, Kerry (A)

Approved Body: Solicitors Family Law Association

Regional Group / Service: Member of Solicitors Family Law Association, telephone 01689 850227 for details

Mediation telephone number: 0117 929 5252

Mediation address: Lawrence Tucketts Solicitors, Bush House, 72 Prince Street, Bristol, Avon BS99 7JZ
Facsimile 0117 929 8313, DX 7830 BRISTOL, E-mail lawrence_tucketts@link.org

Professional qualifications and experience: solicitor LLB (Honours), admitted October 1983

Year qualified in mediation: 1998

Membership of professional bodies and organisations: Solicitors Family Law Association; Bristol Solicitors Family Law Association

Willing to travel outside the region: ✓

(cont'd)

Willing to travel to: anywhere in the South West

Practice offered: All Issues Mediation

Hagan, Glen (M)

Approved Body: National Family Mediation

Regional Group / Service: Family Mediation Service (Greater Manchester)

Mediation telephone number: 0161 797 9910/764 2196

Haines, Andrew John (A)

Approved Body: LawGroup UK

Regional Group / Service: Member of LawGroup UK's Family Mediation Register, telephone 01883 370000 for details

Mediation telephone number: 01482 325242

Haines, Sheila (M)

Approved Body: National Family Mediation

Regional Group / Service: Merseyside Family Mediation Service

Mediation telephone number: 0151 260 9155

Hale, Susan Jane (A)

Approved Body: Family Mediators Association

Regional Group / Service: Milton Keynes and North Buckinghamshire FMA Group

Mediation telephone number: 01908 366960

Mediation address: 28 Huntingdon Crescent, Bletchley, Milton Keynes, Buckinghamshire MK3 5NT

Professional qualifications and experience: FMA foundation training

Year qualified in mediation: 1995

Membership of professional bodies and organisations: FMA

Willing to travel outside the region: ✓

Willing to travel to: Northants, London, Bedfordshire, Oxon

Practice offered: All Issues Mediation

Hall, Christopher Richard (A)

Approved Body: LawGroup UK

Regional Group / Service: Member of LawGroup UK's Family Mediation Register, telephone 01883 370000 for details

Mediation telephone number: 01392 258451

■ **Hall**, Priscilla Mary (A)

> *Approved Body:* Family Mediators Association
>
> *Regional Group / Service:* Essex Family Mediators Association
>
> *Mediation telephone number:* 01206 544434

■ **Halpern**, Delia H (A)

> *Approved Body:* Family Mediators Association
>
> *Regional Group / Service:* London North & Central Family Mediators Association
>
> *Mediation telephone number:* 0171 722 0277

■ **Hamilton**, Catherine (M)

> *Approved Body:* Family Mediation Scotland
>
> *Regional Group / Service:* Family Mediation Grampian
>
> *Mediation telephone number:* 01224 630050

■ **Hamilton**, Christine Mary (A)

> *Approved Body:* Solicitors Family Law Association
>
> *Regional Group / Service:* Member of Solicitors Family Law Association, telephone 01689 850227 for details

■ **Hamilton**, Maria (A)

> *Approved Body:* Solicitors Family Law Association
>
> *Regional Group / Service:* Member of Solicitors Family Law Association, telephone 01689 850227 for details
>
> *Mediation telephone number:* 0171 481 2333

■ **Hammerton**, Robert George (A)

> *Approved Body:* Family Mediators Association
>
> *Regional Group / Service:* Family Mediators South Wales Ltd
>
> *Mediation telephone number:* 01443 400336

■ **Hammock**, Olive Marion (M)

> *Approved Body:* National Family Mediation
>
> *Regional Group / Service:* Kent Family Mediation Service
>
> *Mediation telephone number:* 01795 429689

■ **Hardy**, Peter (A)

> *Approved Body:* LawGroup UK
>
> *Regional Group / Service:* Member of LawGroup UK's Family Mediation Register, telephone 01883 370000 for details
>
> *Mediation telephone number:* 01522 531461

■ **Harmer**, Madeline M (A)

> *Approved Body:* Family Mediators Association
>
> *Regional Group / Service:* Essex Family Mediators Association
>
> *Mediation telephone number:* 01371 872490

■ **Harrington**, Philip James (A)

> *Approved Body:* National Family Mediation
>
> *Regional Group / Service:* Family Mediation Cardiff
>
> *Mediation telephone number:* 01222 229692

■ **Harris**, David Andrew (M)

> *Approved Body:* National Family Mediation
>
> *Regional Group / Service:* Thames Valley Family Mediation
>
> *Mediation telephone number:* 01753 830770

■ **Harris**, Donna Ann (M)

> *Approved Body:* National Family Mediation
>
> *Regional Group / Service:* South East London Family Mediation Bureau
>
> *Mediation telephone number:* 0181 460 4606

■ **Harris**, Jenny (M)

> *Approved Body:* National Family Mediation
>
> *Regional Group / Service:* Oxfordshire Family Mediation Service
>
> *Mediation telephone number:* 01865 741781

■ **Harrison**, Dawn Christine (M)

> *Approved Body:* National Family Mediation
>
> *Regional Group / Service:* Kent Family Mediation Service
>
> *Mediation telephone number:* 01795 429689

■ **Harrison**, Steven (A)

> *Approved Body:* LawGroup UK
>
> *Regional Group / Service:* Member of LawGroup UK's Family Mediation Register, telephone 01883 370000 for details
>
> *Mediation telephone number:* 01843 592361

■ **Harrison**, Susan Kathryn (A)

> *Approved Body:* LawGroup UK
>
> *Regional Group / Service:* Member of LawGroup UK's Family Mediation Register, telephone 01883 370000 for details
>
> *Mediation telephone number:* 0161 278 1800

(M) = Member   (A) = Associate

Harte, Emma Kathleen (A)

Approved Body: Solicitors Family Law Association

Regional Group / Service: Member of Solicitors Family Law Association, telephone 01689 850227 for details

Mediation telephone number: 0171 457 3000

Hartnell, Norman Anthony (M)

Approved Body: Family Mediators Association

Regional Group / Service: Devon Family Mediators Association

Mediation telephone number: 01392 421777

Mediation address: 20 Cathedral Yard, Exeter, Devon EX1 1HB

Professional qualifications and experience: qualified as solicitor 1979; member of The Law Society Children Panel since 1988; trainer for the Relate Quality Partnership and FMA; principal of specialist family law practice with staff of 13

Year qualified in mediation: 1989

Membership of professional bodies and organisations: Member of Relate Quality Partnership

Practice offered: Finance Issues Mediation; Children Issues Mediation; All Issues Mediation; mediation training; Professional Practice Supervision/Consultancy

Additional mediation training:

mediation trainer training	FMA	1997
Professional Practice Supervision/Consultancy	FMA	1997

Harvey, Maggie (M)

Approved Body: Family Mediation Scotland

Regional Group / Service: Family Mediation Lothian

Mediation telephone number: 0131 226 4507

Haskey, Karen Diane (A)

Approved Body: Solicitors Family Law Association

Regional Group / Service: Member of Solicitors Family Law Association, telephone 01689 850227 for details

Mediation telephone number: 0161 832 8087

Haslam, Jenny (A)

Approved Body: Family Mediation Scotland

Regional Group / Service: Family Mediation Lothian

Mediation telephone number: 0131 226 4507

Hawkins, Joanna Catherine (A)

Approved Body: LawGroup UK

Regional Group / Service: Member of LawGroup UK's Family Mediation Register, telephone 01883 370000 for details

Mediation telephone number: 01234 711215

Haworth, James Edward (A)

Approved Body: LawGroup UK

Regional Group / Service: Member of LawGroup UK's Family Mediation Register, telephone 01883 370000 for details

Mediation telephone number: 0116 2551811

Hawthorn, Linda Hazel (M)

Approved Body: Family Mediation Scotland

Regional Group / Service: Family Mediation Borders

Mediation telephone number: 01721 724170

Hayes, Mary (A)

Approved Body: Family Mediators Association

Regional Group / Service: London South & West Family Mediators Association

Mediation telephone number: 0181 744 1999

Healey, Eric (A)

Approved Body: Family Mediators Association

Regional Group / Service: Birmingham Family Mediators Association

Heathcote, Sarah Elizabeth (A)

Approved Body: Solicitors Family Law Association

Regional Group / Service: Member of Solicitors Family Law Association, telephone 01689 850227 for details

Mediation telephone number: 0115 924 3333

Heaver, Malcolm (M)

Approved Body: National Family Mediation

Regional Group / Service: Derbyshire Family Mediation Service

Mediation telephone number: 01246 277422

Hellim, Ann Margaret (A)

Approved Body: Family Mediators Association

Regional Group / Service: Surrey & North Hampshire Family Mediators Association

(cont'd)

Mediation telephone number: 01730 827001

■ **Helm**, Marjorie (M)

Approved Body: National Family Mediation

Regional Group / Service: Cumbria Family Mediation Service; Family Mediation Service (Northumberland & Tyneside)

Mediation telephone number: 0191 261 9212

■ **Henderson**, Anna (M)

Approved Body: Family Mediators Association

Regional Group / Service: London North & Central Family Mediators Association

Mediation telephone number: 0181 868 2363

Mediation address: Greystoke, Mayfield Drive, Pinner, Middlesex HA5 5QT
Facsimile 0181 868 1648

Professional qualifications and experience: solicitor (admitted 1975); 20 years' experience in family law; seven years' experience as a family mediator

Year qualified in mediation: 1991

Membership of professional bodies and organisations: Family Mediators Association; The Law Society; Solicitors Family Law Association; Lawyers Christian Fellowship; Marriage Encounter; Marriage Resource; Care for the Family

Willing to travel outside the region: ✓

Willing to travel to: 30 mile radius of Harrow

Practice offered: Finance Issues Mediation; Children Issues Mediation; All Issues Mediation; Professional Practice Supervision/Consultancy; sole or co-mediation

Additional mediation training:

consultation with children
domestic violence
Professional Practice Supervision/Consultancy

■ **Hey**, Julian Wright (A)

Approved Body: Solicitors Family Law Association

Regional Group / Service: Member of Solicitors Family Law Association, telephone 01689 850227 for details

Mediation telephone number: 01904 632841

Mediation address: 90 Main Street, Fulford, York, North Yorkshire YO1 4PS
Facsimile 01904 651366

(cont'd)

(M) = Member   (A) = Associate

Professional qualifications and experience: BA (Hons) Law & Economics; Solicitor and Notary Public; 25 years' experience in family law

Year qualified in mediation: 1998

Membership of professional bodies and organisations: The Law Society; Notaries Society; Solicitors Family Law Association

Willing to travel outside the region: ✓

Willing to travel to: North, South, East and West Yorkshire

Practice offered: All Issues Mediation

Heywood, Joanna (M)

Approved Body: National Family Mediation

Regional Group / Service: Family Mediation Service (North-West Yorkshire)

Mediation telephone number: 01423 525156

Higgin, Tom (A)

Approved Body: LawWise

Regional Group / Service: Member of LawWise Family Mediators Register, telephone 01483 237300 for details

Mediation telephone number: 01493 857503

Hilder, Carolyn Hayley Jane (A)

Approved Body: National Family Mediation

Regional Group / Service: South Staffordshire Family Mediation Service

Mediation telephone number: 01543 572600

Hill, Christine Maria (A)

Approved Body: National Family Mediation

Regional Group / Service: Merseyside Family Mediation Service

Mediation telephone number: 0151 260 9155

Hill, Irena (M)

Approved Body: National Family Mediation; Family Mediators Association

Regional Group / Service: NCH Action for Children Eye to Eye Mediation

Mediation telephone number: 0171 701 1114

Hill, Kathleen (M)

Approved Body: National Family Mediation

Regional Group / Service: Durham Family Mediation

(cont'd)

Mediation telephone number: 0191 386 5418

Hindley, Ruth (Non-Practising Member)

Approved Body: Family Mediators Association

Regional Group / Service: Sussex Family Mediators Association

Mediation telephone number: 01273 725926

Hirst, Richard Anthony (A)

Approved Body: Family Mediators Association

Regional Group / Service: Lancashire Family Mediators Association

Mediation telephone number: 01524 39760

Hoare, Alison Hilary (M)

Approved Body: National Family Mediation

Regional Group / Service: Durham Family Mediation

Mediation telephone number: 0191 3865418

Hocking, Charles William (M)

Approved Body: National Family Mediation

Regional Group / Service: Durham Family Mediation

Mediation telephone number: 0191 386 5418

Hodson, David (M)

Approved Body: Family Mediators Association

Regional Group / Service: The Family Law Consortium

Mediation telephone number: 0171 420 5000

Mediation address: The Family Law Consortium, 2 Henrietta Street, London WC2E 8PS
Facsimile 0171 420 5005, DX 40012 COVENT GARDEN, E-mail flc@tflc.co.uk

Other mediation address: Guildford (Surrey), (by special arrangement)

Professional qualifications and experience: solicitor; mediator (joint and sole); Deputy District Judge

Year qualified in mediation: 1997

Membership of professional bodies and organisations: FMA; British Association of Lawyer Mediators; Solicitors Family Law Association; Marriage Resource; International Academy of Matrimonial Lawyers; Lawyers Christian Fellowship; Lord Chancellor's Department's Family Proceedings Rules Committee

Willing to travel outside the region: ✓

Willing to travel to: London; Surrey; elsewhere in the world subject to agreeing fees

(cont'd)

Practice offered: All Issues Mediation

Career and Work Experience

Solicitor and partner in The Family Law Consortium, probably England's first multi-disciplinary private practice combining solicitors, mediators and counsellors. It is a Legal Aid Board Mediation Pilot.

Trained as joint and sole mediator with FMA. Specialises in finance cases involving middle and higher income families.

Regular speaker and writer on mediation and family law generally. Contributor to *UK College of Family Mediators Directory & Handbook* (1st and 2nd editions). Co-author, *Divorce Reform: A Guide for Lawyers and Mediators* (FT Law & Tax) and *The Business of Family Law* (Jordans). Speaker at twice annual NFM residential training weekends.

Committee member of British Association of Lawyer Mediators. Member of Solicitors Family Law Association National Committee and chairman of its Good Practice Committee. Family law co-ordinator of Lawyers Christian Fellowship. Trustee of Marriage Resource counselling organisation, one of the Lord Chancellor's pilot marriage support organisations. Deputy District Judge, Principal Registry Family Division. Member LCD's Family Proceedings Rules Committee. Fellow, International Academy of Matrimonial Lawyers.

■ **Holding**, Karen Margrethe **(A)**

Approved Body: LawWise

Regional Group / Service: Member of LawWise Family Mediators Register, telephone 01483 237300 for details

Mediation telephone number: 0171 833 3454

Mediation address: 144 Cloudesley Road, Islington, London N1 0EA Facsimile 0171 833 3454, E-mail futurefocus@hotmail.com

Professional qualifications and experience: solicitor; Certificate in Systemic Counselling (Institute of Family Therapy)

Year qualified in mediation: 1996

Membership of professional bodies and organisations: The Law Society; British Association of Lawyer Mediators

Practice offered: All Issues Mediation

■ **Holleyman**, Graham John **(M)**

Approved Body: Family Mediators Association

Regional Group / Service: Kent Family Mediators Association

Hollidge-Goode, Stephanie Mary (A)

Approved Body: LawWise

Regional Group / Service: Member of LawWise Family Mediators Register, telephone 01483 237300 for details

Mediation telephone number: 01420 82879

Hollywood, Susan Elaine (A)

Approved Body: National Family Mediation

Regional Group / Service: South Staffordshire Family Mediation Service

Mediation telephone number: 01543 572600

Holmes, Patricia Ines (A)

Approved Body: Family Mediators Association

Regional Group / Service: Coventry and South Warwickshire Family Mediators Association

Mediation telephone number: 01203 631000

Holmes, Sara (M)

Approved Body: National Family Mediation

Regional Group / Service: Lancashire Family Mediation Service

Hope, Helen Claire (A)

Approved Body: Solicitors Family Law Association

Regional Group / Service: Member of Solicitors Family Law Association, telephone 01689 850227 for details

Mediation telephone number: 01767 600600

Hope, Nia Frances (A)

Approved Body: LawGroup UK

Regional Group / Service: Member of LawGroup UK's Family Mediation Register, telephone 01883 370000 for details

Mediation telephone number: 0161 480 3431

Hopkin, Sian Gwyneth (M)

Approved Body: Family Mediators Association

Regional Group / Service: Bristol Family Mediators Association

Mediation telephone number: 0117 9292811

Horne, Louise (M)

Approved Body: National Family Mediation

Regional Group / Service: Family Mediation Service (Greater Manchester)

(cont'd)

Mediation telephone number: 0161 797 9910

■ **Horton**, Maeve (M)

>*Approved Body:* National Family Mediation
>
>*Regional Group / Service:* Northamptonshire Family Mediation Service
>
>*Mediation telephone number:* 01604 636651

■ **Hotchkiss**, Elizabeth Susan (M)

>*Approved Body:* National Family Mediation
>
>*Regional Group / Service:* Merseyside Family Mediation Service
>
>*Mediation telephone number:* 0151 260 9155

■ **Hoult**, John Frederick (A)

>*Approved Body:* Family Mediators Association
>
>*Regional Group / Service:* South Yorkshire Family Mediators Association
>
>*Mediation telephone number:* 01724 281312

■ **Howard**, Helen Patricia (A)

>*Approved Body:* Solicitors Family Law Association
>
>*Regional Group / Service:* Member of Solicitors Family Law Association, telephone 01689 850227 for details
>
>*Mediation telephone number:* 01865 798003

■ **Howe**, James (M)

>*Approved Body:* National Family Mediation
>
>*Regional Group / Service:* South Staffordshire Family Mediation Service
>
>*Mediation telephone number:* 01543 572600

■ **Howe**, Jo (M)

>*Approved Body:* National Family Mediation
>
>*Regional Group / Service:* South Yorkshire Family Mediation Service
>
>*Mediation telephone number:* 0114 275 2227

■ **Howe**, Kerrie (M)

>*Approved Body:* Family Mediation Scotland
>
>*Regional Group / Service:* Family Mediation Tayside
>
>*Mediation telephone number:* 01382 201343

■ **Howe**, Nicola Jane (A)

>*Approved Body:* Family Mediators Association
>
>*Regional Group / Service:* Kent Family Mediators Association

(cont'd)

Mediation telephone number: 01892 510000

Howell, Jeremy Wynter (A)

Approved Body: LawGroup UK

Regional Group / Service: Member of LawGroup UK's Family Mediation Register, telephone 01883 370000 for details

Mediation telephone number: 01803 213513

Hughes, Frances Mary Theresa (M)

Approved Body: Family Mediators Association

Regional Group / Service: London South & Central Family Mediators Association

Mediation telephone number: 0171 551 7777

Hugman, John Melvin (A)

Approved Body: LawWise

Regional Group / Service: Member of LawWise Family Mediators Register, telephone 01483 237300 for details

Mediation telephone number: 0151 609 2814

Mediation address: 397 Woodchurch Road, Birkenhead, Wirral L42 8PF Facsimile 0151 608 0624, DX 15503 PRENTON, E-mail llw@compuserve.com

Other mediation address: 6th Floor, 43 Castle Street, Liverpool, Merseyside L2 1JT

Professional qualifications and experience: solicitor 19 years; Family Mediator two years

Year qualified in mediation: 1996

Membership of professional bodies and organisations: BALM; SFLA

Willing to travel outside the region: ✓

Willing to travel to: Cheshire, South Lancashire, Flintshire

Practice offered: All Issues Mediation

Hulland, Vivien Elizabeth (A)

Approved Body: Family Mediators Association

Regional Group / Service: West Yorkshire Family Mediators Association

Mediation telephone number: 01943 461414

Hunter, Alexis Margaret (A)

Approved Body: Family Mediation Scotland

Regional Group / Service: Family Mediation (West of Scotland)

(cont'd)

Mediation telephone number: 0141 332 2731

■ **Hurlow**, Carole Ann (A)

Approved Body: LawGroup UK

Regional Group / Service: Member of LawGroup UK's Family Mediation Register, telephone 01883 370000 for details

Mediation telephone number: 01222 396087

■ **Hutchinson**, Stella (M)

Approved Body: National Family Mediation

Regional Group / Service: Family Mediation (Central Middlesex)

Mediation telephone number: 0181 427 2076

■ **Ievins**, Catherine Ruth (M)

Approved Body: National Family Mediation

Regional Group / Service: Peterborough & District Family Mediation Service

Mediation telephone number: 01733 347353

■ **Iliff**, Catherine Ann Murray (M)

Approved Body: Family Mediators Association

Regional Group / Service: Family Mediation in Norfolk

Mediation telephone number: 01603 723721 (direct line)

Mediation address: Fosters, 60 London Street, Norwich, Norfolk NR2 1JY
Facsimile 01603 624090, DX 5225 NORWICH 1

Other mediation address: Fosters, 3 Trinity Street, Bungay, Suffolk NR35 1EQ

Professional qualifications and experience: solicitor qualified in 1982 specialising in family law; solid experience in all aspects of family work

Year qualified in mediation: Accredited 1994

Membership of professional bodies and organisations: SFLA; FMA

Willing to travel outside the region: ✓

Willing to travel to: East Anglia

Practice offered: Children Issues Mediation; All Issues Mediation

Additional mediation training:

consultation with children	FMA	1997
domestic violence	FMA	1997

Other additional mediation training: sole and anchor mediation practitioners course (FMA) 1997

Irvine, Charles Clouston (M)

Approved Body: Family Mediation Scotland

Regional Group / Service: Family Mediation (West of Scotland)

Mediation telephone number: 0141 332 2731

Izod, Kevin Howard Ralph (A)

Approved Body: LawWise

Regional Group / Service: Member of LawWise Family Mediators Register, telephone 01483 237300 for details

Mediation telephone number: 01252 376282

Jackson, Catherine Elinor (M)

Approved Body: National Family Mediation

Regional Group / Service: Cleveland Family Mediation Service

Mediation telephone number: 01642 222967

Jackson, Dori (M)

Approved Body: Family Mediation Scotland

Regional Group / Service: Family Mediation (West of Scotland)

Mediation telephone number: 01563 572429

Jackson, Susan Elizabeth (A)

Approved Body: LawGroup UK

Regional Group / Service: Member of LawGroup UK's Family Mediation Register, telephone 01883 370000 for details

Mediation telephone number: 01234 303030

Jackson, Tony (A)

Approved Body: National Family Mediation

Regional Group / Service: Cleveland Family Mediation Service

Mediation telephone number: 01642 222967

Jackson-Thomas, Sarah Jane (A)

Approved Body: LawWise; LawGroup UK

Regional Group / Service: Member of LawGroup UK's Family Mediation Register, telephone 01883 370000 for details; Member of LawWise Family Mediators Register, telephone 01483 237300 for details

Mediation telephone number: 01792 454715

Jacob, Steven (A)

Approved Body: Family Mediators Association

Regional Group / Service: The Hertfordshire Comprehensive Mediation Service

Mediation address: 90 Stroud Green Road, London N4 3EN
Facsimile 0181 292 3378, DX 57478 FINSBURY PARK

Professional qualifications and experience: matrimonial solicitor of 11 years' post-admission experience

Year qualified in mediation: 1994

Membership of professional bodies and organisations: The Law Society; Family Mediators Association; Reunite; Relate Quality Partner; Association of Lawyers for Children

Willing to travel outside the region: ✓

Willing to travel to: Hertfordshire, Barnet, Brent and Haringey

Practice offered: All Issues Mediation

Additional Relevant Skills

I qualified in August 1986 and joined a central London firm of solicitors in 1988, where I became head of their matrimonial department. I am fluent in Greek and have an established matrimonial practice with a firm commitment to mediation and conciliation. Additional interests include alternative dispute resolution. My present practice was established in 1995 with a particular emphasis on matrimonial and family-related work.

Jacobs, Michael (M)

Approved Body: National Family Mediation

Regional Group / Service: Herefordshire Family Mediation Service

Mediation telephone number: 01432 264087

James, Bryan Haydn (M)

Approved Body: National Family Mediation

Regional Group / Service: Family Mediation Cardiff

Mediation telephone number: 01222 229692

James, Ralph Lionel (M)

Approved Body: National Family Mediation

Regional Group / Service: Birmingham District Family Mediation

Mediation telephone number: 0121 233 1999

Janko, Moya Emma (A)

Approved Body: Family Mediators Association

Regional Group / Service: South Midlands Family Mediators Association

(cont'd)

Mediation telephone number: 01604 622101

▦ **Jeffrey**, George (M)

Approved Body: National Family Mediation

Regional Group / Service: Suffolk Family Mediation Service

Mediation telephone number: 01502 501935

▦ **Jeffrey**, Joy (M)

Approved Body: National Family Mediation

Regional Group / Service: Suffolk Family Mediation Service

Mediation telephone number: 01502 501935

▦ **Jenkins**, Anthony David (A)

Approved Body: LawWise

Regional Group / Service: Member of LawWise Family Mediators Register, telephone 01483 237300 for details

Mediation telephone number: 01483 562901

▦ **Jennings**, Stephen Paul (A)

Approved Body: Solicitors Family Law Association

Regional Group / Service: Member of Solicitors Family Law Association, telephone 01689 850227 for details

▦ **Johnson**, Angela Jane (A)

Approved Body: Family Mediation Scotland

Regional Group / Service: Family Mediation Grampian

Mediation telephone number: 01779 490790

▦ **Johnson**, Pauline (A)

Approved Body: Family Mediators Association

Regional Group / Service: Hampshire & Isle of Wight Family Mediators Association

Mediation telephone number: 01703 334661

▦ **Jones**, Andrea (M)

Approved Body: National Family Mediation

Regional Group / Service: York Family Mediation Service

Mediation telephone number: 01904 646068

▦ **Jones**, Anne (A)

Approved Body: National Family Mediation

Regional Group / Service: York Family Mediation Service

(cont'd)

Mediation telephone number: 01904 646068

Jones, Brian Anthony (M)

Approved Body: Family Mediators Association

Regional Group / Service: Bath District Family Mediators Association

Mediation telephone number: 01225 448494

Mediation address: Thrings & Long, Midland Bridge, Bath, Bath & NE Somerset BA1 2HQ
Facsimile 01225 319735, DX 8002 BATH

Other mediation address: Nettleton Millhouse, Nettleton, Chippenham, Wiltshire SN14 7NJ

Professional qualifications and experience: solicitor, 20 years' family specialism; accredited mediator, supervisor, sole and anchor

Year qualified in mediation: 1992

Membership of professional bodies and organisations: SFLA; FMA; The Law Society

Willing to travel outside the region: ✓

Willing to travel to: Bath & North East Somerset, North Wiltshire

Practice offered: All Issues Mediation; Professional Practice Supervision/Consultancy; sole mediation

Additional mediation training:

Professional Practice Supervision/Consultancy   FMA   1997

Other additional mediation training: sole and anchor (FMA) 1997

Jones, Graham Kenneth (M)

Approved Body: National Family Mediation

Regional Group / Service: Kent Family Mediation Service

Mediation telephone number: 01795 429689

Jones, Peter Graham (A)

Approved Body: Solicitors Family Law Association

Regional Group / Service: Member of Solicitors Family Law Association, telephone 01689 850227 for details

Mediation telephone number: 0113 246 0055

Mediation address: Pearl Chambers, 22 East Parade, Leeds LS1 5BZ
Facsimile 0113 246 7446, DX 14080 LEEDS PARK SQ

Professional qualifications and experience: solicitor and specialist family lawyer

Year qualified in mediation: 1997

Membership of professional bodies and organisations: The Law Society; Solicitors Family Law Association; UK College of Family Mediators

(cont'd)

Willing to travel outside the region: ✓

Willing to travel to: North of England and London

Practice offered: All Issues Mediation

Jordan, Barbara (A)

Approved Body: Family Mediators Association

Regional Group / Service: Hereford & Worcester Family Mediators Association

Mediation telephone number: 01989 566111

Mediation address: Jordans Solicitors, 51 Broad St, Ross on Wye, Herefordshire HR9 7DY
Facsimile 01989 565566, DX 22498 ROSS ON WYE

Professional qualifications and experience: solicitor and FMA trained mediator

Year qualified in mediation: 1996

Membership of professional bodies and organisations: The Law Society; FMA

Willing to travel outside the region: ✓

Willing to travel to: 35 mile radius of office

Practice offered: Children Issues Mediation; All Issues Mediation

I have worked as a divorce lawyer for a number of years, and recognise that there are some people for whom the legal system offers an unnecessarily lengthy and accrimonious method of divorce or separation.

I believe that my legal background enables me to provide an informed mediation service for those who wish to opt for a settlement of issues based on face-to-face communication, with professional guidance.

Jordan, Paul (A)

Approved Body: LawGroup UK

Regional Group / Service: Member of LawGroup UK's Family Mediation Register, telephone 01883 370000 for details

Mediation telephone number: Freephone 0500 328886

Josse, Jeannette Denise (M)

Approved Body: Family Mediators Association

Regional Group / Service: Cambridge Family Mediators Association

Mediation telephone number: 01223 460122

Joyce, Pauli (M)

Approved Body: National Family Mediation

Regional Group / Service: Somerset Family Mediation Service

(cont'd)

Mediation telephone number: 01823 352013

Kaffel, Dawn (A)

Approved Body: Family Mediators Association

Regional Group / Service: London North & Central Family Mediators Association

Mediation telephone number: 0181 348 4440

Kane, Brigid Mary (M)

Approved Body: Family Mediators Association

Regional Group / Service: London North & Central Family Mediators Association

Mediation telephone number: 0171 435 5553

Katzenberg, Simone Elaine (M)

Approved Body: Family Mediators Association

Regional Group / Service: London North & Central Family Mediators Association

Mediation telephone number: 0171 431 1912

Kelleher, Bruce Stuart (A)

Approved Body: LawGroup UK

Regional Group / Service: Member of LawGroup UK's Family Mediation Register, telephone 01883 370000 for details

Mediation telephone number: 01208 812068

Kelly, Margaret Kelly (A)

Approved Body: Family Mediators Association

Regional Group / Service: London North & Central Family Mediators Association

Mediation telephone number: 0171 700 6006

Kelly, Martin John (A)

Approved Body: Family Mediators Association

Regional Group / Service: Thames Valley Family Mediators Association

Mediation telephone number: 01189 587111

Kemp, Howard (A)

Approved Body: Family Mediators Association

Regional Group / Service: Essex Family Mediators Association

Mediation telephone number: 0181 514 3000

(M) = Member   (A) = Associate

■ **Kendrew,** David Charles (A)

Approved Body: Solicitors Family Law Association

Regional Group / Service: Member of Solicitors Family Law Association, telephone 01689 850227 for details

Mediation telephone number: 01228 522215

Mediation address: Bendles Solicitors, 22 Portland Square, Carlisle, Cumbria CA1 1PE
Facsimile 01228 515442, DX 63010 CARLISLE

Professional qualifications and experience: solicitor of the Supreme Court; 22 years of experience in family law; trained mediator with ADR group; trained family mediator with SFLA

Year qualified in mediation: 1996

Membership of professional bodies and organisations: The Law Society; SFLA

Willing to travel outside the region: ✓

Willing to travel to: North of England

Practice offered: All Issues Mediation

■ **Kennard,** Sheila (M)

Approved Body: National Family Mediation

Regional Group / Service: Plymouth Mediation

Mediation telephone number: 01752 671078

■ **Kennedy,** Evelyn (M)

Approved Body: National Family Mediation

Regional Group / Service: Family Mediation Service: Barnet, Haringey & Hertsmere

Mediation telephone number: 0181 343 9899

■ **Keogh-Smith,** Elizabeth (M)

Approved Body: National Family Mediation

Regional Group / Service: Worcestershire Family Mediation

Mediation telephone number: 01905 610925

■ **Kerr,** Linda Patricia (M)

Approved Body: National Family Mediation

Regional Group / Service: Northern Ireland Family Mediation Service

Mediation telephone number: 01232 322914

Kidd, Paul Garforth (M)

>*Approved Body:* National Family Mediation
>
>*Regional Group / Service:* Salisbury & District Family Mediation Service
>
>*Mediation telephone number:* 01722 332936

King, Jennifer Hilary Laura (M)

>*Approved Body:* Family Mediators Association
>
>*Regional Group / Service:* Wiltshire Family Mediators Association
>
>*Mediation telephone number:* 01635 264406

Kinnear, Olive Jean (M)

>*Approved Body:* Family Mediation Scotland
>
>*Regional Group / Service:* Family Mediation Lothian
>
>*Mediation telephone number:* 0131 226 4507

Kitchener, Miranda (M)

>*Approved Body:* National Family Mediation
>
>*Regional Group / Service:* Family Mediation Cardiff
>
>*Mediation telephone number:* 01222 229692

Klarfeld, Jacqueline Ann (M)

>*Approved Body:* Family Mediators Association
>
>*Regional Group / Service:* London North & Central Family Mediators Association
>
>*Mediation telephone number:* 0181 954 3523

Klauber, Jane Eva (A)

>*Approved Body:* Family Mediators Association
>
>*Regional Group / Service:* London North & Central Family Mediators Association
>
>*Mediation telephone number:* 0181 969 3667

Kleanthous, Valerie Anne (M)

>*Approved Body:* Family Mediators Association
>
>*Regional Group / Service:* Mediation for Families (Thames Valley and Central London)
>
>*Mediation telephone number:* 01923 777739
>
>*Mediation address:* Thatchways, Bridle Lane, Loudwater, Rickmansworth, Hertfordshire WD3 4JG
>Facsimile 01923 897618, E-mail val_kleanthous@link.org

(cont'd)

(M) = Member   (A) = Associate

Professional qualifications and experience: LLB (Lond); solicitor; Mediation Trainer FMA/SFLA

Year qualified in mediation: 1989

Membership of professional bodies and organisations: FMA; SFLA; The Law Society; Hertfordshire Comprehensive Mediation Service

Willing to travel outside the region: ✓

Willing to travel to: also practise in Central London

Practice offered: Finance Issues Mediation; Children Issues Mediation; All Issues Mediation; mediation training; Professional Practice Supervision/Consultancy; mediation in Greek and Jewish communities

Additional mediation training:

consultation with children	FMA	
domestic violence	FMA	
mediation trainer training		1996
Professional Practice Supervision/Consultancy		1995

▪ **Klein**, Wendy T (A)

Approved Body: Family Mediators Association

Regional Group / Service: Thames Valley Family Mediators Association

Mediation telephone number: 0118 984 2856

▪ **Knight**, Susan (M)

Approved Body: National Family Mediation

Regional Group / Service: Sussex Family Mediation Service

Mediation telephone number: 01273 550563

▪ **Koppel**, Hanno (M)

Approved Body: Family Mediators Association

Regional Group / Service: Family Mediators South Wales Ltd

Mediation telephone number: 01222 874000 ext 6490

▪ **Lacy**, Margaret Mary (M)

Approved Body: National Family Mediation

Regional Group / Service: Family Mediation Service (Northumberland & Tyneside)

Mediation telephone number: 0191 261 9212

▪ **Laird**, Doreen (M)

Approved Body: Family Mediation Scotland

Regional Group / Service: Family Mediation (West of Scotland)

Mediation telephone number: 0141 332 2731

Lake-Carroll, Angela (M)

Approved Body: National Family Mediation; Family Mediators Association

Regional Group / Service: Mediation East Anglia; Suffolk Family Mediation Service

Mediation telephone number: 01284 706149

Lambert, Leasa (M)

Approved Body: National Family Mediation

Regional Group / Service: Mediation for Families (East London & City)

Mediation telephone number: 0171 503 7454

Lang, Jean Mary (A)

Approved Body: Solicitors Family Law Association

Regional Group / Service: Member of Solicitors Family Law Association, telephone 01689 850227 for details

Mediation telephone number: 01305 266896

Latham, Annette (M)

Approved Body: Family Mediators Association

Regional Group / Service: Family Mediation Consortium

Mediation telephone number: 01772 257745

Mediation address: 13 Cross Street, Preston, Lancashire PR1 3LT Facsimile 01772 257944, DX 17103

Professional qualifications and experience: solicitor, (LLB); accredited FMA mediator; approved Law Society Children Panel solicitor

Year qualified in mediation: 1996

Willing to travel outside the region: ✓

Willing to travel to: Cumbria (all over), Lancashire (all over)

Practice offered: All Issues Mediation

Other additional mediation training: sole mediation 1998

Laugharne, Andrew (A)

Approved Body: LawGroup UK

Regional Group / Service: Member of LawGroup UK's Family Mediation Register, telephone 01883 370000 for details

Mediation telephone number: 01271 342268

Laughton, Sarah Jane (M)

Approved Body: National Family Mediation

Regional Group / Service: Cambridge Family & Divorce Centre

(cont'd)

Mediation telephone number: 01223 576308

▪ **Lazarus**, Myrna (M)

    Approved Body: National Family Mediation

    Regional Group / Service: Mediation for Families (East London & City)

    Mediation telephone number: 0171 613 1666

▪ **Leach**, Jon (A)

    Approved Body: Family Mediators Association

    Regional Group / Service: West Yorkshire Family Mediators Association

    Mediation telephone number: 01756 794611

▪ **Leach**, Vicky (M)

    Approved Body: National Family Mediation

    Regional Group / Service: NCH Action for Children Eye to Eye Mediation

    Mediation telephone number: 0171 701 1114

▪ **Leask**, Deborah Elizabeth (A)

    Approved Body: Solicitors Family Law Association

    Regional Group / Service: Member of Solicitors Family Law Association, telephone 01689 850227 for details

    Mediation telephone number: 0171 607 0616

▪ **Lee**, Kathryn (M)

    Approved Body: National Family Mediation

    Regional Group / Service: Kent Family Mediation Service

    Mediation telephone number: 01795 429689

▪ **Lee**, Theresa (A)

    Approved Body: Family Mediators Association

    Regional Group / Service: Thames Valley Family Mediators Association

    Mediation telephone number: 0118 9589711

▪ **Leeson**, Mark Alastair (M)

    Approved Body: Family Mediators Association

    Regional Group / Service: Kent Family Mediators Association

    Mediation telephone number: 01732 864411

Le Fleming, Peer Christopher (A)

Approved Body: LawWise

Regional Group / Service: Member of LawWise Family Mediators Register, telephone 01483 237300 for details

Mediation telephone number: 01227 456731

Leggett, Eddie (M)

Approved Body: National Family Mediation

Regional Group / Service: Derbyshire Family Mediation Service

Mediation telephone number: 01246 277422

Leigh, Rose Jacqueline (M)

Approved Body: National Family Mediation

Regional Group / Service: Family Mediation Service – Institute of Family Therapy

Mediation telephone number: 0171 391 9150

Mediation address: The Family Mediation Service – Institute of Family Therapy, 2nd Floor, 24-32 Stephenson Way, London NW1 2HX Facsimile 0171 391 9169

Professional qualifications and experience: lawyer; CAB manager

Year qualified in mediation: 1995

Membership of professional bodies and organisations: UK College of Family Mediators; The Law Society

Willing to travel outside the region: ✓

Willing to travel to: South-East region

Practice offered: Finance Issues Mediation; Children Issues Mediation; All Issues Mediation; welfare benefits; able to work with Jewish and mixed couples

Additional mediation training:

consultation with children	NFM	1996
initial information giving and/or assessment	NFM	1995

Lennon, Pat A (A)

Approved Body: Family Mediators Association

Mediation telephone number: 0114 290 2200

Leonard, Peggy Jean (A)

Approved Body: Family Mediators Association

Regional Group / Service: South West Region Family Mediators Association

Mediation telephone number: 01752 774368

Leonards, Olive (M)

Approved Body: National Family Mediation

Regional Group / Service: Family Mediation Service (Greater Manchester)

Mediation telephone number: 0161 764 2196

Lever, Lynden (M)

Approved Body: Family Mediators Association

Regional Group / Service: Bath District Family Mediators Association

Mediation telephone number: 01225 337599

Mediation address: 13 Queen Square, Bath BA1 2HJ
Facsimile 01225 335437, DX 8001 BATH, E-mail
lyndenlever@stoneking.demon.co.uk

Professional qualifications and experience: solicitor; member FMA; trained in sole and anchor mediation

Year qualified in mediation: 1991

Membership of professional bodies and organisations: FMA; SFLA

Willing to travel outside the region: ✓

Willing to travel to: Somerset, Wiltshire, Bristol, Avon

Practice offered: All Issues Mediation; Professional Practice Supervision/Consultancy

Additional mediation training:

domestic violence	FMA	
initial information giving and/or assessment	FMA	
Professional Practice Supervision/Consultancy	FMA	1996

Other additional mediation training: sole mediation 1996

Levinge, Nicholas Vere (A)

Approved Body: Family Mediators Association

Regional Group / Service: South Midlands Family Mediators Association

Mediation telephone number: 01604 231050

Levy, Deborah Jane (A)

Approved Body: Family Mediators Association

Regional Group / Service: The Hertfordshire Comprehensive Mediation Service

Mediation telephone number: 01923 854887

■ **Lewis**, Ana Josefina (A)

Approved Body: Solicitors Family Law Association

Regional Group / Service: Member of Solicitors Family Law Association, telephone 01689 850227 for details

Mediation telephone number: 01234 270600/0370 675540

■ **Lewis**, Jacqueline Ann (A)

Approved Body: Solicitors Family Law Association

Regional Group / Service: Member of Solicitors Family Law Association, telephone 01689 850227 for details

Mediation telephone number: 0181 977 7633

Mediation address: Infields, 1 Old Bridge Street, Hampton Wick, Kingston-upon-Thames, Surrey KT1 4DB
Facsimile 0181 977 9962, DX 31510 KINGSTON

Professional qualifications and experience: solicitor, admitted 1985; SFLA mediation training

Year qualified in mediation: 1997

Membership of professional bodies and organisations: The Law Society; APIL; SFLA

Practice offered: All Issues Mediation

■ **Lewis**, Margaret Eveline (M)

Approved Body: National Family Mediation

Regional Group / Service: Peterborough & District Family Mediation Service

Mediation telephone number: 01733 347353

■ **Lewis**, Rhiannon (M)

Approved Body: Family Mediators Association

Regional Group / Service: London South & Central Family Mediators Association

Mediation telephone number: 0171 242 2556

■ **Lewis**, Tony (M)

Approved Body: National Family Mediation

Regional Group / Service: Somerset Family Mediation Service; Bristol Family Mediation Service

Mediation telephone number: 0117 929 2002

■ **Liddell**, Katrina Louise (M)

Approved Body: Family Mediation Scotland

Regional Group / Service: Family Mediation Tayside

(cont'd)

Mediation telephone number: 01382 201343

Lidster, Wendy Carol (M)

> *Approved Body:* Family Mediators Association
>
> *Regional Group / Service:* Sussex Family Mediators Association
>
> *Mediation telephone number:* 01273 330262

Lindfield, Sarah (M)

> *Approved Body:* National Family Mediation
>
> *Regional Group / Service:* Gwent Mediation Service
>
> *Mediation telephone number:* 01633 263065

Linn, Pauline (A)

> *Approved Body:* Family Mediation Scotland
>
> *Regional Group / Service:* Family Mediation Lothian
>
> *Mediation telephone number:* 0131 226 4507

Linsley, Wendy Mary (M)

> *Approved Body:* National Family Mediation
>
> *Regional Group / Service:* Family Mediation Service (Northumberland & Tyneside)
>
> *Mediation telephone number:* 0191 261 9212

Little, Peter (M)

> *Approved Body:* National Family Mediation
>
> *Regional Group / Service:* Shropshire Family Mediation Service
>
> *Mediation telephone number:* 01952 502447

Littlewood, Robin (A)

> *Approved Body:* Family Mediators Association
>
> *Regional Group / Service:* Wiltshire Family Mediators Association
>
> *Mediation telephone number:* 01666 822671

Lloyd, Michael James Nicholas (M)

> *Approved Body:* National Family Mediation
>
> *Regional Group / Service:* Sussex Family Mediation Service
>
> *Mediation telephone number:* 01273 550563

Lloyd, Sarah (A)

> *Approved Body:* Solicitors Family Law Association
>
> *Regional Group / Service:* Member of Solicitors Family Law Association, telephone 01689 850227 for details

(cont'd)

Mediation telephone number: 0181 789 9111

Lloyd-Davies, Michael David (A)

Approved Body: Family Mediators Association

Regional Group / Service: Somerset Family Mediators Association

Mediation telephone number: 01823 331293

Lockyear, Catherine Helen Anne (M)

Approved Body: Family Mediators Association

Regional Group / Service: South West Region Family Mediators Association

Mediation telephone number: 01392 420888

Logan, Alastair Douglas Wollaston (M)

Approved Body: LawWise

Regional Group / Service: Member of LawWise Family Mediators Register, telephone 01483 237300 for details

Mediation telephone number: 01483 236237

Mediation address: The Shooting Lodge, Guildford Road, Sutton Green, Guildford, Surrey GU4 7PZ
Facsimile 01483 237004, DX 83171 GUILDFORD 2, E-mail a.logan@cableol.co.uk

Professional qualifications and experience: solicitor; family lawyer; family mediator; commercial mediator; Director of the University of Oxford Postgraduate Diploma in Family Mediation

Year qualified in mediation: 1995

Membership of professional bodies and organisations: The Law Society; Haynes Mediation Training Institute; SFLA, LawWise

Willing to travel outside the region: ✓

Willing to travel to: England and Wales

Practice offered: All Issues Mediation; mediation training; Professional Practice Supervision/Consultancy

Additional mediation training:

initial information giving and/or assessment	HMTI	1995
mediation trainer training	HMTI	1996
Professional Practice Supervision/Consultancy	HMTI 1996, FMA 1997	

Other additional mediation training: Advanced Family Mediation (HMTI) 1996; Commercial Mediation (CEDR) JANUS/Eudispute 1995

Career

I have a degree in Law from University College, London in 1964. Throughout my practising life I have been involved in family law. I am a member of the SFLA.

(cont'd)

I practise in Guildford specialising in family law and mediation. My firm has held a Legal Aid Franchise in family law work for three years. With my wife Pat we run our own mediation centre 'Solutions' offering mediation in both civil and family disputes.

I trained as a family mediator with Dr John Haynes. I undertook advanced mediation training with John Haynes and with experienced mediators in the USA. I trained as a commercial mediator with the Centre for Dispute Resolution (CEDR) in London and JAMS/Endispute the largest providers of mediation in the US, in Boston, Massachusetts.

I am licensed as a trainer of mediators by the Haynes Mediation Training Institute. I train family and commercial mediators in a programme run by my own company, LawWise Limited, the first independent training organisation to be approved as family mediation trainers by the UK College of Family Mediators.

I am a founder member and the Chairman of the British Association of Lawyer Mediators. I am the Director of the University of Oxford Postgraduate Diploma in Family Mediation.

Logan, Crawford John (M)

Approved Body: Family Mediation Scotland

Regional Group / Service: Family Mediation Central Scotland

Mediation telephone number: 01786 472984

Logan, Patricia Anne (M)

Approved Body: LawWise

Regional Group / Service: Member of LawWise Family Mediators Register, telephone 01483 237300 for details

Mediation telephone number: 01483 236237

Mediation address: The Shooting Lodge, Guildford Road, Sutton Green, Guildford, Surrey GU4 7PZ
Facsimile 01483 237004, DX 83171 GUILDFORD 2

Professional qualifications and experience: accountancy; legal practice practice management; legal (solicitors accounts); family law (eight years); commercial mediation

Year qualified in mediation: 1995

Membership of professional bodies and organisations: BALM; SFLA; Haynes Mediation Training Institute; LawWise

Willing to travel outside the region: ✓

Willing to travel to: England and Wales

Practice offered: Finance Issues Mediation; Children Issues Mediation; All Issues Mediation; mediation training; Professional Practice Supervision/Consultancy; mediation extended family; wills and boundary disputes

(cont'd)

Additional mediation training:

consultation with children	LawWise/Angela Lake	
	Carroll	1997
domestic violence	JHTI	1996
initial information giving and/or assessment	HMTI	1997
mediation trainer training	HMTI	1996
Professional Practice Supervision/Consultancy	FMA/HMTI	1997

Other additional mediation training: Advanced Family Mediation (HMTI) 1996; The Boston Mediation Advanced Training 1995

Additional Relevant Skills

Career: Trained as an accountant originally. In my working career I managed a chain of shops and spent four years as a market research analyst. After my children started school I was an infant school teacher for a number of years, the Accommodation Officer at University of Surrey and County Organiser for Surrey Young Farmers.

For the last eight years I have been Practice Manager for the Logan Partnership which involves managing a busy solicitors office which has a franchise from the Legal Aid Board for family work. I have qualifications as a debt counsellor and welfare benefits advisor and practise particularly in connection with the restructuring of family finances as a consequence of divorce or separation with Solutions Mediation Centre for four years, specialising in **Family** and **All Issues Mediation** and have completed over 50 cases.

Training: Trained as a family mediator with John Haynes and since qualified as a Trainer and Supervisor with The Haynes Mediation Institute and LawWise. I have completed the FMA Professional Practice Supervisor Consultant Course, CEDR Commercial Dispute Resolutions in London and JAMS/Endispute, largest providers of mediation in the USA.

I am a founder member and Membership Secretary of the **BALM**.

Longford, Nicholas F W (A)

Approved Body: Solicitors Family Law Association

Regional Group / Service: Member of Solicitors Family Law Association, telephone 01689 850227 for details

Mediation telephone number: 01638 661221

Loram, John Beloe (A)

Approved Body: LawGroup UK

Regional Group / Service: Member of LawGroup UK's Family Mediation Register, telephone 01883 370000 for details

Mediation telephone number: 01392 270867

Lothian, Mary (M)

> *Approved Body:* Family Mediation Scotland
>
> *Regional Group / Service:* Family Mediation Service (Highland)
>
> *Mediation telephone number:* 01463 712100

Love, Lorraine (A)

> *Approved Body:* Family Mediation Scotland
>
> *Regional Group / Service:* Family Mediation Central Scotland
>
> *Mediation telephone number:* 01786 472984

Lowe, Linda (M)

> *Approved Body:* Family Mediation Scotland
>
> *Regional Group / Service:* Family Mediation Service (Highland)
>
> *Mediation telephone number:* 01463 712100

Lowe, Pauline (M)

> *Approved Body:* National Family Mediation
>
> *Regional Group / Service:* South Yorkshire Family Mediation Service
>
> *Mediation telephone number:* 0114 275 2227

Lowe, Tracy Josephine Toni (M)

> *Approved Body:* National Family Mediation
>
> *Regional Group / Service:* Lancashire Family Mediation Service
>
> *Mediation telephone number:* 01722 204248

Lynch, Kathleen Mary (A)

> *Approved Body:* Family Mediation Scotland
>
> *Regional Group / Service:* Family Mediation (West of Scotland)
>
> *Mediation telephone number:* 0141 332 2731

Lynch, Kay Ann (M)

> *Approved Body:* National Family Mediation
>
> *Regional Group / Service:* Hampshire Family Mediation
>
> *Mediation telephone number:* 01705 660919

Lyons, Judi (A)

> *Approved Body:* Family Mediators Association
>
> *Regional Group / Service:* Thames Valley Family Mediators Association
>
> *Mediation telephone number:* 01189 421009

(M) = Member   (A) = Associate

MacBean, Marion (M)

> *Approved Body:* Family Mediators Association
>
> *Regional Group / Service:* Lancashire Family Mediators Association
>
> *Mediation telephone number:* 01524 770507

MacDonald, Alistair (A)

> *Approved Body:* LawGroup UK
>
> *Regional Group / Service:* Member of LawGroup UK's Family Mediation Register, telephone 01883 370000 for details
>
> *Mediation telephone number:* 01227 762888

MacDonald, Sharon Fiona (M)

> *Approved Body:* Family Mediators Association
>
> *Regional Group / Service:* Bath District Family Mediators Association
>
> *Mediation telephone number:* 01225 425731

Macgregor, Jennifer W (M)

> *Approved Body:* Family Mediation Scotland
>
> *Regional Group / Service:* Family Mediation Grampian
>
> *Mediation telephone number:* 01224 630050

Machin, Sandra (A)

> *Approved Body:* LawGroup UK
>
> *Regional Group / Service:* Member of LawGroup UK's Family Mediation Register, telephone 01883 370000 for details
>
> *Mediation telephone number:* 01264 353411

MacKechnie-Jarvis, Susan Margaret (A)

> *Approved Body:* LawWise
>
> *Regional Group / Service:* Member of LawWise Family Mediators Register, telephone 01483 237300 for details
>
> *Mediation telephone number:* 01223 500919

MacLellan, Virginia Mary (M)

> *Approved Body:* National Family Mediation; Family Mediation Scotland
>
> *Regional Group / Service:* Coventry & Warwickshire Family Mediation Service
>
> *Mediation telephone number:* 01203 717109

■ **MacLeod**, Alastair John Robert (A)

>*Approved Body:* LawGroup UK
>
>*Regional Group / Service:* Member of LawGroup UK's Family Mediation Register, telephone 01883 370000 for details
>
>*Mediation telephone number:* 01392 258451

■ **Macleod**, Donna (M)

>*Approved Body:* Family Mediation Scotland
>
>*Regional Group / Service:* Family Mediation Service Western Isles
>
>*Mediation telephone number:* 01851 706868

■ **Maher**, Carol Lesley (M)

>*Approved Body:* National Family Mediation; Family Mediators Association
>
>*Regional Group / Service:* Lancashire Family Mediation Service; Lancashire Family Mediation Consortium
>
>*Mediation telephone number:* 01772 861308

■ **Maidment**, Susan (A)

>*Approved Body:* Family Mediators Association
>
>*Regional Group / Service:* London North & Central Family Mediators Association
>
>*Mediation telephone number:* 0171 625 9101

■ **Mair**, Leonard (M)

>*Approved Body:* Family Mediation Scotland
>
>*Regional Group / Service:* Family Mediation Lothian
>
>*Mediation telephone number:* 0131 550 1001
>
>*Mediation address:* 19 York Place, Edinburgh EH1 Facsimile 0131 550 1003, DX ED119
>
>*Other mediation address:* Family Mediation Lothian, 37 George Street, Edinburgh EH2 2HN
>
>*Professional qualifications and experience:* BA (Hons), LLB, NP, WS; qualified as solicitor 1976; qualified as mediator (non-family) 1993; qualified as family mediator 1994
>
>*Membership of professional bodies and organisations:* The Law Society of Scotland; Family Mediation Scotland
>
>*Willing to travel outside the region:* ✓
>
>*Willing to travel to:* Borders, Tayside
>
>*Practice offered:* Finance Issues Mediation; Children Issues Mediation; All Issues Mediation; issues other than family, eg contract, boundary, neighbour issues

▪ **Manock**, Penelope Jane (A)

Approved Body: Solicitors Family Law Association

Regional Group / Service: Member of Solicitors Family Law Association, telephone 01689 850227 for details

Mediation telephone number: 01422 362737

▪ **Markey**, Lindsay Margaret (M)

Approved Body: LawWise

Regional Group / Service: Member of LawWise Family Mediators Register, telephone 01483 237300 for details

Mediation telephone number: 01222 867111

▪ **Markwell**, Jessica (M)

Approved Body: National Family Mediation

Regional Group / Service: Berkshire Family Mediation

Mediation telephone number: 0118 957 1159

▪ **Marshall**, Ruby (M)

Approved Body: National Family Mediation

Regional Group / Service: Cleveland Family Mediation Service

Mediation telephone number: 01642 222967

▪ **Martens**, Greta (A)

Approved Body: Family Mediators Association

Regional Group / Service: Lancashire Family Mediators Association

Mediation telephone number: 01768 372080

▪ **Martin**, Peter Derek (M)

Approved Body: Family Mediators Association

Regional Group / Service: London North & Central Family Mediators Association

Mediation telephone number: 0181 349 0321

Mediation address: c/o Osmond Gaunt & Rose, Winston House, 349 Regents Park Road, London N3 1DH
Facsimile 0181 346 8605, DX 57254 FINCHLEY 2, E-mail pmartin@ogr-law.com

Willing to travel outside the region: ✓

Practice offered: All Issues Mediation; mediation training; additional practice experience/knowledge; sole and co-mediation models; expert in Anglo/Swedish family law; mediation of international and child abduction issues

(cont'd)

Additional mediation training:

mediation trainer training	FMA	1995

Other additional mediation training: sole mediation (FMA) 1994

Having been a specialist family lawyer for many years, I felt there had to be a better solution for many clients than litigation, even litigation with sensible negotiation. I therefore trained in mediation in 1991. My experience in numerous mediations since then have shown my initial view to be correct. I am a past secretary to the board of FMA and chair of its Training and Development Group. I am active in training mediators. I also sit on the Professional Standards Committee of the UK College of Family Mediators. I practise as a co-mediator and a sole mediator in All Issues Mediation from my office in Finchley, north London; in central London; and in Northwood. I have particular expertise in international family law matters and an almost unique specialisation of being an expert in Anglo/Swedish family law.

▪ **Martin**, Sara Kay (A)

Approved Body: Solicitors Family Law Association

Regional Group / Service: Member of Solicitors Family Law Association, telephone 01689 850227 for details; Lancashire Family Mediation Consortium

Mediation telephone number: 01524 66277

▪ **Matthews**, Beryl Joan (M)

Approved Body: National Family Mediation; Family Mediators Association

Regional Group / Service: Family Mediation in Norfolk; Norfolk Family Mediation Service

▪ **Maudsley**, Laurence Stewart (A)

Approved Body: LawGroup UK

Regional Group / Service: Member of LawGroup UK's Family Mediation Register, telephone 01883 370000 for details

Mediation telephone number: 01268 572131

▪ **Mayne**, Theresa (M)

Approved Body: National Family Mediation

Mediation telephone number: 0191 386 4860

▪ **McCann**, Anne (M)

Approved Body: National Family Mediation

Regional Group / Service: Lancashire Family Mediation Service

Mediation telephone number: 01772 204246

■ **McColgan**, Katie (M)

Approved Body: Family Mediators Association

Regional Group / Service: Family Mediators South Wales Ltd

Mediation telephone number: 01656 645525

Mediation address: Family Mediators South Wales Ltd, Brackla House, Brackla Street, Bridgend CF31 1BZ
Facsimile 01656 645174, DX 38004 BRIDGEND

Professional qualifications and experience: LLB; FMA accredited; Member of UK College of Family Mediators last year

Year qualified in mediation: 1992

Membership of professional bodies and organisations: The Law Society; FMA; UK College of Family Mediators

Willing to travel outside the region: ✓

Willing to travel to: Cardiff, Bridgend, Swansea and surrounding areas

Practice offered: Finance Issues Mediation; Children Issues Mediation; All Issues Mediation; Professional Practice Supervision/Consultancy

Additional mediation training:

Professional Practice Supervision/Consultancy   FMA   1996

Having qualified as a solicitor in 1986, I have specialised in family law ever since. I was extremely interested in the practice of family mediation as soon as this came to my attention and therefore took up training in the winter 1991/92. When I qualified in the spring of 1992, I became the first solicitor/mediator in family law in South Wales. I was appointed chair and regional co-ordinator of the South Wales group in February 1995 and became an accredited member of the FMA in December 1995 and a full Member of the UK College of Family Mediators upon its formation in February 1996.

I have been providing professional practice consultancy to members and associates within the South Wales area since December 1996 and am now the managing director of the company, Family Mediators South Wales Ltd.

■ **McDonald**, Neil (M)

Approved Body: National Family Mediation

Regional Group / Service: Family Mediation Service (Greater Manchester)

Mediation telephone number: 0161 797 9910

■ **McEldowney**, Patrick David (M)

Approved Body: Family Mediators Association

Regional Group / Service: Hampshire & Isle of Wight Family Mediators Association

Mediation telephone number: 01705 492295

(cont'd)

Mediation address: 42 Market Parade, Havant, Hampshire PO9 1QF

Professional qualifications and experience: solicitor (admitted 1972); Member of the The Law Society Children Panel

Year qualified in mediation: 1991

Membership of professional bodies and organisations: SFLA; BALM; Lawyers for Children

Practice offered: Finance Issues Mediation; Children Issues Mediation; All Issues Mediation; Professional Practice Supervision/Consultancy

Additional mediation training:

Professional Practice Supervision/Consultancy   FMA

Other additional mediation training: sole and anchor mediation

McIntosh, Marie Elizabeth (M)

Approved Body: Family Mediation Scotland

Regional Group / Service: NCH Action for Children Dumfries & Galloway Family Mediation Service

Mediation telephone number: 01387 263185

McKay, Alison Maureen (M)

Approved Body: Family Mediation Scotland

Regional Group / Service: Family Mediation Tayside

Mediation telephone number: 01382 201343

McKenzie, Annie Morrison Gray (M)

Approved Body: Family Mediation Scotland

Regional Group / Service: NCH Action for Children Dumfries & Galloway Family Mediation Service

Mediation telephone number: 01387 263185

McKenzie, John (A)

Approved Body: Family Mediation Scotland

Regional Group / Service: Family Mediation (West of Scotland)

Mediation telephone number: 01563 572429

McKibbin, Maura Alexandra (A)

Approved Body: Solicitors Family Law Association

Regional Group / Service: Member of Solicitors Family Law Association, telephone 01689 850227 for details

Mediation telephone number: 0161 832 3000

McLaren, Jane Wright (M)

Approved Body: Family Mediation Scotland

Regional Group / Service: Family Mediation Lothian

Mediation telephone number: 0131 226 4507

McNeil, Stuart (A)

Approved Body: Family Mediators Association

Regional Group / Service: Wiltshire Family Mediators Association

Mediation telephone number: 01793 848900

McRorie, Rhonda (M)

Approved Body: Family Mediation Scotland

Regional Group / Service: Family Mediation Service (Highland)

Meads, William Anthony (A)

Approved Body: Family Mediators Association

Regional Group / Service: Hampshire & Isle of Wight Family Mediators Association

Mediation telephone number: 01705 812511

Medvei, Elizabeth (A)

Approved Body: Solicitors Family Law Association

Regional Group / Service: Member of Solicitors Family Law Association, telephone 01689 850227 for details

Mediation telephone number: 01379 852664

Mehlig, Anne (M)

Approved Body: National Family Mediation

Regional Group / Service: Sussex Family Mediation Service

Mediation telephone number: 01273 550563

Meisel, Mari (A)

Approved Body: Family Mediators Association

Regional Group / Service: Birmingham Family Mediators Association

Mediation telephone number: 0121 200 3026

Melbourne, Vinnette (M)

Approved Body: National Family Mediation

Regional Group / Service: Family Mediation (Central Middlesex)

Mediation telephone number: 0181 952 9723

Mellalieu, Rowan Nicola (A)

> *Approved Body:* Solicitors Family Law Association
>
> *Regional Group / Service:* Member of Solicitors Family Law Association, telephone 01689 850227 for details
>
> *Mediation telephone number:* 01772 562222

Middleton, Judith (A)

> *Approved Body:* LawGroup UK
>
> *Regional Group / Service:* Member of LawGroup UK's Family Mediation Register, telephone 01883 370000 for details
>
> *Mediation telephone number:* 01325 381600

Midha, Seema (A)

> *Approved Body:* Family Mediators Association
>
> *Mediation telephone number:* 0118 984 2266

Miles, Elizabeth Margaret (M)

> *Approved Body:* National Family Mediation
>
> *Regional Group / Service:* Suffolk Family Mediation Service

Millen, Paul Michael Patrick (A)

> *Approved Body:* Family Mediators Association
>
> *Regional Group / Service:* West Yorkshire Family Mediators Association
>
> *Mediation telephone number:* 0113 255 2269

Miller, Carole Anne (A)

> *Approved Body:* Family Mediation Scotland
>
> *Regional Group / Service:* NCH Action for Children Family Mediation Fife
>
> *Mediation telephone number:* 01592 751095

Miller, Gill (A)

> *Approved Body:* National Family Mediation
>
> *Regional Group / Service:* Worcestershire Family Mediation
>
> *Mediation telephone number:* 01905 610925

Mills, Corey (A)

> *Approved Body:* LawWise; LawGroup UK
>
> *Regional Group / Service:* Member of LawGroup UK's Family Mediation Register, telephone 01883 370000 for details; Member of LawWise Family Mediators Register, telephone 01483 237300 for details
>
> *Mediation telephone number:* 01227 456321

Miln, Rory McQueen Andrew (A)

Approved Body: LawGroup UK

Regional Group / Service: Member of LawGroup UK's Family Mediation Register, telephone 01883 370000 for details

Mediation telephone number: 01392 258451

Milroy, Ann (M)

Approved Body: National Family Mediation

Regional Group / Service: Mediation in Divorce

Mediation telephone number: 0181 891 6860

Minchella, Diane (M)

Approved Body: National Family Mediation

Regional Group / Service: Sunderland & South Tyneside Family Mediation Service

Mediation telephone number: 0191 568 0433

Mitchell, Anthony Paul (A)

Approved Body: Family Mediators Association

Regional Group / Service: South Midlands Family Mediators Association

Mediation telephone number: 01604 258524

Mediation address: The Family Mediation Centre, Toller Hales & Collcutt, 2 Castilian Street, Northampton, Northamptonshire NN1 1JX Facsimile 01604 258500, DX 12422

Other mediation address: Boxhedge House, Astwood Road, near Cranfield, Bedfordshire MK43 0AT

Professional qualifications and experience: solicitor; Deputy District Judge; Recorder licensed in family law; family lawyer; member of The Law Society Children Panel

Year qualified in mediation: 1992/3

Membership of professional bodies and organisations: The Law Society; FMA; Association of Lawyers for Children; SFLA

Willing to travel outside the region: ✓

Willing to travel to: Bedfordshire and Buckinghamshire

Practice offered: All Issues Mediation

Mitchell, David Stuart (A)

Approved Body: Solicitors Family Law Association

Regional Group / Service: Member of Solicitors Family Law Association, telephone 01689 850227 for details

Mediation telephone number: 0117 942 8214

Mitchell, John Ewan (A)

Approved Body: LawGroup UK

Regional Group / Service: Member of LawGroup UK's Family Mediation Register, telephone 01883 370000 for details

Mediation telephone number: 01522 542211

Mitchell, June Alma (A)

Approved Body: National Family Mediation

Regional Group / Service: Family Mediation Service (Greater Manchester)

Mediation telephone number: 0161 797 9910

Mitchels, Barbara Mary (A)

Approved Body: Solicitors Family Law Association

Regional Group / Service: Member of Solicitors Family Law Association, telephone 01689 850227 for details

Mediation telephone number: 01603 660341

Mediation address: Tombland Mediation Centre at Russell Steward, 5 Tombland, Norwich, Norfolk NR3 1HH
Facsimile 01603 666443, DX 5211 NORWICH, E-mail mitchels@netcom.co.uk

Other mediation address: Point House, 42 Yarmouth Road, Norwich, Norfolk NR7 0EQ

Professional qualifications and experience: LLB (Hons) Lond, solicitor since 1975; The Law Society Children Panel; Dip Counselling and Psychotherapy; BAC accredited; UKRC Registered Counsellor

Year qualified in mediation: 1996

Membership of professional bodies and organisations: British Association for Counselling; The Law Society; SFLA; BAAF

Willing to travel outside the region: ✓

Willing to travel to: London East Anglia, Suffolk

Practice offered: Finance Issues Mediation; Children Issues Mediation; All Issues Mediation; mediation training; training in listening and communication skills, child law, child protection, and other mediation-related topics

Additional mediation training:

consultation with children	Working with Children 1990-1997
domestic violence	Working with Children 1996&1998
mediation trainer training	Mediation UK, Community Mediation 1996

Other additional mediation training: legal seminars and psychotherapy courses including cognitive-behavioural treatment of bereavement,

(cont'd)

loss, trauma and de-briefing 1990-1998

■ **Mollison**, Helen Wilson (M)

Approved Body: Family Mediation Scotland

Regional Group / Service: Family Mediation Grampian

Mediation telephone number: 01224 630050

■ **Montgomery**, Paul Adrian (M)

Approved Body: Family Mediators Association

Regional Group / Service: Milton Keynes and North Buckinghamshire FMA Group

■ **Mooney**, Irene (A)

Approved Body: Family Mediation Scotland

Regional Group / Service: Family Mediation Tayside

Mediation telephone number: 01382 201343

■ **Moore**, Anthony Nigel (A)

Approved Body: LawGroup UK

Regional Group / Service: Member of LawGroup UK's Family Mediation Register, telephone 01883 370000 for details

Mediation telephone number: 0117 962 1205

■ **Moore**, Fiona Jenny (A)

Approved Body: Family Mediators Association

Regional Group / Service: South Midlands Family Mediators Association

Mediation telephone number: 01933 279000

■ **Moore**, Wendy (M)

Approved Body: National Family Mediation

Regional Group / Service: Berkshire Family Mediation

Mediation telephone number: 0118 957 1159

■ **Moran**, Mike (A)

Approved Body: National Family Mediation

Regional Group / Service: York Family Mediation Service

Mediation telephone number: 01904 646068

■ **Morcom**, Caroline Susan (M)

Approved Body: National Family Mediation

Regional Group / Service: Mediation in Divorce

(cont'd)

A–Z College Members and Associates

C

Mediation telephone number: 0181 891 6860

Morgan, Carole Ann (A)

> *Approved Body:* Family Mediators Association
>
> *Regional Group / Service:* Family Mediators South Wales Ltd
>
> *Mediation telephone number:* 01792 792810

Morgan, Carole June (A)

> *Approved Body:* LawGroup UK
>
> *Regional Group / Service:* Member of LawGroup UK's Family Mediation Register, telephone 01883 370000 for details
>
> *Mediation telephone number:* 01522 512321

Morkham, Trevor James (M)

> *Approved Body:* National Family Mediation
>
> *Regional Group / Service:* Bristol Family Mediation Service
>
> *Mediation telephone number:* 0117 929 2002

Morris, Allan (M)

> *Approved Body:* National Family Mediation
>
> *Regional Group / Service:* Family Mediation Service – Institute of Family Therapy
>
> *Mediation telephone number:* 0171 391 9150

Morris, Richard (A)

> *Approved Body:* LawGroup UK
>
> *Regional Group / Service:* Member of LawGroup UK's Family Mediation Register, telephone 01883 370000 for details
>
> *Mediation telephone number:* 01234 303030

Morrison, Cynthia Mary Louise (M)

> *Approved Body:* National Family Mediation
>
> *Regional Group / Service:* Herefordshire Family Mediation Service
>
> *Mediation telephone number:* 01432 264087

Morrison, Isabel Colville (M)

> *Approved Body:* Family Mediation Scotland
>
> *Regional Group / Service:* Family Mediation Tayside
>
> *Mediation telephone number:* 01382 201343

Morse-Brown, Jennifer Saunders (A)

Approved Body: Solicitors Family Law Association

Regional Group / Service: Member of Solicitors Family Law Association, telephone 01689 850227 for details

Mediation telephone number: 01273 329797

Moss, Bernard Roger (M)

Approved Body: National Family Mediation

Regional Group / Service: Mediation Advisory Service for Stafford and North Staffordshire

Mediation telephone number: 01785 214933

Mediation address: SDVS Centre, 131-141 North Walls, Stafford, Staffordshire ST16 3AD
E-mail b.r.moss@staffs.ac.uk

Professional qualifications and experience: MA (Econ); CQSW Manchester University; former Probation Officer; now Senior Lecturer in Social Work, Staffordshire University; mediation teaching at Law School Staffordshire University

Year qualified in mediation: 1996

Practice offered: Children Issues Mediation

Moss, Stephen (M)

Approved Body: National Family Mediation

Regional Group / Service: Swindon Family Mediation Service

Mediation telephone number: 01793 527141

Motley, Paul Jeffrey (A)

Approved Body: Solicitors Family Law Association

Regional Group / Service: Member of Solicitors Family Law Association, telephone 01689 850227 for details

Mediation telephone number: 01767 600600

Muir, Jean (M)

Approved Body: Family Mediation Scotland

Regional Group / Service: Family Mediation Service (Highland)

Muir, William (M)

Approved Body: Family Mediation Scotland

Regional Group / Service: Family Mediation Tayside

Mediation telephone number: 01382 201343

Mullins, Patrick (A)

Approved Body: LawWise

Regional Group / Service: Member of LawWise Family Mediators Register, telephone 01483 237300 for details

Mediation telephone number: 01773 715334

Munro, Moira (M)

Approved Body: Family Mediation Scotland

Regional Group / Service: Family Mediation (West of Scotland)

Mediation telephone number: 0141 332 2731

Murton, Frances E (M)

Approved Body: National Family Mediation

Regional Group / Service: Cambridge Family & Divorce Centre

Mediation telephone number: 01223 576308

Mushett, Geraldine (A)

Approved Body: Family Mediators Association

Regional Group / Service: London South & Central Family Mediators Association

Mediation telephone number: 0171 733 1216

Myerscough, Seona Elizabeth Cecile (A)

Approved Body: Family Mediators Association

Regional Group / Service: Thames Valley Family Mediators Association

Mediation telephone number: 0118 957 4018

Naish, Christopher John (A)

Approved Body: LawGroup UK

Regional Group / Service: Member of LawGroup UK's Family Mediation Register, telephone 01883 370000 for details

Mediation telephone number: 01392 255777

Nazareth, Marianne (A)

Approved Body: Solicitors Family Law Association

Regional Group / Service: Member of Solicitors Family Law Association, telephone 01689 850227 for details

Mediation telephone number: 0181 534 1653

Neill, Gail Frances (M)

Approved Body: National Family Mediation

Regional Group / Service: NCH Action for Children Eye to Eye Mediation

Mediation telephone number: 0171 701 1114

Neilson, Kath (A)

Approved Body: National Family Mediation

Regional Group / Service: Coventry & Warwickshire Family Mediation Service

Mediation telephone number: 01203 717109

Neuborn, Danuta Jadwiga (A)

Approved Body: Family Mediators Association

Regional Group / Service: South Midlands Family Mediators Association

Mediation telephone number: 01536 411698

Neves, Mark William (A)

Approved Body: National Family Mediation

Regional Group / Service: Suffolk Family Mediation Service

Newbould, Ann Mary (M)

Approved Body: National Family Mediation

Regional Group / Service: Family Mediation Service (Greater Manchester)

Mediation telephone number: 0161 797 9910

Newman, Paul Michael (A)

Approved Body: LawGroup UK

Regional Group / Service: Member of LawGroup UK's Family Mediation Register, telephone 01883 370000 for details

Mediation telephone number: 01472 358234

Newport, Jacqueline (A)

Approved Body: Family Mediators Association

Regional Group / Service: Birmingham Family Mediators Association

Mediation telephone number: 01543 483015

Ng, Alastair (A)

Approved Body: Solicitors Family Law Association

Regional Group / Service: Member of Solicitors Family Law Association, telephone 01689 850227 for details

(cont'd)

Mediation telephone number: 01483 770708

Nicholas, Thomas Philip (M)

Approved Body: National Family Mediation

Regional Group / Service: Family Mediation Cardiff

Mediation telephone number: 01222 229692

Nicholl, Christine (A)

Approved Body: Family Mediators Association

Regional Group / Service: South West Region Family Mediators Association

Mediation telephone number: 01363 774706

Nichols, Therese Mary (A)

Approved Body: Solicitors Family Law Association

Regional Group / Service: Member of Solicitors Family Law Association, telephone 01689 850227 for details

Mediation telephone number: 0181 546 6111

Mediation address: Bishops Palace House, Kingston Bridge, Kingston-upon-Thames KT1 1QN
Facsimile 0181 541 4404, DX 31546 KINGSTON-UPON-THAMES, E-mail nicholst@russell-cooke.co.uk

Professional qualifications and experience: mediator trained with SFLA

Year qualified in mediation: 1997

Membership of professional bodies and organisations: SFLA

Willing to travel outside the region: ✓

Willing to travel to: Surrey, London, Hampshire, Sussex, Berkshire

Practice offered: All Issues Mediation

Other additional mediation training: SFLA course 1997

Nicol, Walter (M)

Approved Body: Family Mediation Scotland

Regional Group / Service: Family Mediation (West of Scotland)

Mediation telephone number: 0141 332 2731

Nicolle, Donella (M)

Approved Body: Family Mediators Association

Mediation telephone number: 0115 947 6651

Mediation address: Ashton Bond Gigg Solicitors, Pearl Assurance House, Friar Lane, Nottingham NG1 6BX
Facsimile 0115 947 5244, DX 10002 NOTTM

(cont'd)

Professional qualifications and experience: qualified solicitor and FMA trained mediator; worked in exclusively family law for seven years; Head of Family Law Department and partner in firm

Year qualified in mediation: 1997

Membership of professional bodies and organisations: SFLA; Association of Women Solicitors; Fairplay

Willing to travel outside the region: ✓

Willing to travel to: Midlands (East), ie Leicestershire, Derbyshire, Nottinghamshire

Practice offered: Finance Issues Mediation; Children Issues Mediation; All Issues Mediation

Noall, John Mark (M)

Approved Body: National Family Mediation

Regional Group / Service: Family Mediation Service (Greater Manchester)

Mediation telephone number: 0161 764 2196

Noon, Maggie (A)

Approved Body: Family Mediators Association

Regional Group / Service: Family Mediators South Wales Ltd

Mediation telephone number: 01291 673534

Norris, Marion Elizabeth (M)

Approved Body: Family Mediation Scotland

Regional Group / Service: Family Mediation (West of Scotland)

Mediation telephone number: 01563 572429

Norton, Alison Sheila (M)

Approved Body: National Family Mediation

Regional Group / Service: Milton Keynes Family Mediation

Mediation telephone number: 01462 434686

Nott, Dorothy Arkell (M)

Approved Body: National Family Mediation

Regional Group / Service: York Family Mediation Service

Mediation telephone number: 01904 646068

Nunn, Elaine Janet (A)

Approved Body: Family Mediators Association

Regional Group / Service: Northants, Bucks and Leics Family Mediators Association

(cont'd)

Mediation telephone number: 01604 881716

Nunnerley, Margaret Lorna (M)

Approved Body: National Family Mediation

Regional Group / Service: West Yorkshire Family Mediation Service

Mediation telephone number: 01274 732768

Nye, Cyril Marcus (A)

Approved Body: Family Mediators Association

Regional Group / Service: Shropshire Family Mediators Association

Mediation telephone number: 01743 270077

Oakes, Jane (A)

Approved Body: Solicitors Family Law Association

Regional Group / Service: Member of Solicitors Family Law Association, telephone 01689 850227 for details

Mediation telephone number: 01799 523441

O'Brien, Kit (Catherine) (A)

Approved Body: Solicitors Family Law Association

Regional Group / Service: Member of Solicitors Family Law Association, telephone 01689 850227 for details

Mediation telephone number: 01935 423685

O'Byrne, Patrick (M)

Approved Body: National Family Mediation

Regional Group / Service: Bradford Metropolitan Family Mediation Service

Mediation telephone number: 01274 732768

Offord, Deirdre Patricia (A)

Approved Body: National Family Mediation

Regional Group / Service: Nottinghamshire Children & Families Mediation Service (FAME)

Mediation telephone number: 0115 985 8855

O'Hagan, Orla (A)

Approved Body: Family Mediators Association

Regional Group / Service: Sussex Family Mediators Association

(cont'd)

Mediation telephone number: 01903 764517

■ **Oldroyd**, John Norton (A)

Approved Body: National Family Mediation

Regional Group / Service: Cumbria Family Mediation Service

Mediation telephone number: 01539 733705

■ **O'Meara**, Carol Ann (M)

Approved Body: National Family Mediation

Regional Group / Service: Kent Family Mediation Service

Mediation telephone number: 01795 429689

■ **Orr**, Muriel Jean (M)

Approved Body: National Family Mediation

Regional Group / Service: Northern Ireland Family Mediation Service

Mediation telephone number: 01232 322914

■ **Osman**, Margaret Lynn (A)

Approved Body: Solicitors Family Law Association

Regional Group / Service: Member of Solicitors Family Law Association, telephone 01689 850227 for details

Mediation telephone number: 01704 878501

Mediation address: Whitfields, Marion House, 23-25 Elbow Lane, Formby, Merseyside L37 4AB
Facsimile 01704 872145, DX 15403 FORMBY

Professional qualifications and experience: LLB (Hons); solicitor; 20 years' experience in family matters

Year qualified in mediation: 1997

Membership of professional bodies and organisations: The Law Society; SFLA

Willing to travel outside the region: ✓

Willing to travel to: within 75 miles of Liverpool

Practice offered: All Issues Mediation

Other additional mediation training: SFLA training course 1997

■ **O'Sullivan**, Fiona (A)

Approved Body: Solicitors Family Law Association

Regional Group / Service: Member of Solicitors Family Law Association, telephone 01689 850227 for details

Mediation telephone number: 0121 426 4171

O Sullivan, John Joseph (M)

> *Approved Body:* National Family Mediation
>
> *Regional Group / Service:* Suffolk Family Mediation Service
>
> *Mediation telephone number:* 01473 225845

Oswald, Anne Kerr (M)

> *Approved Body:* Family Mediation Scotland
>
> *Regional Group / Service:* Family Mediation Grampian
>
> *Mediation telephone number:* 01224 630050

Oswald, Christopher Stephen Thomas (M)

> *Approved Body:* National Family Mediation
>
> *Regional Group / Service:* Swindon Family Mediation Service
>
> *Mediation telephone number:* 01793 527285

Oswald, Rosalind Amanda Jennie (M)

> *Approved Body:* National Family Mediation
>
> *Regional Group / Service:* Swindon Family Mediation Service
>
> *Mediation telephone number:* 01793 527285

Otten, Guy Nicholas (M)

> *Approved Body:* Family Mediators Association
>
> *Regional Group / Service:* Greater Manchester Family Mediators Association
>
> *Mediation telephone number:* 0161 945 1431

Packer, Nigel Robert (A)

> *Approved Body:* Family Mediators Association
>
> *Regional Group / Service:* Family Mediators South Wales Ltd
>
> *Mediation telephone number:* 01792 892166

Paddison, Mark Stewart (A)

> *Approved Body:* Family Mediators Association
>
> *Regional Group / Service:* South West Region Family Mediators Association
>
> *Mediation telephone number:* 01242 574244

Palmer, Lynn (M)

> *Approved Body:* Family Mediation Scotland
>
> *Regional Group / Service:* Family Mediation (West of Scotland)
>
> *Mediation telephone number:* 0141 332 2731

■ **Paris**, Patricia (M)

> *Approved Body:* National Family Mediation
>
> *Regional Group / Service:* Nottinghamshire Children & Families Mediation Service (FAME)
>
> *Mediation telephone number:* 0115 985 8855

■ **Parker**, Beverly Ann (A)

> *Approved Body:* Family Mediators Association
>
> *Regional Group / Service:* South Midlands Family Mediators Association; Smith Chamberlain – The Mediation Service
>
> *Mediation telephone number:* 0930 756010 (day) 01604 719443 (eve)

■ **Parker**, Diana (M)

> *Approved Body:* Solicitors Family Law Association
>
> *Regional Group / Service:* Member of Solicitors Family Law Association, telephone 01689 850227 for details
>
> *Mediation telephone number:* 0171 936 1000

■ **Parkhouse**, Jenny (M)

> *Approved Body:* National Family Mediation
>
> *Regional Group / Service:* Dorset Family Mediation Service
>
> *Mediation telephone number:* 01202 314600

■ **Parkinson**, Lisa (M)

> *Approved Body:* Family Mediators Association; LawGroup UK
>
> *Regional Group / Service:* Bristol Family Mediators Association; Member of LawGroup UK's Family Mediation Register, telephone 01883 370000 for details
>
> *Mediation telephone number:* 0117 950 0140
>
> *Mediation address:* The Old House, Rectory Gardens, Henbury, Bristol BS10 7AQ
> Facsimile 0117 950 0140, E-mail tparkinson@compuserve.com
>
> *Other mediation address:* Lawgroup UK, Orbital House, 85 Croydon Road, Caterham, Surrey CR3 6PD
>
> *Professional qualifications and experience:* MA (Oxon, 1st Class Honours Degree 1961); postgraduate diploma in Social Studies, University of London 1969; Certificate of Qualification in social work, University of Bristol 1976; social work experience with couples, children and families 1964-74.
>
> *Year qualified in mediation:* 1978
>
> *Membership of professional bodies and organisations:* FMA; Academy of Family Mediators; Association of Family and Conciliation Courts; World Mediation Forum; LawGroup UK Family Mediators Register

(cont'd)

Willing to travel outside the region: ✓

Willing to travel to: UK and other English, French, German and Spanish speaking countries

Practice offered: Children Issues Mediation; All Issues Mediation; mediation training; Professional Practice Supervision/Consultancy; consulting with children; domestic violence issues in mediation; mediation intake and assessment; advanced mediation skills

Additional mediation training:

consultation with children	Academy of Family Mediators	1997
domestic violence	Academy of Family Mediators	1997
initial information giving and/or assessment	Academy of Family Mediators	1997
mediation trainer training	Academy of Family Mediators	1997
Professional Practice Supervision/Consultancy	FMA	1992

Other additional mediation training: transformative mediation and workshops with John Haynes 1997

Mediation Career

Current Positions

i) Director of Family Mediation Training Lawgroup UK

ii) Director of Family Mediation Training, CALM (Comprehensive Accredited Lawyer Mediators), Scotland

iii) Member of editorial board, *Mediation Quarterly*

iv) Member of editorial board, *Family & Conciliation Courts Review*

v) Trainer, European Institute of Family Mediation.

Recent Publications

Family Mediation, Sweet & Maxwell, 1997; 'Family Mediation' in *Family Law in Practice*, Blackstone Press, 1997; 'Comprehensive Mediation' in *Family Conciliation in the UK*, (ed Fisher, revised 1992), also articles in *Family Law*, *Mediation Quarterly* and *British Journal of Social Work*.

Conferences and Training

International conferences and family mediation training courses include USA and la Reunion (1997); University of Nantes, Paris and Madrid (1996); France, Spain and Canada (1995); France, South Africa and Spain (1994).

Career Details

Involved in setting up the first family mediation service in the UK, as founder member and first co-ordinator of Bristol Family Mediation Service (1977-83); founder member of NFCC (now NFM) and NFCC's first training co-ordinator (1983-6); founder member of 'Solicitors in

(cont'd)

Mediation' (1985-8); member of the Marre Committee on the Future of the Legal Profession (Report, 1988); founder member and first director of FMA (1988-94); trainer with CALM, Scotland (1993-); member of Bristol FMA's Phase 1 Pilot with Legal Aid Board (1997-), now running family mediation training (foundation and advanced training) for several mediation organisations in the UK and in other countries.

Parsons, Caroline Jane (A)

Approved Body: LawGroup UK

Regional Group / Service: Member of LawGroup UK's Family Mediation Register, telephone 01883 370000 for details

Mediation telephone number: 01992 300333

Parsons, Donna Caroline (A)

Approved Body: Solicitors Family Law Association

Regional Group / Service: Member of Solicitors Family Law Association, telephone 01689 850227 for details

Mediation telephone number: 01223 316666

Paterson, Catherine Mary (M)

Approved Body: Family Mediation Scotland

Regional Group / Service: Family Mediation Service Western Isles

Mediation telephone number: 01851 706868

Paterson, Murielle Joyce (M)

Approved Body: Family Mediation Scotland

Regional Group / Service: Family Mediation Central Scotland

Mediation telephone number: 01786 472984

Patrick, Jill Louise (A)

Approved Body: National Family Mediation

Regional Group / Service: Cleveland Family Mediation Service

Mediation telephone number: 01642 222967

Patterson, David John (M)

Approved Body: National Family Mediation

Regional Group / Service: Exeter & District Family Mediation Service

Mediation telephone number: 01392 410529

Payne, John (A)

Approved Body: Family Mediators Association

Regional Group / Service: The Hertfordshire Comprehensive Mediation Service

(cont'd)

(M) = Member   (A) = Associate

Mediation telephone number: 01923 836595

Payne, Monica Louise (M)

Approved Body: Family Mediators Association

Regional Group / Service: Oxford Family Mediators Association

Mediation telephone number: 01865 724977

Mediation address: Faulkners Solicitors, 42 Westgate, Oxford OX1 1PD Facsimile 01865 791300, DX 4317 OXFORD 1

Professional qualifications and experience: solicitor & qualified family mediator for past 6 years; Member of The Law Society's Children Panel

Year qualified in mediation: 1992

Membership of professional bodies and organisations: Family Mediators Association; Solicitors Family Law Association

Practice offered: All Issues Mediation

Payne, Yvonne (M)

Approved Body: National Family Mediation

Regional Group / Service: Surrey Family Mediation Service

Mediation telephone number: 01306 741777

Peacock, John (A)

Approved Body: LawGroup UK

Regional Group / Service: Member of LawGroup UK's Family Mediation Register, telephone 01883 370000 for details

Mediation telephone number: 01472 358234

Pearce, Marshall Davie (M)

Approved Body: National Family Mediation

Regional Group / Service: Kent Family Mediation Service

Mediation telephone number: 01795 429689

Pearson, Carmela (M)

Approved Body: National Family Mediation; Family Mediators Association

Regional Group / Service: Cambridge Family & Divorce Centre

Mediation telephone number: 01223 546308 (NFM); 01438 871364 (FMA)

Peck, Alan Thomas (A)

Approved Body: LawWise

Regional Group / Service: Member of LawWise Family Mediators Register, telephone 01483 237300 for details

(cont'd)

Mediation telephone number: 01536 315615

Mediation address: 55 Headlands, Kettering, Northants NN15 7EY
Facsimile 01536 315600, DX MDX 12801 KETTERING

Professional qualifications and experience: solicitor, qualified 1989;
trained with LawWise

Year qualified in mediation: 1998

Membership of professional bodies and organisations: BALM (British
Association of Lawyer Mediators)

Willing to travel outside the region: ✓

Willing to travel to: East Midlands

Practice offered: All Issues Mediation

Peffer, Linda (M)

Approved Body: National Family Mediation

Regional Group / Service: Mediation for Families (East London & City)

Mediation telephone number: 0171 613 1666

Peiser, Jennifer Ann (M)

Approved Body: National Family Mediation

Regional Group / Service: Family Mediation (Central Middlesex)

Mediation telephone number: 0181 427 2076

Pemberton, Adam James (M)

Approved Body: Family Mediators Association

Regional Group / Service: South Yorkshire Family Mediators
Association

Mediation telephone number: 0114 275 3350

Pendlebury, Margaret (M)

Approved Body: National Family Mediation

Regional Group / Service: Mediation in Divorce

Mediation telephone number: 0181 891 6860

Penning, Marlene (A)

Approved Body: LawWise

Regional Group / Service: Member of LawWise Family Mediators
Register, telephone 01483 237300 for details

Mediation telephone number: 01303 850120

Mediation address: Resolutions Family Mediation Centre, 5th Floor,
Europa House, Sandgate Road, Folkestone, Kent CT20 1TD
Facsimile 01303 221424, E-mail mgabs@aol.com

(cont'd)

A–Z College Members and Associates

C

Professional qualifications and experience: Post-graduate Teaching Diploma; Legal Executive with seven years' experience of family law dealing with disputes relating to domestic violence, marital breakdown, finance, property and Children Act matters. Trained by John Haynes and LawWise in 1996 as an All Issues mediator

Year qualified in mediation: 1996

Membership of professional bodies and organisations: Solicitors Family Law Association (SFLA); British Association of Lawyer Mediators

Willing to travel outside the region: ✓

Willing to travel to: Sussex, Kent

Practice offered: All Issues Mediation

Additional mediation training:

consultation with children	LawWise	1998
domestic violence	LawWise	1998
initial information giving and/or assessment	LawWise	1998

Other additional mediation training: one day children dispute mediation (LawWise) 1997

Perring, Elizabeth (M)

Approved Body: Family Mediators Association

Regional Group / Service: Surrey & North Hampshire Family Mediators Association

Mediation telephone number: 01428 652163

Perry, Katherine (A)

Approved Body: National Family Mediation

Regional Group / Service: Cambridge Family & Divorce Centre

Mediation telephone number: 01223 576308

Perry, Malcolm Charles (A)

Approved Body: Solicitors Family Law Association

Regional Group / Service: Member of Solicitors Family Law Association, telephone 01689 850227 for details

Mediation telephone number: 01375 383731

Perry, Terence Henry (A)

Approved Body: LawWise

Regional Group / Service: Member of LawWise Family Mediators Register, telephone 01483 237300 for details

Mediation telephone number: 01530 563700

Mediation address: 6-8 Kilwardby Street, Ashby-de-la-Zouch, Leics LE6 5FU Facsimile 01530 416146, DX 22651 ASHBY-DE-LA-ZOUCH

Professional qualifications and experience: solicitor with over 30 years' family law experience

(cont'd)

Year qualified in mediation: 1997

Membership of professional bodies and organisations: The Law Society; BALM member

Practice offered: All Issues Mediation

Additional mediation training:

consultation with children

Phillips, Anthony (M)

Approved Body: National Family Mediation

Regional Group / Service: NCH Action for Children Eye to Eye Mediation

Mediation telephone number: 0171 701 1114

Pickwell, Christine Elizabeth (A)

Approved Body: LawGroup UK

Regional Group / Service: Member of LawGroup UK's Family Mediation Register, telephone 01883 370000 for details

Mediation telephone number: 01522 561005

Piggott, Lesley (M)

Approved Body: National Family Mediation

Regional Group / Service: Peterborough & District Family Mediation Service

Mediation telephone number: 01733 347353

Pigott, Simon (M)

Approved Body: Family Mediators Association

Regional Group / Service: London South & Central Family Mediators Association

Mediation telephone number: 0171 556 2400

Pitt, Michael John (A)

Approved Body: Family Mediators Association

Regional Group / Service: Somerset Family Mediators Association

Mediation telephone number: 01823 666622

Place, Frances (M)

Approved Body: LawWise

Regional Group / Service: Member of LawWise Family Mediators Register, telephone 01483 237300 for details

Mediation telephone number: 0117 924 3880

A–Z College Members and Associates

Plant, Samantha (A)

Approved Body: LawGroup UK

Regional Group / Service: Member of LawGroup UK's Family Mediation Register, telephone 01883 370000 for details

Mediation telephone number: 01626 203366

Poles, Yvonne (M)

Approved Body: Family Mediators Association

Regional Group / Service: Family Mediation in Norfolk; Mediation East Anglia

Mediation telephone number: 01362 820543

Poole, Melloney (A)

Approved Body: LawWise

Regional Group / Service: Member of LawWise Family Mediators Register, telephone 01483 237300 for details

Mediation telephone number: 01995 61087

Porter, Jane Elizabeth Helen (A)

Approved Body: Solicitors Family Law Association

Regional Group / Service: Member of Solicitors Family Law Association, telephone 01689 850227 for details

Mediation telephone number: 01483 887766

Postle, Karen Margaret (Non-Practising Member)

Approved Body: National Family Mediation

Regional Group / Service: Hampshire Family Mediation

Mediation telephone number: 01705 660919

Power, Suzy (M)

Approved Body: Family Mediators Association

Regional Group / Service: London North & Central Family Mediators Association

Mediation telephone number: 0181 341 6154

Mediation address: 21 Palace Road, Crouch End, London N8 8QL

Professional qualifications and experience: BA (Hons) Soc Sci; Certificate of Qualification in Social Work (CQSW)

Year qualified in mediation: 1991

Membership of professional bodies and organisations: Accredited Member Family Mediators Association

Willing to travel outside the region: ✓

Willing to travel to: Hertfordshire

(cont'd)

Practice offered: Children Issues Mediation; All Issues Mediation; mediation training; Professional Practice Supervision/Consultancy

Additional mediation training:

consultation with children		1998
domestic violence		1998
mediation trainer training	FMA	1997
Professional Practice Supervision/Consultancy	FMA	1996

Career

I completed a combined social science degree and professional social work qualification at Sheffield University in 1977. I worked with children and families in a variety of therapeutic settings for 12 years and during this time focused on the needs of separating couples and their children. The importance of facilitating couples in reaching decisions about their future led me to become increasingly interested in mediation and I trained with the Family Mediators Association in 1991. Since that time I have worked with a substantial number of couples at various stages of separation. I have also lectured in child development for seven years and am qualified as an NVQ assessor. I provide professional practice consultancy for a number of mediators in my area and act as assessor on the Solicitors Family Law Association family mediation training courses. I practise as a co-mediator with solicitors in north and central London.

Preston, Diana Margaret (A)

Approved Body: Family Mediation Scotland

Regional Group / Service: Family Mediation Orkney

Mediation telephone number: 01856 870571

Price, Gillian Marise (A)

Approved Body: Family Mediators Association

Regional Group / Service: Greater Manchester Family Mediators Association

Mediation telephone number: 0161 945 4836

Price, Jonathan (M)

Approved Body: National Family Mediation

Regional Group / Service: Gwent Mediation Service

Mediation telephone number: 01633 263065

Pringle, Ingrid (M)

Approved Body: Family Mediation Scotland

Regional Group / Service: Family Mediation Grampian

Mediation telephone number: 01224 630050

Pritchard, Wendy Anne (M)

> *Approved Body:* National Family Mediation; Family Mediators Association
>
> *Regional Group / Service:* Cambridge Family Mediators Association
>
> *Mediation telephone number:* 01223 321066

Pryce, Andrew Nicholas (A)

> *Approved Body:* LawGroup UK
>
> *Regional Group / Service:* Member of LawGroup UK's Family Mediation Register, telephone 01883 370000 for details
>
> *Mediation telephone number:* 01803 559257

Pucknell, Indra (A)

> *Approved Body:* Family Mediators Association
>
> *Regional Group / Service:* Kent Family Mediators Association
>
> *Mediation telephone number:* 0181 325 5514
>
> *Mediation address:* 48 Courtfield Rise, West Wickham, Bromley, Kent BR4 9BH
>
> *Other mediation address:* 9 North Road, West Wickham, Kent BR4 0JS
>
> *Professional qualifications and experience:* Registered General Nurse Therapist (17 years); EMDR Therapist; trainer couples counsellor
>
> *Year qualified in mediation:* 1997
>
> *Membership of professional bodies and organisations:* BAC; ESST; FMA
>
> *Willing to travel outside the region:* ✓
>
> *Willing to travel to:* South East, South West and Central London, Croydon, Bromley, Kent
>
> *Practice offered:* All Issues Mediation; mediation training
>
> *Other additional mediation training:* neighbour mediation training 1997

Pugsley, Judith Mary (A)

> *Approved Body:* Family Mediators Association
>
> *Regional Group / Service:* Birmingham Family Mediators Association
>
> *Mediation telephone number:* 01335 360097

Purser, Candida Nicola Kirby (A)

> *Approved Body:* LawWise
>
> *Regional Group / Service:* Member of LawWise Family Mediators Register, telephone 01483 237300 for details
>
> *Mediation telephone number:* 01223 500919

■ **Quinn,** Patrick (A)

> *Approved Body:* Family Mediators Association
>
> *Regional Group / Service:* London South & West Family Mediators Association
>
> *Mediation telephone number:* 0181 924 5326

■ **Raeside,** Dominic (M)

> *Approved Body:* Family Mediators Association
>
> *Regional Group / Service:* London South & Central Family Mediators Association
>
> *Mediation telephone number:* 0171 420 5000
>
> *Mediation address:* The Family Law Consortium, 2 Henrietta Street, London WC2E 8PS
> Facsimile 0171 420 5005, DX 40012 COVENT GARDEN, E-mail flc@tflc.co.uk
>
> *Other mediation address:* 154 Elsenham Street, Southfields, London SW18 5NP
>
> *Professional qualifications and experience:* CQSW – 1984 Brunel University; Dip FT – UCL
>
> *Year qualified in mediation:* 1990
>
> *Membership of professional bodies and organisations:* FMA; UKCP
>
> *Willing to travel outside the region:* ✓
>
> *Practice offered:* Finance Issues Mediation; Children Issues Mediation; All Issues Mediation; mediation training; Professional Practice Supervision/Consultancy; consulting with children
>
> *Additional mediation training:*

consultation with children	IFT	1993
domestic violence	IFT	1992
initial information giving and/or assessment	NFM	1990
mediation trainer training	John Haynes	1991
Professional Practice Supervision/Consultancy	FMA	1995

> *Other additional mediation training:* anti-racist training 1988 ; sole and anchor mediation training, FMA 1996

> **Professional Experience**
>
> Professional background includes: psychiatric social worker, probation officer, family court welfare officer and Guardian ad Litem. Social worker from 1980 – specialised in working with children and families in the process of divorce and separation since 1988. Trained as a family therapist (1987) – currently an accredited member of UK Council for Psychotherapy. Mediator since 1988 – professional practice consultant/supervisor with the FMA and member of the Family Mediation Service, Institute of Family Therapy (London). Founder member of the Divorce Mediation Group. Presenter and trainer on mediation, family therapy and related areas, co-author of *Divorce Reform: A Guide for Lawyers and Mediators* (FT Law and Tax). Mediator-counsellor consultant with
> *(cont'd)*

the Family Law Consortium (the first multi-disciplinary legal practice)
Covent Garden, London WC2. Available as an independent mediator to
co-mediate or supervise/consult with FMA, SFLA, LawGroup and
LawWise trained mediators.

Raikes, Benjamin Kennedy (M)

Approved Body: National Family Mediation

Regional Group / Service: Family Mediation Service (Greater
Manchester)

Mediation telephone number: 0161 797 9910

Ralph, Elizabeth (M)

Approved Body: National Family Mediation

Regional Group / Service: Derbyshire Family Mediation Service

Mediation telephone number: 01246 277422

Ramm, Helen (M)

Approved Body: Family Mediators Association

Regional Group / Service: Bristol Family Mediators Association

Mediation telephone number: 01453 842665

Randall, Richard Maurice (A)

Approved Body: LawWise

Regional Group / Service: Member of LawWise Family Mediators
Register, telephone 01483 237300 for details

Mediation telephone number: 01245 264764

Randle, John Charles William (A)

Approved Body: Solicitors Family Law Association

Regional Group / Service: Member of Solicitors Family Law Association,
telephone 01689 850227 for details

Mediation telephone number: 01225 444882

Mediation address: 24 Queen Square, Bath, Bath & North East
Somerset BA1 2HY
Facsimile 01225 445208, DX 8003 BATH

Professional qualifications and experience: qualified as solicitor in 1984;
member of The Law Society's Children Panel; specialist in family law
and member of SFLA Education Committee

Year qualified in mediation: 1996

Membership of professional bodies and organisations: The Law Society;
SFLA; The Law Society's Children Panel

Willing to travel outside the region: ✓

Willing to travel to: South West England

(cont'd)

Practice offered: All Issues Mediation

Ray, Margot (M)

Approved Body: National Family Mediation

Regional Group / Service: Northamptonshire Family Mediation Service

Mediation telephone number: 01604 636651

Raymont, Mary Catherine (A)

Approved Body: Solicitors Family Law Association

Regional Group / Service: Member of Solicitors Family Law Association, telephone 01689 850227 for details

Mediation telephone number: 01622 690691

Mediation address: Brachers, Somerfield House, 59 London Road, Maidstone, Kent ME16
Facsimile 01622 690824, DX 4806 MAIDSTONE 1

Professional qualifications and experience: LLB; LSF; SFLA member; qualified October 1992; member of The Law Society's Children Panel since 1996

Year qualified in mediation: 1996

Membership of professional bodies and organisations: Solicitors Family Law Association

Willing to travel outside the region: ✓

Willing to travel to: London and South East

Practice offered: All Issues Mediation

Read, Fiona Bridget (A)

Approved Body: Solicitors Family Law Association

Regional Group / Service: Member of Solicitors Family Law Association, telephone 01689 850227 for details

Mediation telephone number: 0181 789 9111

Read, Jane (M)

Approved Body: National Family Mediation

Regional Group / Service: South Staffordshire Family Mediation Service

Mediation telephone number: 01543 572600

Read, Polly (M)

Approved Body: National Family Mediation

Regional Group / Service: Kent Family Mediation Service

Mediation telephone number: 01795 476949

Rebello, Andre Joseph Anthony (A)

Approved Body: Solicitors Family Law Association

Regional Group / Service: Member of Solicitors Family Law Association, telephone 01689 850227 for details

Mediation telephone number: 01254 696121

Redhead, Hedley (M)

Approved Body: National Family Mediation

Regional Group / Service: Sunderland & South Tyneside Family Mediation Service

Mediation telephone number: 0191 5680433

Reed, Jane (A)

Approved Body: Family Mediation Scotland

Regional Group / Service: Family Mediation Tayside

Mediation telephone number: 01382 201343

Rees, David William Harold (A)

Approved Body: Solicitors Family Law Association

Regional Group / Service: Member of Solicitors Family Law Association, telephone 01689 850227 for details

Mediation telephone number: 01952 810307

Rees, Gillian Anne (A)

Approved Body: National Family Mediation

Regional Group / Service: Family Mediation Cardiff

Mediation telephone number: 01222 229692

Reeves, Nicholas Bruce (A)

Approved Body: Solicitors Family Law Association

Regional Group / Service: Member of Solicitors Family Law Association, telephone 01689 850227 for details

Mediation telephone number: 01603 660744

Mediation address: Greenland Houchen Solicitors, 38 Prince of Wales Road, Norwich, Norfolk NR1 1HZ
Facsimile 01603 610700, DX 5217 NORWICH 1

Professional qualifications and experience: solicitor; Member of Children Panel

Year qualified in mediation: 1997

Membership of professional bodies and organisations: SFLA

Practice offered: All Issues Mediation

Regi, Susan (A)

> *Approved Body:* LawWise
>
> *Regional Group / Service:* Member of LawWise Family Mediators Register, telephone 01483 237300 for details
>
> *Mediation telephone number:* 01273 735289

Reibstein, Janet (M)

> *Approved Body:* Family Mediators Association
>
> *Regional Group / Service:* Cambridge Family Mediators Association
>
> *Mediation telephone number:* 01223 359260
>
> *Mediation address:* 2 Tenison Avenue, Cambridge CB1 2DY Facsimile 01223 359260, E-mail reib@monsell.u-net.com
>
> *Professional qualifications and experience:* MA; PhD; C Psychol; Diploma Family Therapy
>
> *Year qualified in mediation:* 1993
>
> *Membership of professional bodies and organisations:* FMA; BPS; AFT
>
> *Willing to travel outside the region:* ✓
>
> *Willing to travel to:* London
>
> *Practice offered:* Children Issues Mediation; All Issues Mediation

Rennie, Katherine Mary (M)

> *Approved Body:* National Family Mediation
>
> *Regional Group / Service:* Salisbury & District Family Mediation Service
>
> *Mediation telephone number:* 01722 332936

Rennie, Sarah (M)

> *Approved Body:* National Family Mediation
>
> *Regional Group / Service:* Worcestershire Family Mediation
>
> *Mediation telephone number:* 01905 610925

Renton, Clare (A)

> *Approved Body:* Family Mediators Association
>
> *Regional Group / Service:* London South & Central Family Mediators Association
>
> *Mediation telephone number:* 0171 831 2626

Reynard, John Allanson (M)

> *Approved Body:* National Family Mediation
>
> *Regional Group / Service:* York Family Mediation Service
>
> *Mediation telephone number:* 01904 646068

Richards, Christopher Guy (M)

Approved Body: National Family Mediation

Regional Group / Service: Surrey Family Mediation Service; Hampshire Family Mediation; Mediation in Divorce; Thames Valley Family Mediation; Chiltern Family & Mediation Centre

Mediation telephone number: 0181 847 5979

Richards, Debbie (A)

Approved Body: LawGroup UK

Regional Group / Service: Member of LawGroup UK's Family Mediation Register, telephone 01883 370000 for details

Mediation telephone number: 01685 371168

Richardson, Madeleine Joan (A)

Approved Body: Family Mediators Association

Regional Group / Service: Sussex Family Mediators Association

Mediation telephone number: 01273 504385

Ridley, Margaret Helen (M)

Approved Body: Family Mediators Association

Regional Group / Service: Essex Family Mediators Association

Mediation telephone number: 01702 337315

Mediation address: 56 London Road, Southend-on-Sea SS1 1QQ Facsimile 01702 431438, DX 2805 SOUTHEND

Professional qualifications and experience: Margaret Ridley trained with the FMA in 1992 and is an accredited member and professional practice supervisor/consultant. She is a solicitor with experience in general litigation who has specialised in family law since 1978 when she joined her present firm where she is a partner and head of the family law department. She is a member of the Solicitors Family Law Association, Legal Aid Area Committee and a chair of Child Support and Social Security Appeal Tribunals.

Year qualified in mediation: 1992

Membership of professional bodies and organisations: The Law Society; UK College of Family Mediators; Solicitors Family Law Association; Family Mediators Association; Director of South Essex Relate

Willing to travel outside the region: ✓

Willing to travel to: Central & East London

Practice offered: Finance Issues Mediation; Children Issues Mediation; All Issues Mediation; mediation training; Professional Practice Supervision/Consultancy

(cont'd)

Additional mediation training:

consultation with children		1998
domestic violence		1998
Professional Practice Supervision/Consultancy	FMA	1996

Other additional mediation training: sole and anchor mediation 1996

Ritchie, Sheila S (M)

Approved Body: Family Mediation Scotland

Regional Group / Service: Family Mediation Tayside

Mediation telephone number: 01382 201343

Robb, Barbara Yvonne (M)

Approved Body: National Family Mediation

Regional Group / Service: Suffolk Family Mediation Service

Mediation telephone number: 01502 500101

Roberts, Gillian (M)

Approved Body: Family Mediators Association

Regional Group / Service: Essex Family Mediators Association

Mediation telephone number: 01277 211755

Roberts, Marian (M)

Approved Body: National Family Mediation

Regional Group / Service: South East London Family Mediation Bureau

Mediation telephone number: 0181 460 4606

Mediation address: South East London Family Mediation Bureau, 5 Upper Park Road, Bromley, Kent BR1 3HN
Facsimile 0181 466 6572

Professional qualifications and experience: BA (Cape Town, 1964); postgraduate diploma in Social Studies (with distinction), (University of London, 1966); barrister (1979)

Year qualified in mediation: 1982

Membership of professional bodies and organisations: The General Council of the Bar

Practice offered: Children Issues Mediation; mediation training

Additional mediation training:

consultation with children	NFM	1996
domestic violence	NFM	1998
initial information giving and/or assessment	LAB v Child Poverty Action Group	1997
mediation trainer training	NFM	1988

Other additional mediation training: All Issues Mediation (John Haynes) 1990; All Issues Mediation (NFM) 1993

(cont'd)

Mediation Career

Career Details (relevant to mediation) Mediator, SE London
Family Mediation Bureau (1982-); Mediation Consultant (1985-88);
Mediation Trainer for NFCC (now NFM) (1988-89); Training Co-
ordinator, NFCC (now NFM) (1989-95); Assistant Director
(Professional Practice & Training), NFM (1995-); Member of
Professional Standards Committee, UK College of Family Mediators
(1996-); External Assessor, Mediators Institute Ireland (1997-).

International Conferences/Seminars: Papers on family mediation
presented in Amsterdam 1992, Lisbon 1993, Rome 1993, Onati 1994,
Brussels 1995, Madrid 1995 and Glasgow 1997.

Overseas Training Consultancies: Milan 1994 and Lisbon 1995.

Selected Publications:
Mediation in Family Disputes: Principles of Practice, Arena, 1997 (2nd
edition); with Gwynn Davis, *Access to Agreement*, Open University
Press, 1988.
Selected articles and chapters have appeared in: *Mediation Quarterly
Vol 10, No 1, 1992; Journal of Social Welfare and Family Law*, No 5,
1992; *Family Conciliation in the UK: Policy and Practice* (ed Fisher, T)
Family Law, 1992; *Journal of Social Welfare and Family Law*, No 4,
1994; *La Mediazoni Familiare*, Guiffre Editore, Milano, 1994; *Family
Law*, Vol 26, April, 1996; *UK College of Family Mediators Directory and
Handbook*, 1997/98.

Robertson, Barbara (M)

Approved Body: National Family Mediation

Regional Group / Service: Merseyside Family Mediation Service

Mediation telephone number: 0151 260 9155

Robertson, Hazel Muriel (M)

Approved Body: Family Mediation Scotland

Regional Group / Service: Family Mediation Borders

Mediation telephone number: 01721 724170

Robey, Jane Alison (A)

Approved Body: National Family Mediation

Regional Group / Service: Exeter & District Family Mediation Service

Mediation telephone number: 01392 410529

Robinson, Margaret Elisabeth (M)

Approved Body: National Family Mediation

Mediation telephone number: 01962 777368

■ **Robinson**, Neil (A)

> *Approved Body:* Family Mediators Association
>
> *Regional Group / Service:* Birmingham Family Mediators Association
>
> *Mediation telephone number:* 01785 252377

■ **Robinson**, Sara Catherine (M)

> *Approved Body:* Family Mediators Association
>
> *Regional Group / Service:* London South & Central Family Mediators Association
>
> *Mediation telephone number:* 0171 420 5000
>
> *Mediation address:* 2 Henrietta Street, Covent Garden, London WC2E 8PS
> Facsimile 0171 420 5005, DX 40012 COVENT GARDEN, E-mail flc@tflc.co.uk
>
> *Professional qualifications and experience:* LLB Hons Law Degree; 18 years' post-qualification experience in practice
>
> *Year qualified in mediation:* 1991
>
> *Membership of professional bodies and organisations:* The Law Society; Solicitors Family Law Association
>
> *Willing to travel outside the region:* ✓
>
> *Willing to travel to:* Devon
>
> *Practice offered:* Finance Issues Mediation; All Issues Mediation; Professional Practice Supervision/Consultancy
>
> *Additional mediation training:*

mediation trainer training	SFLA	1996
Professional Practice Supervision/Consultancy	FMA	1997

> *Other additional mediation training:* John Haynes 1994

> **Career/Experience**
>
> Partner in The Family Law Consortium, the first multi-disciplinary service in the United Kingdom to offer access to mediation, counselling, legal advice and representation under one roof. This service is a Legal Aid Board Mediation Pilot.
>
> Trained as a mediator with The Family Mediators Association in 1991, achieving accreditation in 1992. Undertook further training as sole mediator in 1996 and was appointed a trainer and consultant to the Solicitors Family Law Association Mediation Training Faculty. Undertakes SFLA mediation training assessment and provides professional practice consultancy to FMA and SFLA trainees. Founder member of the Divorce Mediation Group. Co-author of *Divorce Reform: A Guide for Lawyers and Mediators* (FT Law & Tax), practises as a co-mediator and as a sole mediator.

Robinson, Susan Jane (A)

> *Approved Body:* Family Mediators Association
>
> *Regional Group / Service:* Shropshire Family Mediators Association
>
> *Mediation telephone number:* 01743 248545

Robinson, Zoe Ruth (A)

> *Approved Body:* LawGroup UK
>
> *Regional Group / Service:* Member of LawGroup UK's Family Mediation Register, telephone 01883 370000 for details
>
> *Mediation telephone number:* 01423 566666

Robson, Bridget Mary (M)

> *Approved Body:* National Family Mediation
>
> *Regional Group / Service:* West Yorkshire Family Mediation Service
>
> *Mediation telephone number:* 0345 419403

Robson, Isobel Ann (A)

> *Approved Body:* LawGroup UK
>
> *Regional Group / Service:* Member of LawGroup UK's Family Mediation Register, telephone 01883 370000 for details
>
> *Mediation telephone number:* 01482 325242

Rodak, Mary (A)

> *Approved Body:* Solicitors Family Law Association
>
> *Regional Group / Service:* Member of Solicitors Family Law Association, telephone 01689 850227 for details
>
> *Mediation telephone number:* 01706 644187

Roper, Nancy Lynne (A)

> *Approved Body:* LawGroup UK
>
> *Regional Group / Service:* Member of LawGroup UK's Family Mediation Register, telephone 01883 370000 for details
>
> *Mediation telephone number:* 01264 353411

Ross, Claire Rose (M)

> *Approved Body:* Family Mediation Scotland
>
> *Regional Group / Service:* Family Mediation Grampian
>
> *Mediation telephone number:* 01343 540801

Ross, Martin Edward (M)

> *Approved Body:* National Family Mediation
>
> *Regional Group / Service:* West Essex Family Mediation Service *(cont'd)*

Mediation telephone number: 0171 482 1974

■ **Rowe**, Vivienne (M)

Approved Body: National Family Mediation

Regional Group / Service: Exeter & District Family Mediation Service

Mediation telephone number: 01392 410529

■ **Rowland**, Michael (A)

Approved Body: LawWise

Regional Group / Service: Member of LawWise Family Mediators Register, telephone 01483 237300 for details

Mediation telephone number: 01622 656500

■ **Rumbold**, Henry John Sebastian (A)

Approved Body: Solicitors Family Law Association

Regional Group / Service: Member of Solicitors Family Law Association, telephone 01689 850227 for details

Mediation telephone number: 0171 242 2556

Mediation address: Dawson Cornwell & Co, 16 Red Lion Square, London WC1R 4QT
Facsimile 0171 831 0478, DX 351725 BLOOMSBURY, E-mail mail@dawsoncornwell.co.uk

Professional qualifications and experience: solicitor; specialist in family law for 17 years; trained as an All Issues Mediator by SFLA

Year qualified in mediation: 1997

Membership of professional bodies and organisations: The Law Society; Solicitors Family Law Association

Willing to travel outside the region: ✓

Willing to travel to: South West (Wiltshire, Somerset, Dorset)

Practice offered: Finance Issues Mediation; Children Issues Mediation; All Issues Mediation

■ **Rutherford**, Alan Petrie (M)

Approved Body: National Family Mediation

Regional Group / Service: Family Mediation Service (Northumberland & Tyneside)

Mediation telephone number: 0191 261 9212

■ **Ryan**, Anne (A)

Approved Body: LawWise

Regional Group / Service: Member of LawWise Family Mediators Register, telephone 01483 237300 for details

(cont'd)

Mediation telephone number: 0161 746 7776

▨ **Ryder**, Catherine Ann (A)

> *Approved Body:* LawGroup UK
>
> *Regional Group / Service:* Member of LawGroup UK's Family Mediation Register, telephone 01883 370000 for details
>
> *Mediation telephone number:* 01242 514674

▨ **Sabberton**, Joanne (A)

> *Approved Body:* Solicitors Family Law Association
>
> *Regional Group / Service:* Member of Solicitors Family Law Association, telephone 01689 850227 for details
>
> *Mediation telephone number:* 01493 844308

▨ **Sabine**, Christa (A)

> *Approved Body:* Solicitors Family Law Association
>
> *Regional Group / Service:* Member of Solicitors Family Law Association, telephone 01689 850227 for details
>
> *Mediation telephone number:* 0171 354 1800

▨ **Sadleir**, Jack (A)

> *Approved Body:* Solicitors Family Law Association
>
> *Regional Group / Service:* Member of Solicitors Family Law Association, telephone 01689 850227 for details
>
> *Mediation telephone number:* 0171 242 9971

▨ **Sale**, Susan (M)

> *Approved Body:* National Family Mediation
>
> *Regional Group / Service:* Durham Family Mediation
>
> *Mediation telephone number:* 0191 386 3057

▨ **Sands**, Rosemary (M)

> *Approved Body:* Family Mediators Association
>
> *Regional Group / Service:* Cambridge Family Mediators Association
>
> *Mediation telephone number:* 01293 576 308/9

▨ **Saunders**, Kate (A)

> *Approved Body:* LawGroup UK
>
> *Regional Group / Service:* Member of LawGroup UK's Family Mediation Register, telephone 01883 370000 for details
>
> *Mediation telephone number:* 01522 531461

(M) = Member   (A) = Associate

■ **Savage**, Robert Adam (A)

> *Approved Body:* Solicitors Family Law Association
>
> *Regional Group / Service:* Member of Solicitors Family Law Association, telephone 01689 850227 for details
>
> *Mediation telephone number:* 01747 834209
>
> *Mediation address:* Farnfields Family Mediation Service, The Square, Gillingham, Dorset SP8 4AX
> Facsimile 01747 822204, DX 100050 GILLINGHAM DORSET
>
> *Other mediation address:* Farnfields Family Mediation Service, 24 Warminster Road, Westbury, Wiltshire BA13 9PE
>
> *Professional qualifications and experience:* solicitor with over 30 years' experience in family law work
>
> *Year qualified in mediation:* 1997
>
> *Membership of professional bodies and organisations:* The Law Society; SFLA; BALM; RQP (Relate Quality Partnership)
>
> *Willing to travel outside the region:* ✓
>
> *Willing to travel to:* Wiltshire – my firm has offices at Warminster and Westbury
>
> *Practice offered:* All Issues Mediation
>
> *Other additional mediation training:* Relate Quality Partnership 1997

■ **Sayers**, Beverley Anne (M)

> *Approved Body:* Family Mediators Association
>
> *Regional Group / Service:* Greater Manchester Family Mediators Association
>
> *Mediation telephone number:* 01925 740261

■ **Schaffer**, Lorraine (M)

> *Approved Body:* National Family Mediation
>
> *Regional Group / Service:* NCH Action for Children Eye to Eye Mediation
>
> *Mediation telephone number:* 0171 701 1114

■ **Schatzburger**, Rosie (M)

> *Approved Body:* National Family Mediation
>
> *Regional Group / Service:* York Family Mediation Service
>
> *Mediation telephone number:* 01904 646068

■ **Schmit**, Jenny (A)

> *Approved Body:* Family Mediators Association
>
> *Regional Group / Service:* Surrey & North Hampshire Family Mediators Association

(cont'd)

Mediation telephone number: 01252 321859

■ **Scofield**, Ian Donald (M)

Approved Body: Family Mediators Association

Regional Group / Service: Devon Family Mediators Association

Mediation telephone number: 01803 213251

■ **Scott**, Judith Elinor (M)

Approved Body: National Family Mediation

Regional Group / Service: West Yorkshire Family Mediation Service

Mediation telephone number: 01274 882019

Mediation address: West Yorkshire FMS, Law Courts, Exchange Square, Drake Street, Bradford, West Yorkshire BD1 1JA

Other mediation address: 17 Brookfield Road, Leeds, West Yorkshire LS6 4EJ

Professional qualifications and experience: CQSW; 20 years as community worker and social worker with children and families

Year qualified in mediation: 1993

Willing to travel outside the region: ✓

Willing to travel to: Greater Manchester and anywhere in the North East

Practice offered: Children Issues Mediation; Professional Practice Supervision/Consultancy

Additional mediation training:

consultation with children	NFM	1996
domestic violence	NFM	1997
initial information giving and/or assessment	NFM	1994
Professional Practice Supervision/Consultancy		1997

■ **Scourfield**, Marion (M)

Approved Body: Family Mediators Association

Regional Group / Service: The Hertfordshire Comprehensive Mediation Service

Mediation telephone number: 01494 672167

Mediation address: Grays Cottage, Church Road, Seer Green, Beaconsfield, Buckinghamshire HP9 2XZ

Professional qualifications and experience: Certificate of Qualification in Social Work; 20 years' experience of working with families

Year qualified in mediation: Accredited 1996

Membership of professional bodies and organisations: UK College of Family Mediators; FMA; National Association of Probation Officers; Association of Family Court Welfare Officers

(cont'd)

Willing to travel outside the region: ✓

Willing to travel to: London (Central, West, North-West), Berks, Bucks, Oxon, Herts.

Practice offered: All Issues Mediation

Seagreaves, Emma Mary (A)

Approved Body: LawWise

Regional Group / Service: Member of LawWise Family Mediators Register, telephone 01483 237300 for details

Mediation telephone number: 0161 746 7776

Sealey, Alan (M)

Approved Body: Family Mediators Association

Regional Group / Service: Wiltshire Family Mediators Association

Shah, Damayanti (M)

Approved Body: National Family Mediation

Regional Group / Service: Bradford Metropolitan Family Mediation Service

Mediation telephone number: 01274 732768

Shannahan, Debra Laraine (A)

Approved Body: National Family Mediation

Regional Group / Service: Sussex Family Mediation Service

Mediation telephone number: 01273 220813

Sharp, Richard William James (A)

Approved Body: Family Mediators Association

Regional Group / Service: Wiltshire Family Mediators Association

Mediation telephone number: 01793 410800

Shaw, Anthony (M)

Approved Body: National Family Mediation

Regional Group / Service: Dorset Family Mediation Service

Mediation telephone number: 01202 314600

Shaw, Gillian Catherine (A)

Approved Body: LawWise

Regional Group / Service: Member of LawWise Family Mediators Register, telephone 01483 237300 for details

Mediation telephone number: 01773 715334

Shearmur, Rachael Ann (A)

Approved Body: LawGroup UK

Regional Group / Service: Member of LawGroup UK's Family Mediation Register, telephone 01883 370000 for details

Mediation telephone number: 01392 258451

Shingleton, Harry (M)

Approved Body: Family Mediators Association

Regional Group / Service: Derbyshire Family Mediators Association

Mediation telephone number: 01773 822307

Mediation address: The Triangle, 131 Bridge Street, Belper, Derbyshire DE56 1BJ
Facsimile 01773 826518, DX 15301 BELPER

Professional qualifications and experience: accredited mediator UK College of Family Mediators; FMA supervisor; sole and anchor mediation; solicitor

Year qualified in mediation: 1993

Practice offered: All Issues Mediation; Professional Practice Supervision/Consultancy

Additional mediation training:

Professional Practice Supervision/Consultancy   FMA   1996

Other additional mediation training: sole and anchor mediation (FMA) 1997; AIM mediation (NFM) 1998

Shirres, Kate (M)

Approved Body: Family Mediation Scotland

Regional Group / Service: Family Mediation Lothian

Mediation telephone number: 0131 226 4507

Shore, Barbara (M)

Approved Body: National Family Mediation

Regional Group / Service: Herefordshire Family Mediation Service

Mediation telephone number: 01432 264087

Short, Saeeda (M)

Approved Body: National Family Mediation

Regional Group / Service: NCH Action for Children Eye to Eye Mediation

Mediation telephone number: 0171 701 1114

Simela, Aggrey John (M)

Approved Body: National Family Mediation

Regional Group / Service: Mediation for Families (East London & City); African Caribbean Family Mediation Service

Mediation telephone number: 0171 613 1666/737 2366

Simmons, Gloria (M)

Approved Body: National Family Mediation; Family Mediators Association

Regional Group / Service: Family Mediation (Central Middlesex); London North & Central Family Mediators Association

Mediation telephone number: 0181 361 3740

Mediation address: Timbers, 64 Manor Drive, Whetstone, London N20 0DU

Professional qualifications and experience: Relate individual and marital counsellor; family psychotherapist (UKCP accredited); Relate psychosexual counsellor

Year qualified in mediation: 1992

Membership of professional bodies and organisations: Relate; NFM; FMA

Willing to travel outside the region: ✓

Willing to travel to: Within North and Central London region, South Herts and Middlesex

Practice offered: Children Issues Mediation; All Issues Mediation

Additional mediation training:

consultation with children	NFM	1988
domestic violence	NFM	1997
initial information giving and/or assessment	FMA	1992

Other additional mediation training: sole and anchor 1996

Simmons, Russell (M)

Approved Body: National Family Mediation

Regional Group / Service: Derbyshire Family Mediation Service

Mediation telephone number: 01246 277422

Simnett, George William (A)

Approved Body: Solicitors Family Law Association

Regional Group / Service: Member of Solicitors Family Law Association, telephone 01689 850227 for details

Mediation telephone number: 01283 564716

(M) = Member   (A) = Associate

Simpson, Margaret Mary (M)

>*Approved Body:* National Family Mediation
>
>*Regional Group / Service:* Gloucestershire Family Mediation
>
>*Mediation telephone number:* 01452 411843

Singer, Laurence Maurice (M)

>*Approved Body:* National Family Mediation
>
>*Regional Group / Service:* Thames Valley Family Mediation; Surrey Family Mediation Service
>
>*Mediation telephone number:* 01494 431400

Singleton, Judith Elizabeth (M)

>*Approved Body:* National Family Mediation
>
>*Regional Group / Service:* Family Mediation Service (Northumberland & Tyneside)
>
>*Mediation telephone number:* 0191 261 9212

Sisk, Nicola (A)

>*Approved Body:* Solicitors Family Law Association
>
>*Regional Group / Service:* Member of Solicitors Family Law Association, telephone 01689 850227 for details
>
>*Mediation telephone number:* 01842 754151

Skelly, Agnes Catherine (A)

>*Approved Body:* LawWise
>
>*Regional Group / Service:* Member of LawWise Family Mediators Register, telephone 01483 237300 for details

Slingsby, Anthony Francis (M)

>*Approved Body:* National Family Mediation
>
>*Regional Group / Service:* Sussex Family Mediation Service; Family Mediation Service – Institute of Family Therapy
>
>*Mediation telephone number:* 01273 494054

Smale-Adams, Marion June (M)

>*Approved Body:* National Family Mediation
>
>*Regional Group / Service:* Mediation in Divorce
>
>*Mediation telephone number:* 0181 891 6860

■ **Small**, Annie Duncan Gow (M)

>*Approved Body:* Family Mediation Scotland
>
>*Regional Group / Service:* Family Mediation (West of Scotland)
>
>*Mediation telephone number:* 01563 572429

■ **Smallacombe**, Ruth (M)

>*Approved Body:* Family Mediators Association
>
>*Regional Group / Service:* London South & Central Family Mediators Association
>
>*Mediation telephone number:* 0181 648 2212
>
>*Mediation address:* The Family Law Consortium, 2 Henrietta Street, London WC2E 8PS
>Facsimile 0171 420 5005, DX 40012 COVENT GARDEN, E-mail flc@tflc.co.uk
>
>*Other mediation address:* The Counselling Concern, Mitcham Hall House, London Road, Mitcham, London Borough of Merton CR4 4BF
>
>*Professional qualifications and experience:* mediator; counsellor; social worker; trainer; (PPSC) supervisor-consultant
>
>*Year qualified in mediation:* 1991 (accredited 1993)
>
>*Membership of professional bodies and organisations:* FMA; British Association for Counselling (BAC)
>
>*Willing to travel outside the region:* ✓
>
>*Willing to travel to:* South East; worldwide by agreement
>
>*Practice offered:* Finance Issues Mediation; Children Issues Mediation; All Issues Mediation; mediation training; Professional Practice Supervision/Consultancy; co-mediation and sole/anchor mediation
>
>*Additional mediation training:*
>
>| | | |
>|---|---|---|
>| domestic violence | FMA | 1995 |
>| mediation trainer training | FMA | 1995 |
>| Professional Practice Supervision/Consultancy | FMA | 1996 |
>
>*Other additional mediation training:* sole mediator (FMA) 1996; welfare benefits 1997

■ **Smart**, Julia Bryony (A)

>*Approved Body:* LawWise
>
>*Regional Group / Service:* Member of LawWise Family Mediators Register, telephone 01483 237300 for details
>
>*Mediation telephone number:* 0117 9253311

■ **Smith**, Caroline (A)

>*Approved Body:* Family Mediation Scotland
>
>*Regional Group / Service:* Family Mediation Lothian

(cont'd)

Mediation telephone number: 0131 226 4507

Smith, Colin Alan (M)

Approved Body: Family Mediators Association

Regional Group / Service: Essex Family Mediators Association; Mediation East Anglia

Mediation telephone number: 01245 264764

Mediation address: Leonard Gray Solicitors, 72-74 Duke Street, Chelmsford, Essex CM1 1JY
Telephone 01245 490728, DX 3309 CHELMSFORD 1

Professional qualifications and experience: solicitor/partner, Leonard Gray solicitors, Chelmsford, Essex; FMA mediator

Year qualified in mediation: 1995

Membership of professional bodies and organisations: The Law Society; SFLA; FMA; Association of Lawyers for Children; Vice-Chair Relate Mid-Essex; Member UK College of Family Mediators

Practice offered: All Issues Mediation

Additional mediation training:

Professional Practice Supervision/Consultancy	FMA	1996

Other additional mediation training: CEDR current course (four days)

Smith, Jacky (A)

Approved Body: Family Mediators Association

Regional Group / Service: Family Mediators South Wales Ltd

Mediation telephone number: 01291 421121

Mediation address: 78A Chepstow Road, Caldicot, Monmouthshire NP6 4HZ
Facsimile 01291 421133, E-mail sdent87095@aol.com

Professional qualifications and experience: Postgraduate Diploma in Counselling; member of Family Mediators Association; broad financial background as director in personal finance companies; building society manager; experienced counsellor and debt counsellor

Year qualified in mediation: Newly-qualified

Membership of professional bodies and organisations: Family Mediators Association; British Association of Counselling

Willing to travel outside the region: ✓

Willing to travel to: South West England – Bristol, Bath, M4 corridor

Practice offered: All Issues Mediation

Additional mediation training:

initial information giving and/or assessment	FMA	1997

Smith, Jonathan Mark Weston (M)

Approved Body: National Family Mediation

Regional Group / Service: South Staffordshire Family Mediation Service

Mediation telephone number: 01543 572600

Smith, Susan Katharine (M)

Approved Body: National Family Mediation

Regional Group / Service: Hampshire Family Mediation

Mediation telephone number: 01705 660919

Smith, Valerie (M)

Approved Body: National Family Mediation

Regional Group / Service: Sunderland & South Tyneside Family Mediation Service

Mediation telephone number: 0191 568 0433

Sorrell, Andrea (A)

Approved Body: National Family Mediation

Regional Group / Service: West Essex Family Mediation Service

Mediation telephone number: 01279 426 6749

Speed, Judith Mary (A)

Approved Body: Family Mediators Association

Regional Group / Service: Nottinghamshire Family Mediators Association

Mediation telephone number: 0115 936 9369

Spooner, Margaret Alma (A)

Approved Body: Family Mediation Scotland

Regional Group / Service: Family Mediation Orkney

Mediation telephone number: 01856 870571

Squires, Renella Mary (M)

Approved Body: National Family Mediation; LawWise

Regional Group / Service: Hampshire Family Mediation; Member of LawWise Family Mediators Register, telephone 01483 237300 for details

Mediation telephone number: 01243 786668 or 0800 132342

Mediation address: George Ide Phillips, Solicitors Mediation Service, Lion House, 79 St Pancras, Chichester, West Sussex PO19 4NL Facsimile 01243 787566, DX 30306 CHICHESTER

(cont'd)

Professional qualifications and experience: lawyer mediator in children's issues, finance and property issues; also experience in mediating with children and domestic violence

Year qualified in mediation: 1995

Membership of professional bodies and organisations: BALM; NFM; SFLA

Willing to travel outside the region: ✓

Willing to travel to: Sussex, Hampshire, Surrey

Practice offered: All Issues Mediation

Stacey, Howard Walter (A)

Approved Body: Solicitors Family Law Association

Regional Group / Service: Member of Solicitors Family Law Association, telephone 01689 850227 for details

Mediation telephone number: 0171 631 1050

Staff, Jane (A)

Approved Body: Solicitors Family Law Association

Regional Group / Service: Member of Solicitors Family Law Association, telephone 01689 850227 for details

Mediation telephone number: 01782 639827

Stanton, Joseph William (M)

Approved Body: Family Mediators Association

Regional Group / Service: South West Region Family Mediators Association

Mediation telephone number: 01392 420888

Staples, Mary (M)

Approved Body: National Family Mediation

Regional Group / Service: York Family Mediation Service

Mediation telephone number: 01904 646068

Stebbing, Colin Peter (A)

Approved Body: LawGroup UK

Regional Group / Service: Member of LawGroup UK's Family Mediation Register, telephone 01883 370000 for details

Mediation telephone number: 0151 931 2777

Stephany, Jane Susan (A)

Approved Body: Family Mediators Association

Regional Group / Service: Herts & Bucks Family Mediators Association

(cont'd)

Mediation telephone number: 01923 853545

Stephenson, Suzanne (A)

Approved Body: Family Mediators Association

Regional Group / Service: The Hertfordshire Comprehensive Mediation Service

Mediation telephone number: 01582 724501

Stephenson, Tracy (A)

Approved Body: National Family Mediation

Regional Group / Service: Cleveland Family Mediation Service

Mediation telephone number: 01642 222967

Stevens, Catherine Louise (A)

Approved Body: Solicitors Family Law Association

Regional Group / Service: Member of Solicitors Family Law Association, telephone 01689 850227 for details

Mediation telephone number: 0115 924 3333

Stevenson, Catherine Anne (M)

Approved Body: Family Mediation Scotland

Regional Group / Service: NCH Action for Children Family Mediation Fife

Mediation telephone number: 01592 751095

Stevenson, John Morrison (M)

Approved Body: Family Mediation Scotland

Regional Group / Service: Family Mediation Service (Highland)

Stevenson, Marion Emma Lander (M)

Approved Body: National Family Mediation; Family Mediators Association

Regional Group / Service: Oxfordshire Family Mediation Service; Oxford Family Mediators Association

Mediation telephone number: 01865 553321

Stocks, David (A)

Approved Body: LawWise

Regional Group / Service: Member of LawWise Family Mediators Register, telephone 01483 237300 for details

Mediation telephone number: 0161 969 3131/976 5298

▨ **Stocks**, Susan (A)

Approved Body: LawGroup UK

Regional Group / Service: Member of LawGroup UK's Family Mediation Register, telephone 01883 370000 for details

Mediation telephone number: 01522 512321

▨ **Strutt**, Christopher (A)

Approved Body: LawGroup UK

Regional Group / Service: Member of LawGroup UK's Family Mediation Register, telephone 01883 370000 for details

Mediation telephone number: 01323 509191

▨ **Stuart-Smith**, Mary (M)

Approved Body: Family Mediators Association

Regional Group / Service: Kent Family Mediators Association

Mediation telephone number: 01580 240395

▨ **Stylianou**, Katherine Dora (M)

Approved Body: National Family Mediation

Regional Group / Service: NCH Action for Children Eye to Eye Mediation

Mediation telephone number: 0171 703 1114/0181 460 4606

▨ **Sutton**, Guy Christopher (A)

Approved Body: LawWise

Regional Group / Service: Member of LawWise Family Mediators Register, telephone 01483 237300 for details

Mediation telephone number: 0171 734 6505

▨ **Swanson**, Elizabeth Anne (M)

Approved Body: National Family Mediation

Regional Group / Service: Merseyside Family Mediation Service

Mediation telephone number: 0151 260 9155

▨ **Swenson**, Adrian (M)

Approved Body: Family Mediators Association

Regional Group / Service: Lancashire Family Mediators Association

Mediation telephone number: 01524 762508

▨ **Swenson**, Veronica J (M)

Approved Body: National Family Mediation

Regional Group / Service: Cumbria Family Mediation Service

(cont'd)

Mediation telephone number: 01524 762508

■ **Swift**, Sue (M)

Approved Body: Family Mediators Association

Regional Group / Service: Kent Family Mediators Association

Mediation telephone number: 01892 783207

■ **Swindells**, Rhoda D (M)

Approved Body: National Family Mediation; Family Mediators Association

Regional Group / Service: South Yorkshire Family Mediators Association; South Yorkshire Family Mediation Service

Mediation telephone number: 0114 2302891

■ **Sydney**, Barbara (M)

Approved Body: National Family Mediation

Regional Group / Service: Cleveland Family Mediation Service

Mediation telephone number: 01642 222967

■ **Symons**, Jacqueline Mary (M)

Approved Body: Family Mediation Scotland

Regional Group / Service: Family Mediation Borders

■ **Tait**, Rosemary (A)

Approved Body: LawWise

Regional Group / Service: Member of LawWise Family Mediators Register, telephone 01483 237300 for details

Mediation telephone number: 0191 384 5440

■ **Tank**, Helen Katharine (A)

Approved Body: Solicitors Family Law Association

Regional Group / Service: Member of Solicitors Family Law Association, telephone 01689 850227 for details

Mediation telephone number: 01432 272401

■ **Tattum**, Sally Elizabeth (A)

Approved Body: Family Mediation Scotland

Regional Group / Service: Family Mediation Service (Highland)

■ **Taylor**, Adam Kane (M)

Approved Body: Family Mediators Association

Regional Group / Service: Sussex Family Mediators Association

(cont'd)

Mediation telephone number: 01243 531551

Taylor, Julian Nicholas (A)

Approved Body: LawWise

Regional Group / Service: Member of LawWise Family Mediators Register, telephone 01483 237300 for details

Mediation telephone number: 01484 559050/1

Taylor, Karen (M)

Approved Body: National Family Mediation

Regional Group / Service: Swindon Family Mediation Service; Oxfordshire Family Mediation Service

Mediation telephone number: 01793 527285/01865 741781

Taylor, Kathryn Lesley (A)

Approved Body: Family Mediators Association

Regional Group / Service: Essex Family Mediators Association

Mediation telephone number: 01206 733733

Taylor, Patricia Rosemary (A)

Approved Body: Family Mediators Association

Regional Group / Service: Essex Family Mediators Association

Mediation telephone number: 01787 224876/97

Temple-Harris, Linda (A)

Approved Body: Family Mediators Association

Regional Group / Service: The Hertfordshire Comprehensive Mediation Service

Mediation telephone number: 0181 950 5149

Terry, Caroline (A)

Approved Body: LawGroup UK

Regional Group / Service: Member of LawGroup UK's Family Mediation Register, telephone 01883 370000 for details

Mediation telephone number: 01689 833657

Terry, Julia Helen (A)

Approved Body: National Family Mediation

Regional Group / Service: York Family Mediation Service

Mediation telephone number: 01904 646068

■ **Thickett**, Rosalyn (A)

Approved Body: LawWise

Regional Group / Service: Member of LawWise Family Mediators Register, telephone 01483 237300 for details

Mediation telephone number: 01603 610911

■ **Thomas**, Ann (A)

Approved Body: Solicitors Family Law Association

Regional Group / Service: Member of Solicitors Family Law Association, telephone 01689 850227 for details

Mediation telephone number: 01223 363111

Mediation address: Few & Kester Solicitors & Attorneys, Chequers House, 77-81 Newmarket Road, Cambridge CB5 8EU
Facsimile 01223 323370, DX 122893 CAMBRIDGE 4, E-mail
few.kester@dial.pipex.com

Professional qualifications and experience: LLB (Hons); solicitor

Year qualified in mediation: 1998

Membership of professional bodies and organisations: The Law Society; Solicitors Family Law Association

Willing to travel outside the region: ✓

Willing to travel to: Suffolk

Practice offered: All Issues Mediation

■ **Thomas**, Christopher Norman (A)

Approved Body: Family Mediators Association

Regional Group / Service: South West Region Family Mediators Association

Mediation telephone number: 01626 332266

■ **Thomas**, Pamela Dawn (A)

Approved Body: Family Mediators Association

Regional Group / Service: Herts & Bucks Family Mediators Association

Mediation telephone number: 01582 696482

■ **Thomas**, William Neale (A)

Approved Body: LawGroup UK

Regional Group / Service: Member of LawGroup UK's Family Mediation Register, telephone 01883 370000 for details

Mediation telephone number: 0468 688379

■ **Thompson**, Andrea (A)

> *Approved Body:* Solicitors Family Law Association
>
> *Regional Group / Service:* Member of Solicitors Family Law Association, telephone 01689 850227 for details
>
> *Mediation telephone number:* 01767 315040
>
> *Mediation address:* Leeds Day, 20 Hitchin Street, Biggleswade, Bedfordshire SG18 8BE
> Facsimile 01767 316573, DX 37156 BIGGLESWADE, E-mail mailbox@leedsday.demon.co.uk
>
> *Other mediation address:* 7-8 Market Hill, Huntingdon, Cambridgeshire PE18 6NT
>
> *Professional qualifications and experience:* Fellow of the Institute of Legal Executives; ten years' experience as a family lawyer; SFLA approved mediator
>
> *Year qualified in mediation:* 1996
>
> *Membership of professional bodies and organisations:* SFLA; ILEX
>
> *Willing to travel outside the region:* ✓
>
> *Willing to travel to:* offices in Sandy, Biggleswade, St Neots, Huntingdon, St Ives
>
> *Practice offered:* Finance Issues Mediation; Children Issues Mediation; All Issues Mediation

■ **Thompson**, Deborah (A)

> *Approved Body:* Solicitors Family Law Association
>
> *Regional Group / Service:* Member of Solicitors Family Law Association, telephone 01689 850227 for details
>
> *Mediation telephone number:* 0115 941 9141

■ **Thompson**, Janet Rosamond (A)

> *Approved Body:* Family Mediators Association
>
> *Regional Group / Service:* Cambridge Family Mediators Association
>
> *Mediation telephone number:* 01733 892237

■ **Thompson**, Lars Anders (M)

> *Approved Body:* National Family Mediation
>
> *Regional Group / Service:* Family Mediation Service (North-West Yorkshire); West Yorkshire Family Mediation Service; Bradford Metropolitan Family Mediation Service
>
> *Mediation telephone number:* 01483 860013

■ **Thompson**, Richard Paxton (A)

> *Approved Body:* Family Mediators Association
>
> *Regional Group / Service:* Sussex Family Mediators Association

(cont'd)

Mediation telephone number: 01273 570030

Thompson, Valerie Susan (A)

Approved Body: Solicitors Family Law Association

Regional Group / Service: Member of Solicitors Family Law Association, telephone 01689 850227 for details

Mediation telephone number: 01691 659194

Mediation address: The Albany, 37-39 Willow Street, Oswestry, Shropshire SY11 1AQ
Facsimile 01691 652755, DX 26605 OSWESTRY, E-mail awbrownlloyd@btinternet.com

Professional qualifications and experience: BA (Hons); eight years' specialisation in family law

Year qualified in mediation: 1998

Membership of professional bodies and organisations: SFLA

Willing to travel outside the region: ✓

Willing to travel to: Staffordshire

Practice offered: All Issues Mediation

Thomson, Anne Elisabeth (A)

Approved Body: LawGroup UK

Regional Group / Service: Member of LawGroup UK's Family Mediation Register, telephone 01883 370000 for details

Mediation telephone number: 01402 366566

Thorn, Paul (A)

Approved Body: Solicitors Family Law Association

Regional Group / Service: Member of Solicitors Family Law Association, telephone 01689 850227 for details

Mediation telephone number: 0114 224 2080

Mediation address: 6 Campo Lane, Sheffield S1 2EF
Telephone 0114 266 6660, Facsimile 0114 273 1956, DX 10534 SHEFFIELD, E-mail legal@wake-smith.co.uk

Other mediation address: 68 Clarkehouse Road, Sheffield S10 2LF

Professional qualifications and experience: solicitor; SFLA trained mediator; Deputy District Judge

Year qualified in mediation: 1997

Membership of professional bodies and organisations: The Law Society; SFLA

Willing to travel outside the region: ✓

Willing to travel to: North Derbyshire, North Nottinghamshire

(cont'd)

Practice offered: All Issues Mediation

■ **Thorneycroft**, Philip Michael (A)

Approved Body: Solicitors Family Law Association

Regional Group / Service: Member of Solicitors Family Law Association, telephone 01689 850227 for details

Mediation telephone number: 01752 251154

Mediation address: 60 North Hill, Plymouth, Devon PL4 8GP Telephone 01752 663295, Facsimile 01752 672021, DX 8206 PLYMOUTH

Other mediation address: 6/7/8 Addison Road, Sherwell, Plymouth, Devon PL4 8LN

Professional qualifications and experience: solicitor; member of SFLA local committee; member of The Law Society Children Panel; committee member of Plymouth Relate; SFLA trained mediator

Year qualified in mediation: 1997

Membership of professional bodies and organisations: SFLA; The Law Society Children Panel

Willing to travel outside the region: ✓

Willing to travel to: Devon and Cornwall

Practice offered: All Issues Mediation

■ **Thorpe**, Virginia (M)

Approved Body: National Family Mediation

Regional Group / Service: Surrey Family Mediation Service

Mediation telephone number: 01306 741777

■ **Tilley**, Susan (A)

Approved Body: Family Mediators Association

Regional Group / Service: Kent Family Mediators Association

Mediation telephone number: 0181 768 7000

■ **Tish**, Roberta Sandra (A)

Approved Body: Family Mediators Association

Regional Group / Service: London South & Central Family Mediators Association

Mediation telephone number: 0171 223 6966

■ **Tovey**, Geoffrey Arthur (A)

Approved Body: Solicitors Family Law Association

Regional Group / Service: Member of Solicitors Family Law Association, telephone 01689 850227 for details

(cont'd)

Mediation telephone number: 01277 223767

Mediation address: 47 Kings Road, Brentwood, Essex CM14 4RS
Facsimile 01277 234237, DX 5006 BRENTWOOD

Other mediation address: 147 High Road, Loughton, Essex IG10 4LY

Professional qualifications and experience: solicitor; over 20 years'
experience in family law

Year qualified in mediation: 1998

Membership of professional bodies and organisations: The Law Society;
Solicitors Family Law Association

Willing to travel outside the region: ✓

Willing to travel to: Loughton and Harlow, Essex

Practice offered: All Issues Mediation

Townend, Freda **(M)**

Approved Body: Family Mediation Scotland

Regional Group / Service: Family Mediation Central Scotland

Mediation telephone number: 01786 472984

Tracey, Denise **(M)**

Approved Body: National Family Mediation

Regional Group / Service: Coventry & Warwickshire Family Mediation
Service

Mediation telephone number: 01203 717109

Trelfa, Jill Marian **(A)**

Approved Body: Solicitors Family Law Association

Regional Group / Service: Member of Solicitors Family Law Association,
telephone 01689 850227 for details

Mediation telephone number: 0181 941 1249

Tremeer, Helen **(A)**

Approved Body: LawGroup UK

Regional Group / Service: Member of LawGroup UK's Family Mediation
Register, telephone 01883 370000 for details

Mediation telephone number: 01392 436244

Tresidder, Charles **(A)**

Approved Body: LawWise

Regional Group / Service: Member of LawWise Family Mediators
Register, telephone 01483 237300 for details

Mediation telephone number: 01303 850120

(cont'd)

Mediation address: Resolutions Family Mediation Centre, 5th Floor, Europa House, Sandgate Road, Folkestone, Kent CT20 1TD Facsimile 01303 221424, DX 4909 FOLKESTONE, E-mail mgabs@aol.com

Professional qualifications and experience: solicitor with 24 years of experience of family law dealing with disputes relating to domestic violence, finance, property and child matters (residence/contact). Trained by John Haynes and LawWise in 1996 as All Issues family mediator

Year qualified in mediation: 1996

Membership of professional bodies and organisations: Member of the Law Society's Children Panel; Solicitors Family Law Association (SFLA); British Association of Lawyer Mediators; The Relate Quality Partnership

Willing to travel outside the region: ✓

Willing to travel to: Kent, Sussex

Practice offered: All Issues Mediation

Additional mediation training:

consultation with children	LawGroup UK/	
	LawWise	1998
domestic violence	LawGroup UK/	
	LawWise	1998
initial information giving and/or assessment	LawGroup UK/	
	LawWise	1998

Other additional mediation training: advanced mediation course (LawWise) 1998

Tresman, Janet Iris Louise (M)

Approved Body: Family Mediators Association

Regional Group / Service: London North & Central Family Mediators Association

Mediation telephone number: 0171 431 7262

Mediation address: Cawdery Kaye Fireman & Taylor, 25/26 Hampstead High Street, London NW3 1QA Facsimile 0171 431 7605, DX 57567 HAMPSTEAD

Professional qualifications and experience: solicitor; mediator; Deputy District Judge

Year qualified in mediation: 1990

Membership of professional bodies and organisations: The Law Society; SFLA; FMA; National Step Families Association

Willing to travel outside the region: ✓

Willing to travel to: North London, Middlesex and Hertfordshire through Central London through to Wimbledon and nearby areas

(cont'd)

Practice offered: All Issues Mediation

Other additional mediation training: sole/anchor mediation training 1995

Career

I bring to mediation extensive experience and qualifications as follows: 22 years of practice in family law, also dealing with employment, housing, immigration, crime, domestic and commercial conveyancing and probate. In 1990 I trained as a mediator using a co-mediation model with family counsellors. A member of SFLA since 1983 and of its Working Party on Mediation since 1991. Trained as a sole mediator in September 1995 with FMA. As well as being an occasional family law lecturer, I have three different roles as a solicitor, mediator and Deputy District Judge since January 1993: I therefore have thorough knowledge of family law and practice and can inform on all aspects from this position of unusual authority. I also bring particular sensitivity in step family issues, as a step mother of three of wide age ranges and a recent former member of the Board of National Step Families Association for four years.

Trevis, Robert James (A)

Approved Body: LawGroup UK

Regional Group / Service: Member of LawGroup UK's Family Mediation Register, telephone 01883 370000 for details

Mediation telephone number: 0171 395 9507

Truscott, Ann (M)

Approved Body: Family Mediators Association

Regional Group / Service: Devon Family Mediators Association

Mediation telephone number: 01726 822685

Tucker, Frederick Edward (A)

Approved Body: Family Mediators Association

Regional Group / Service: Wiltshire Family Mediators Association

Mediation telephone number: 01793 526601

Turner, Jenni (M)

Approved Body: National Family Mediation

Regional Group / Service: Durham Family Mediation

Turner, Paul John (A)

Approved Body: Family Mediators Association

Regional Group / Service: South Midlands Family Mediators Association

Mediation telephone number: 01933 356131

Tweedale, Beryl (M)

Approved Body: National Family Mediation

Regional Group / Service: Family Mediation Service (Greater Manchester)

Mediation telephone number: 0161 797 9910

Uncles, Linda Jane (M)

Approved Body: National Family Mediation

Regional Group / Service: Berkshire Family Mediation

Mediation telephone number: 0118 957 1159

Vale, Margaret Jane (M)

Approved Body: Family Mediation Scotland

Regional Group / Service: Family Mediation Central Scotland

Mediation telephone number: 01786 472984

Valentine, Averil Margaret (M)

Approved Body: Family Mediation Scotland

Regional Group / Service: Family Mediation Tayside

Mediation telephone number: 01382 201343

Vaughan, Valerie (M)

Approved Body: National Family Mediation

Regional Group / Service: Family Mediation Service (Northumberland & Tyneside)

Mediation telephone number: 0191 261 9212

Mediation address: Family Mediation Service (Northumberland & Tyneside), MEA House, Ellison Place, Newcastle upon Tyne NE1 8XS

Professional qualifications and experience: MCFM; R S Hom

Year qualified in mediation: 1990

Membership of professional bodies and organisations: Member of the UK College of Mediators; Registered Member of the Society of Homeopaths; Fellow of RSA

Practice offered: Children Issues Mediation; All Issues Mediation; Professional Practice Supervision/Consultancy

Additional mediation training:

Professional Practice Supervision/Consultancy   NFM

Vickerman, Catherine Anne (M)

Approved Body: National Family Mediation

Regional Group / Service: Family Mediation Service (Greater Manchester)

(cont'd)

      Mediation telephone number: 0161 797 9910

Vincent, Margaret Mary (A)

Approved Body: National Family Mediation

Regional Group / Service: Surrey Family Mediation Service

Mediation telephone number: 01306 740967

Vincent, Marina Pauline (A)

Approved Body: Solicitors Family Law Association

Regional Group / Service: Member of Solicitors Family Law Association, telephone 01689 850227 for details

Mediation telephone number: 0181 909 1199

Mediation address: Littlejohn & Co, 118 Kenton Road, Kenton, Harrow, Middlesex HA3 8AN
Facsimile 0181 909 1121, DX 47509 KENTON

Professional qualifications and experience: SFLA trained mediator; LLB (Hons) Warwick University

Year qualified in mediation: 1997

Membership of professional bodies and organisations: SFLA; The Law Society

Practice offered: All Issues Mediation

Vogel, Susan Marie (A)

Approved Body: Family Mediators Association

Regional Group / Service: Birmingham Family Mediators Association

Mediation telephone number: 0121 784 8484

Mediation address: 41 Church Street, Birmingham B3 2RT
Facsimile 0121 783 4935, DX 13047 BIRMINGHAM

Professional qualifications and experience: BA (Hons); admitted as solicitor 1982; mediator

Year qualified in mediation: 1994

Willing to travel outside the region: ✓

Willing to travel to: West Midlands

Practice offered: Children Issues Mediation; All Issues Mediation

Other additional mediation training: sole and anchor practitioners course 1998

von Benzon, Nicholas (M)

Approved Body: Family Mediators Association

Regional Group / Service: Wiltshire Family Mediators Association

Mediation telephone number: 01985 840278

Wainwright, Andrea Jill (M)

> *Approved Body:* Family Mediators Association
>
> *Regional Group / Service:* The Hertfordshire Comprehensive Mediation Service; Mediation for Families (Thames Valley and Central London)
>
> *Mediation telephone number:* 01494 433177

Waite, Fiona Elizabeth (M)

> *Approved Body:* Family Mediation Scotland
>
> *Regional Group / Service:* NCH Action for Children Dumfries & Galloway Family Mediation Service
>
> *Mediation telephone number:* 01387 263185

Wakefield, Diana Madeleine (M)

> *Approved Body:* National Family Mediation
>
> *Regional Group / Service:* Family Mediation Service (North-West Yorkshire)
>
> *Mediation telephone number:* 01423 525156

Wakem, Mary Theresa (A)

> *Approved Body:* LawGroup UK
>
> *Regional Group / Service:* Member of LawGroup UK's Family Mediation Register, telephone 01883 370000 for details
>
> *Mediation telephone number:* 01865 792300

Wakeman, Isabel Margaret (M)

> *Approved Body:* National Family Mediation
>
> *Regional Group / Service:* York Family Mediation Service
>
> *Mediation telephone number:* 01904 646068

Walczak, Yvette (M)

> *Approved Body:* Family Mediators Association
>
> *Regional Group / Service:* London North & Central Family Mediators Association
>
> *Mediation telephone number:* 0181 886 9520

Walker, Alexis Jane (M)

> *Approved Body:* National Family Mediation
>
> *Regional Group / Service:* West Yorkshire Family Mediation Service
>
> *Mediation telephone number:* 0345 419403

(M) = Member   (A) = Associate

Walker, Caroline Ann (M)

Approved Body: National Family Mediation

Regional Group / Service: Family Mediation Service (North-West Yorkshire)

Mediation telephone number: 01423 525156

Walker, David John (A)

Approved Body: National Family Mediation

Regional Group / Service: NCH Action for Children Eye to Eye Mediation

Mediation telephone number: 0171 701 1114

Walker, Frances Mary (M)

Approved Body: National Family Mediation

Regional Group / Service: Sunderland & South Tyneside Family Mediation Service

Mediation telephone number: 0191 568 0533

Walker, Gillian Ryden (M)

Approved Body: National Family Mediation

Regional Group / Service: Cleveland Family Mediation Service

Mediation telephone number: 01642 222967

Walker, Linda Mary (A)

Approved Body: Solicitors Family Law Association

Regional Group / Service: Member of Solicitors Family Law Association, telephone 01689 850227 for details

Mediation telephone number: 01226 212345

Wall, Anne-Lise (M)

Approved Body: Family Mediators Association

Regional Group / Service: London South & Central Family Mediators Association

Mediation telephone number: 0181 744 1999

Wall, Linda Margaret (A)

Approved Body: Solicitors Family Law Association

Regional Group / Service: Member of Solicitors Family Law Association, telephone 01689 850227 for details

Mediation telephone number: 01273 327241

Walsh, Eileen (M)

Approved Body: Family Mediators Association

Regional Group / Service: London South & Central Family Mediators Association

Mediation telephone number: 0181 995 1934

Walsh, Elizabeth (M)

Approved Body: National Family Mediation

Regional Group / Service: Chiltern Family & Mediation Centre; Thames Valley Family Mediation

Mediation telephone number: 01494 724833

Walsh, Gaynor (A)

Approved Body: Family Mediators Association; LawGroup UK

Regional Group / Service: Member of LawGroup UK's Family Mediation Register, telephone 01883 370000 for details; Family Mediators South Wales Ltd

Mediation telephone number: 01685 371168

Ward, Janet Elfrida Frances (M)

Approved Body: National Family Mediation

Regional Group / Service: Coventry & Warwickshire Family Mediation Service

Mediation telephone number: 01203 717109

Wardill, Diana (M)

Approved Body: National Family Mediation

Regional Group / Service: Cleveland Family Mediation Service

Mediation telephone number: 01642 222967

Wareing, Andrew David (A)

Approved Body: Family Mediators Association

Regional Group / Service: South Yorkshire Family Mediators Association

Mediation telephone number: 01724 281616

Warne, Anna Jane (A)

Approved Body: LawGroup UK

Regional Group / Service: Member of LawGroup UK's Family Mediation Register, telephone 01883 370000 for details

Mediation telephone number: 01392 210700

A–Z College Members and Associates C

Waterman, Jill (A)

Approved Body: National Family Mediation

Regional Group / Service: Family Mediation Cardiff

Mediation telephone number: 01222 229692

Waterston, Robin James (M)

Approved Body: Family Mediation Scotland

Regional Group / Service: NCH Action for Children Family Mediation Fife

Mediation telephone number: 01592 751095

Watkins, Diane (A)

Approved Body: Family Mediators Association

Regional Group / Service: Family Mediators South Wales Ltd

Mediation telephone number: 01222 560862

Watkins, Helen Margaret (M)

Approved Body: Family Mediators Association

Regional Group / Service: Cambridge Family Mediators Association

Mediation telephone number: 01945 467131

Watson, Liza Helen (A)

Approved Body: LawGroup UK

Regional Group / Service: Member of LawGroup UK's Family Mediation Register, telephone 01883 370000 for details

Mediation telephone number: 0151 256 7777

Watts, John (A)

Approved Body: Family Mediators Association

Regional Group / Service: Hereford & Worcester Family Mediators Association

Mediation telephone number: 01684 563318

Way, Philip Morton (A)

Approved Body: Solicitors Family Law Association

Regional Group / Service: Member of Solicitors Family Law Association, telephone 01689 850227 for details

Mediation telephone number: 0113 209 2282

Mediation address: Addleshaw Booth & Co, Sovereign House, Sovereign Street, Leeds, West Yorkshire LS1 1HQ
Facsimile 0113 209 2060, DX MDX 12004 LEEDS, E-mail
pmw@addleshaw-booth.co.uk

(cont'd)

Professional qualifications and experience: BA (Hons); solicitor; SFLA trained mediator

Year qualified in mediation: 1997

Membership of professional bodies and organisations: The Law Society; SFLA

Willing to travel outside the region: ✓

Willing to travel to: anywhere in the North of England

Practice offered: All Issues Mediation

Webb, Colin Thomas (M)

Approved Body: National Family Mediation; Family Mediators Association

Regional Group / Service: NCH Action for Children Eye to Eye Mediation; Bromley Mediation Bureau

Mediation telephone number: 0171 701 1114

Webb, Irene Jean (A)

Approved Body: LawGroup UK

Regional Group / Service: Member of LawGroup UK's Family Mediation Register, telephone 01883 370000 for details

Mediation telephone number: 01803 853266/864888

Webster, Marilyn Joyce (M)

Approved Body: National Family Mediation

Regional Group / Service: Shropshire Family Mediation Service

Mediation telephone number: 01952 502447

Weedon, Julie (M)

Approved Body: Family Mediators Association

Regional Group / Service: Thames Valley Family Mediators Association

Mediation telephone number: 01491 875786

Weir, Jeannie (M)

Approved Body: National Family Mediation

Regional Group / Service: Suffolk Family Mediation Service

Mediation telephone number: 01473 225845

Welch, Jane (A)

Approved Body: Solicitors Family Law Association

Regional Group / Service: Member of Solicitors Family Law Association, telephone 01689 850227 for details

Mediation telephone number: 0161 624 4971

(cont'd)

Mediation address: 25-27 Queen Street, Oldham, Lancashire OL1 1RN
Facsimile 0161 624 2589, DX 23603

Professional qualifications and experience: solicitor

Year qualified in mediation: 1997

Membership of professional bodies and organisations: The Law Society;
The Law Society Children Panel; Child Concern

Willing to travel outside the region: ✓

Willing to travel to: anywhere in the North West

Practice offered: Children Issues Mediation; All Issues Mediation

■ **Welsh**, Sarah (M)

Approved Body: Family Mediation Scotland

Regional Group / Service: Family Mediation Central Scotland

Mediation telephone number: 01786 472984

■ **Weyland**, Ines (M)

Approved Body: National Family Mediation; Family Mediators
Association

Regional Group / Service: London North & Central Family Mediators
Association; Family Mediation Service: Barnet, Haringey & Hertsmere

Mediation telephone number: 0181 340 7764

■ **Whatling**, Tony (M)

Approved Body: National Family Mediation

Regional Group / Service: Peterborough & District Family Mediation
Service

Mediation telephone number: 01733 347353

■ **Wheeler**, David (A)

Approved Body: Family Mediators Association

Regional Group / Service: Bath District Family Mediators Association

Mediation telephone number: 01225 448494

■ **White**, Felicity (M)

Approved Body: Family Mediators Association

Regional Group / Service: Oxford Family Mediators Association

Mediation telephone number: 01869 347955

■ **White**, Morag (M)

Approved Body: Family Mediation Scotland

Regional Group / Service: NCH Action for Children Family Mediation
Fife

(cont'd)

(M) = Member   (A) = Associate

Mediation telephone number: 01592 751095

Whittaker, William George (M)

> *Approved Body:* National Family Mediation
>
> *Regional Group / Service:* North Devon Family Mediation Service
>
> *Mediation telephone number:* 01271 321888

Whittington, Richard Charles (A)

> *Approved Body:* LawWise
>
> *Regional Group / Service:* Member of LawWise Family Mediators Register, telephone 01483 237300 for details
>
> *Mediation telephone number:* 01276 686222

Wicherek, Ann Marie (A)

> *Approved Body:* LawWise
>
> *Regional Group / Service:* Member of LawWise Family Mediators Register, telephone 01483 237300 for details
>
> *Mediation telephone number:* 0171 797 6000

Wicks, Judith Ann Russel (A)

> *Approved Body:* Solicitors Family Law Association
>
> *Regional Group / Service:* Member of Solicitors Family Law Association, telephone 01689 850227 for details
>
> *Mediation telephone number:* 0171 465 8000

Wieselberg, Huguette-Deborah (M)

> *Approved Body:* National Family Mediation
>
> *Regional Group / Service:* Family Mediation Service – Institute of Family Therapy
>
> *Mediation telephone number:* 0171 391 9150

Wilkinson, Adele Lesley (A)

> *Approved Body:* LawGroup UK
>
> *Regional Group / Service:* Member of LawGroup UK's Family Mediation Register, telephone 01883 370000 for details
>
> *Mediation telephone number:* 01482 325242

Wilkinson, Sharon (A)

> *Approved Body:* Solicitors Family Law Association
>
> *Regional Group / Service:* Member of Solicitors Family Law Association, telephone 01689 850227 for details
>
> *Mediation telephone number:* 01203 641642

■ **Williams,** Alan Charles (M)

> *Approved Body:* Family Mediators Association
>
> *Regional Group / Service:* Oxford Family Mediators Association; Mediation for Families (Oxfordshire)
>
> *Mediation telephone number:* 01865 771917

■ **Williams,** Eldred (M)

> *Approved Body:* National Family Mediation
>
> *Regional Group / Service:* Mediation for Families (East London & City)
>
> *Mediation telephone number:* 0171 613 1666

■ **Williams,** Gail (M)

> *Approved Body:* National Family Mediation
>
> *Regional Group / Service:* Family Mediation Service (Northumberland & Tyneside)
>
> *Mediation telephone number:* 0191 261 9212

■ **Williams,** Jane (A)

> *Approved Body:* LawGroup UK
>
> *Regional Group / Service:* Member of LawGroup UK's Family Mediation Register, telephone 01883 370000 for details
>
> *Mediation telephone number:* 01222 461480

■ **Williams,** Jane Rhiannon (A)

> *Approved Body:* LawWise
>
> *Regional Group / Service:* Member of LawWise Family Mediators Register, telephone 01483 237300 for details
>
> *Mediation telephone number:* 01222 385600

■ **Williamson,** Michael (M)

> *Approved Body:* National Family Mediation
>
> *Regional Group / Service:* NCH Action for Children Eye to Eye Mediation
>
> *Mediation telephone number:* 0171 701 1114

■ **Williamson,** Sue Valerie (M)

> *Approved Body:* National Family Mediation
>
> *Regional Group / Service:* North Devon Family Mediation Service
>
> *Mediation telephone number:* 01271 321888

■ **Wilson,** Barbara Dian (M)

> *Approved Body:* National Family Mediation; Family Mediators Association

(cont'd)

Regional Group / Service: Hampshire Family Mediation; Hampshire & Isle of Wight Family Mediators Association

Mediation telephone number: 01705 812799/0402 315941 mobile

Wilson, Christopher Derek Neil (A)

Approved Body: Family Mediators Association

Regional Group / Service: Shropshire Family Mediators Association

Mediation telephone number: 01743 248545

Wilson, Donald James (A)

Approved Body: National Family Mediation

Regional Group / Service: Worcestershire Family Mediation

Mediation telephone number: 01905 610925

Wilson, Heather (M)

Approved Body: National Family Mediation

Regional Group / Service: Family Mediation Service (Northumberland & Tyneside)

Mediation telephone number: 0191 261 9212

Wilson, Hilary Edith (Non-Practising Member)

Approved Body: National Family Mediation

Mediation telephone number: 01473 658692

Wilson, Maggie (M)

Approved Body: National Family Mediation

Regional Group / Service: Family Mediation Service (Greater Manchester)

Mediation telephone number: 0161 797 9910

Wilson, Pamela Anne (A)

Approved Body: Solicitors Family Law Association

Regional Group / Service: Member of Solicitors Family Law Association telephone 01689 850227 for details

Mediation telephone number: 0161 764 5266

Wilson, Robin Anthony (A)

Approved Body: Family Mediators Association

Regional Group / Service: Hampshire & Isle of Wight Family Mediators Association

Mediation telephone number: 01705 524521

■ **Winter**, Julia Susan (M)

>*Approved Body:* National Family Mediation; Family Mediators Association
>
>*Regional Group / Service:* Shropshire Family Mediation Service
>
>*Mediation telephone number:* 01952 502447

■ **Wisniewski**, Andrew Christopher (A)

>*Approved Body:* Solicitors Family Law Association
>
>*Regional Group / Service:* Member of Solicitors Family Law Association, telephone 01689 850227 for details
>
>*Mediation telephone number:* 0116 253 8585
>
>*Mediation address:* 32 Friar Lane, Leicester, Leicestershire LE1 5RA Facsimile 0116 253 0212, DX MDX 10830 LEICESTER
>
>*Professional qualifications and experience:* LLB (Hons); LLM (Welfare Law); six years' post-qualification experience
>
>*Year qualified in mediation:* 1997
>
>*Membership of professional bodies and organisations:* SFLA
>
>*Willing to travel outside the region:* ✓
>
>*Willing to travel to:* Derby, Nottingham, Northampton
>
>*Practice offered:* All Issues Mediation

■ **Wolfenden**, Martin John (A)

>*Approved Body:* LawGroup UK
>
>*Regional Group / Service:* Member of LawGroup UK's Family Mediation Register, telephone 01883 370000 for details
>
>*Mediation telephone number:* 0181 885 1415

■ **Wood**, Anthony (A)

>*Approved Body:* LawGroup UK
>
>*Regional Group / Service:* Member of LawGroup UK's Family Mediation Register, telephone 01883 370000 for details
>
>*Mediation telephone number:* 01254 56762

■ **Wood**, Geoffrey Ian (A)

>*Approved Body:* Solicitors Family Law Association
>
>*Regional Group / Service:* Member of Solicitors Family Law Association, telephone 01689 850227 for details
>
>*Mediation telephone number:* 0121 643 5531
>
>*Mediation address:* Neville House, 14 Waterloo Street, Birmingham B2 5UF
>Facsimile 0121 643 5711, DX 13065 BIRMINGHAM

(cont'd)

A–Z College Members and Associates

C

Professional qualifications and experience: LLB; over 20 years' post-admission experience in matrimonial and property matters

Year qualified in mediation: 1998

Membership of professional bodies and organisations: The Law Society; SFLA

Willing to travel outside the region: ✓

Willing to travel to: West Midlands, Warwickshire

Practice offered: All Issues Mediation

Woodward, David (A)

Approved Body: Family Mediators Association

Regional Group / Service: Bristol Family Mediators Association

Mediation telephone number: 0117 946 8261

Woodward, Hilary Diana (M)

Approved Body: National Family Mediation

Regional Group / Service: Bristol Family Mediation Service

Mediation telephone number: 0117 929 2002

Woolridge, Gillian (M)

Approved Body: National Family Mediation

Regional Group / Service: Mediation Advisory Service for Stafford and North Staffordshire

Mediation telephone number: 01785 214933

Wragge, Eileen (M)

Approved Body: National Family Mediation; Family Mediators Association

Regional Group / Service: York Family Mediation Service

Mediation telephone number: 01904 646068

Wright, Adrian Charles (M)

Approved Body: Family Mediators Association

Regional Group / Service: Northants, Bucks and Leics Family Mediators Association

Mediation telephone number: 01536 516342

Wright, Barbara Janet (M)

Approved Body: Family Mediators Association

Regional Group / Service: Kent Family Mediators Association

Mediation telephone number: 01892 510000

■ **Wright**, Barbara Mary (A)

Approved Body: Solicitors Family Law Association

Regional Group / Service: Member of Solicitors Family Law Association, telephone 01689 850227 for details

Mediation telephone number: 01483 755575

Mediation address: Southern House, Guildford Road, Woking, Surrey GU22 7UY
Facsimile 01483 729933, DX 2902 WOKING, E-mail bw@robbinsolivey.co.uk

Professional qualifications and experience: LLB (Hons); nine years' experience in family law – now specialising solely in this area

Year qualified in mediation: 1997

Membership of professional bodies and organisations: Solicitors Family Law Association (committee member of local branch)

Willing to travel outside the region: ✓

Willing to travel to: anywhere in Surrey, London and areas bordering Home Counties

Practice offered: All Issues Mediation

■ **Wright**, Gillian (A)

Approved Body: Family Mediators Association

Regional Group / Service: Oxford Family Mediators Association

Mediation telephone number: 01844 212305

■ **Wright**, Hazel Katherine (M)

Approved Body: Family Mediators Association

Regional Group / Service: London South & Central Family Mediators Association

Mediation telephone number: 0171 242 0422

■ **Yarnold**, Maureen Helen (M)

Approved Body: National Family Mediation

Regional Group / Service: West Essex Family Mediation Service

Mediation telephone number: 01279 426749

■ **Yates**, Meredith (M)

Approved Body: National Family Mediation

Regional Group / Service: Divorce Mediation & Counselling Service

Mediation telephone number: 0181 209 1729

Yellowlees, Fiona (A)

Approved Body: Solicitors Family Law Association

Regional Group / Service: Member of Solicitors Family Law Association, telephone 01689 850227 for details

Mediation telephone number: 01582 410041

York, Helen Elizabeth (A)

Approved Body: LawWise

Regional Group / Service: Member of LawWise Family Mediators Register, telephone 01483 237300 for details

Mediation telephone number: 0930 756010 (mobile) 01933 224971 (office)

Young, Claire Jane (A)

Approved Body: Solicitors Family Law Association

Regional Group / Service: Member of Solicitors Family Law Association, telephone 01689 850227 for details

Mediation telephone number: 0161 832 3000

Zneimer, Cynthia (M)

Approved Body: Family Mediators Association

Regional Group / Service: London North & Central Family Mediators Association

Mediation telephone number: 0181 868 1882

DIRECTORY

Groups/Services Index

This index provides an A to Z listing of the names of all the regional groups and services listed in the directory. The page number given is for the full group/service entry in Part B of the directory.

Groups/Services Index

DIRECTORY

**Regional Index of
Members/Associates**

This index lists all the UK College of
Family Mediators Members and
Associates by the region in which they
are located. The page number given is for
the full individual entry in Part C of the
directory.

Regional Index of Members/Associates

North East

Northern Ireland

Scotland

anthony gold
lerman & muirhead
S O L I C I T O R S

MANAGER/CO-ORDINATOR: KIM BEATSON

43 Streatham Hill
London SW2 4TP

Tel: 0181 678 5500

New London Bridge House
25 London Bridge Street
London SE1 9TW
Tel: 0171 940 4000

Affiliation Bodies:

Family Mediators' Association & Solicitors' Family Law Association; Location London

Members	Date Trained	Finance	Children	All Issues
Caroline Attwood	1997	√	√	√
Kim Beatson	1989	√	√	√
Mark Harper	1996	√	√	√

Facilities:

Two mediation rooms; separate waiting rooms; disabled access arrangements can be made.

Geographical area covered:

Central and South London

Areas of Practice:

All issues including a Legal Aid mediation franchise

Areas of Speciality:

Financial cases including cohabitee disputes

Mediation is an integral part of the Family Law Department at Anthony Gold since we adopt a constructive and conciliatory approach to resolving Family problems arising from relationship breakdown. We are able to offer access to mediation, legal advice and representation from our offices. Kim Beatson was one of the first solicitors in the country to qualify as a lawyer mediator. She is a member of the Family Mediators' Association and the Solicitors' Family Law Association Mediation Training Board. Mark Harper and Caroline Attwood are also trained mediators and offer all issues mediation.